THE CATHOLIC LITURGY BOOK

Choral Edition and Organ Accompaniment

General Editor
JAMES E. SCHAEFER

HELICON
Baltimore, Maryland

By special arrangement with Romda, Ltd., *The Catholic Liturgy Book* is distributed and promoted by Helicon Press, Inc., 1120 North Calvert Street, Baltimore, Maryland 21202.

The Catholic Liturgy Book has been designed and edited in accordance with the guidelines and suggestions of the Bishops' Committee on the Liturgy for books used by the congregation for Roman Catholic use.

Music Engraving, typesetting and editing of music notation was prepared by Capital Music Service, 10905 Fort Washington Road, Washington, D.C. 20022

Nihil Obstat: William J. Freburger, Censor Deputatus

Imprimatur: William D. Borders, D.D., Archbishop of Baltimore,
April 7, 1975

Editorial Board of The Catholic Liturgy Book

The Catholic Liturgy Book was prepared, designed and edited with the aid and assistance of hundreds of pastors, liturgists, musicians, scripture scholars, and diocesan liturgical commissions under the general editorship of Dr. Ralph A. Keifer. The Choral Edition and Organ Accompaniment was prepared under the general editorship of James E. Schaefer.

Acknowledgements

Grateful acknowledgement is made to the authors, composers and owners of various hymns and tunes used in *The Catholic Liturgy Book*.

Acta Foundation: 454
F.A. Brooks: 338
H. Barrie Cabena: 8, 9, 10, 14, 20
The Church Hymnal Corporation: 145, 205, 222, 328, 429, 465, 508
F. von Christierson: 312
Evelyn Atwater Commins: 486
Paul Cross: 308
Peter DeRosa: 363
Ignace de Sutter: 422
L. do Vocht: 252, 358
J. Dudley-Smith: 434
Eleanor Farjeon, Estate of: 323
FEL Publications, Ltd.: 94
Franciscan Communications Center: 439, 519
Galaxy Music Corp.: 312, 500
David Head: 337
Martin B. Hellriegel, Estate of: 452
Douglas Hyde: 309
Winfred Hyde: 229
Hymns Ancient and Modern, Proprietors of: 273
Fred Kaan: 382, 384, 502
Ronald A. Knox, Estate of: 271, 290, 370
John May: 460
Mayhew-McCrimmon Ltd.: 344, 350, 385
James McMullen: 366
Frits Mehrtens: 334, 364
C.J Marivoet: 252, 334, 358, 364, 369, 422
Stanley Mountjoy: 337
A. Gregory Murray: 350, 352
John W. Norris: 518
John H. Oliver: 74, 98, 104
One Hundred Hymns, Proprietors of: 516, 523, 524
John Oxenham, Estate of: 517
Oxford University Press: 75, 201, 247, 283, 285, 303, 304, 340, 403, 415, 514,
Tom Parker: 57
James Quinn: 342, 329
D.J. Reagan: 81, 99
J. Athelston Riley: 371
Sacred Heart Publications, Ltd.: 251, 259
St. Joseph's Abbey: 209
St. Martin's Press: 253, 260, 265, 266, 303, 305, 314, 353, 360, 423, 431
R.Y.B. Scott: 520

Robert N. Spencer: 340
The Swallow Press: 368
F. Bland Tucker: 261, 376, 441, 504
Irvin Udulutsch: 232, 241, 359
World Council of Churches: 364
Special acknowledgement and thanks is extended to:
Robert Grogan: 35, 36, 37, 38
The Liturgical Press: 47, 48, 49, 347, 348, 354, 367, 375, 375, 410
Thomas McGuire: 22, 26, 39, 40, 41, 42, 52, 72, 96, 105
Roger Nachtwey: 17, 24, 27, 54, 83, 209, 256
National Council for Liturgy, the Canadian Catholic Conference for its generous help and cooperation.
C. Alexander Peloquin: 33, 50, 51
Elmer F. Pfeil: 34
Peter J. Scagnelli: responsorial psalm refrains
Francis V. Strahan: 208, psalm tones for Morning and Evening Prayer
Robert F. Twynham: for special music for the Holy Week Services.
Andrew J. McArdle for the accompaniment to the chants and acclamations.
James E. Schaefer for the settings in the appendix and other miscelleneous peices.
Rev. Charles Knoll for the psalmody in Morning and Evening Prayer.

Table of Contents

Introduction

Music is an essential part of liturgical celebration. To a greater degree than the mere spoken word, it enables the worshipper to feel at one with his fellow Christian and to express his unity with the universal church. Moreover, music carries the particular theme of the day's worship to the congregation much more dramatically and forcefully than the spoken word.

It is, therefore, most important that the music director plan the musical program for each liturgical event carefully and with specific knowledge. He must be familiar with the overall message of the day's readings and prayers, and offer a program which will reinforce that message. Ideally, he will consult with the celebrant concerning the contents of the homily or sermon so that a unified service can be created with a maximum impact for all present.

The use of a competent song leader cannot be overemphasized. Responsible parishioners with adequate vocal ability should be recruited to lead *all* the music sung by the congregation, whether an entire hymn or a simple responsory answering the choir's psalm verses. The song leader may also double as lector or commentator, provided he or she has the vocal ability and sufficient stage presence to lead the congregation in song. Or the organist or a choir member provided with a microphone connected to the public address system may also act as song leader. This latter arrangement, however—particularly in churches with gallery organs and/or choirs—is less than ideal, since the song leader should be a visible member of the sanctuary personnel.

This volume was prepared as both a choral book and accompaniment to the people's edition. Use of chords were made for instruments wherever appropriate. Many accompaniments were set in lower keys for those congregations who would find the higher and more traditional key not suited to their vocal resources.

In the average parish community, a basic repertory of music is a necessary adjunct of liturgical service. The music director/organist, together with the priests, sisters and other staff, can jointly determine when innovative music is needed. However, it should be kept in mind that the congregation needs a cushion of familiar material, drawn from a basic repertory in order to avoid feeling disoriented or "left out." It is therefore important that new materials be introduced gradually—at best, on specific festive occasions or at the beginning of an obviously new liturgical season. It is essential that new hymns or new chants not be thrust into the liturgy without warning the congregation sufficiently.

The music in this volume, both the "Chants and Acclamations" and the "Hymns and Songs" sections, is intended to provide a basic congregational repertory. No attempt has been made to provide a selection of commercially popular music or "ad hoc" songs, which from time to time will need to be incorporated into a well-developed parochial music program. Such essentially ephemeral music could not possibly be included in a permanent collection for universal distribution—at least not in any meaningful numbers.

The music director/organist is of course expected to take advantage of the flexibility of the contemporary liturgical rites. Many parishes throughout the country have supplemented their standard pew-book with inexpensive "Parish Collections." This practice is not discouraged. However, the purpose of *The Catholic Liturgy Book* is to provide a universally acceptable selection of hymns and music styles for the vast majority of American parishes. This volume stands on its own merit as a complete hymnal for normal parish needs.

Practical Suggestions for the Organist

When accompanying congregational singing, the organist must remember that he is to lead the singing, not follow. A strong, bright sound—even to the use of reed stops—gives the congregation confidence and direction. The organist sets the tempo and the level of musical achievement for the song leader and the people in the pews. If the organist drags behind the singing and does not keep fractionally ahead of the singers, he will soon discover he is following silence.

A useful practice is for the organist to play through the congregational music to be used as the parishioners arrive at church and take their places in the pews. This is particularly helpful when introducing new repertory. It is hoped that the organist can make judicious choices of incidental music that will musically complement the sung portions of the liturgy. Voluntaries melodically related to the hymns to be sung provide a subtle refreshment of memory to the congregation.

If a short rehearsal is practical, immediately prior to a service, it is useful to play the melody (at least for the first and second time through) on a powerful solo stop, again slightly ahead of the tempo of the singers. This is also a useful method of accompanying new hymns, even without rehearsal. This can also be done with a pedal reed which will penetrate the entire building.

The choir is an invaluable help in teaching new material to the congregation. With their lead, they encourage the timid in the pews to join in. The use of harmony and descants with the hymns will give the congregation a sense of being part of a larger event and make impact on all present.

Chants and Acclamations

Chants and Acclamations

One of the most significant changes which has taken place in the liturgical reform and its resulting renewal has been in church music. This has been a direct response to the challenges and guidelines laid down by Vatican II. Among the many concepts that have made their impress these past ten years, two stand out: participation and celebration.

Our liturgical worship manifests the Church to be a community in which there is a diversity of order, talents, and offices. This is quite evident in the way the Church has assigned musical roles to each of the ministries of celebrant and choir and to the people. Such was true when the Mass was in Latin but, as time and national custom eroded the people's knowledge of Latin, their role was naturally diminished. In the past chants and acclamations have been solely identified with the monastic tradition with the resulting effect that parish and ordinary community life was often deprived of a truly singable and appropriate repertoire. Vatican II pointed out this disparity. Consequently, a principal goal of the liturgical reform was precisely to emphasize the active participation of the faithful *in song.*

Celebration is another key concept in understanding the rites of our sacraments and the eucharistic liturgy. Here again music is emphasized, for celebration without music is practically alien to human experience. This participation and this celebration by the faithful is nothing more than a return to our ancient tradition which has always considered music to be an *integral* part of liturgical service.

The use of English has restored the ancient balance because it has emphasized the tradition of *singing the Mass* and not just singing at Mass, or worse, merely listening without understanding. The Roman Catholic tradition has been steadfastly unique in its adherence to chants, especially the ordinary ones such as the *Kyrie, Gloria, Sanctus.* Where the Gregorian plainsong seemed inappropriate to our English tongue we have been fortunate over the past decade to begin to develop a musically sound approach to liturgical service in English. Furthermore, an emphasis on our biblical heritage as illustrated in the three cycles of readings has restored the use of responses. A response indicates a dialogue and while it is primarily taken from the Bible as, for instance, the people's response to a biblical verse, we also respond in a different sense in the dialogue between priest and people, such as his "The Lord be with you" and our "And with you also."

It is by acclamation that the people express prayer and praise. Ancient tradition has always accorded acclamations as belonging to the people and the liturgical reform has restored and reinforced this tradition by adding many possibilities (such as the memorial acclamations) and options to the liturgy of the service. We can surely see its formative impact when the acclamations in the doxology sing forth an affirmation of great faith.

Precisely because of the distinctiveness of our Roman heritage, the editors have set aside this section of Acclamations, Chants and Responses to encourage song *whenever* possible in liturgical service. At the same time, we hope that composers, choirs, scholas, cantors, and choir masters continue within their tradition by way of contributing modern compositions, special acclamations and responses for specific occasions and communities.

1

Advent
Psalm 25:1
Peter Scagnelli, 1975
To you, O Lord, I lift my soul.

2

Advent
Psalm 85:8
Peter Scagnelli, 1975
Lord, let us see your kind - ness.

3

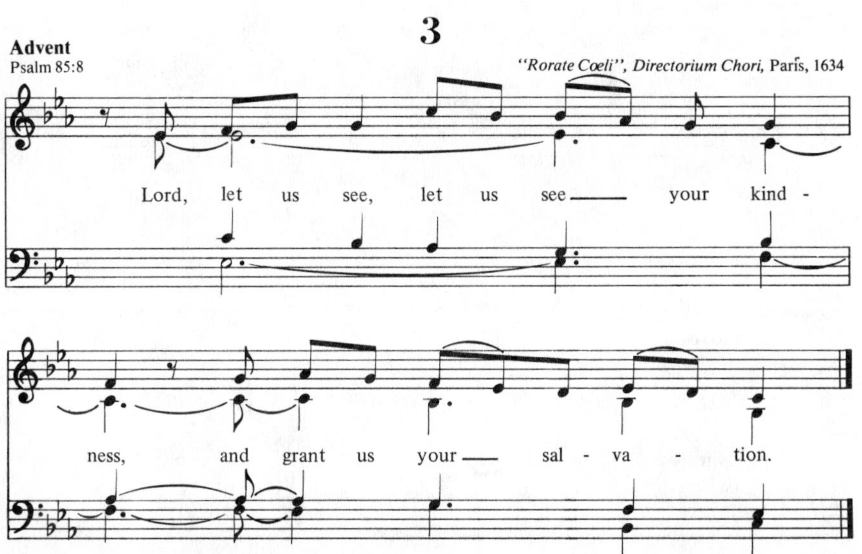
Advent
Psalm 85:8
"Rorate Cœli", Directorium Chori, Paris, 1634
Lord, let us see, let us see your kind -
ness, and grant us your sal - va - tion.

4

Christmas
Psalm 98:3

Peter Scagnelli, 1975
Harm., A. McA.

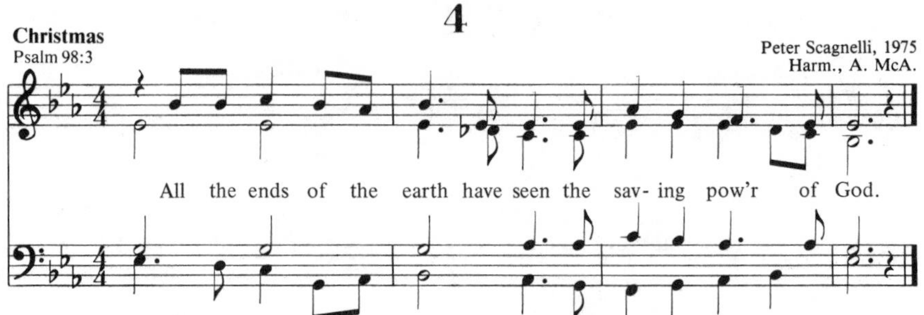
All the ends of the earth have seen the sav- ing pow'r of God.

5

Epiphany
Psalm 72:11

Peter Scagnelli, 1975
Harm., A. McA.

Lord, ev - 'ry na - tion — on earth will — a - dore you.

6

Lent
Psalm 51:3

Peter Scagnelli, 1975
Harm., A. McA.

Be mer - ci - ful, O Lord, for we have sinned.

7

Lent
Psalm 91:15

Peter Scagnelli, 1975
Harm., A. McA.

Be with me, Lord when I am in trou- ble; — be with — me, Lord.

8

Lent
Psalm 91:15

H. Barrie Cabena, adapt., 1975

Be with me, Lord, when I am in trou - ble.

9

Lent
Psalm 130:7

H. Barrie Cabena, 1972

With the Lord there is mer - cy and full - ness of re - demp - tion.

10

Holy Week
Psalm 22:2

H. Barrie Cabena, adapt., 1975

3
3
My God, my God, why have you a - ban - doned me?
3
3

11

Easter Vigil
Psalm 136

Peter Scagnelli, 1975
Harm., A. McA.

His love is ev - er last - ing, his love is ev - er - last - ing.

12

Easter Season
Psalm 118:24

Peter Scagnelli, 1975
Harm., A. McA.

This is the day the Lord has made; let us re-joice and be glad!

13

Easter Season
Psalm 66:1

Peter Scagnelli, 1975
Harm., A. McA.

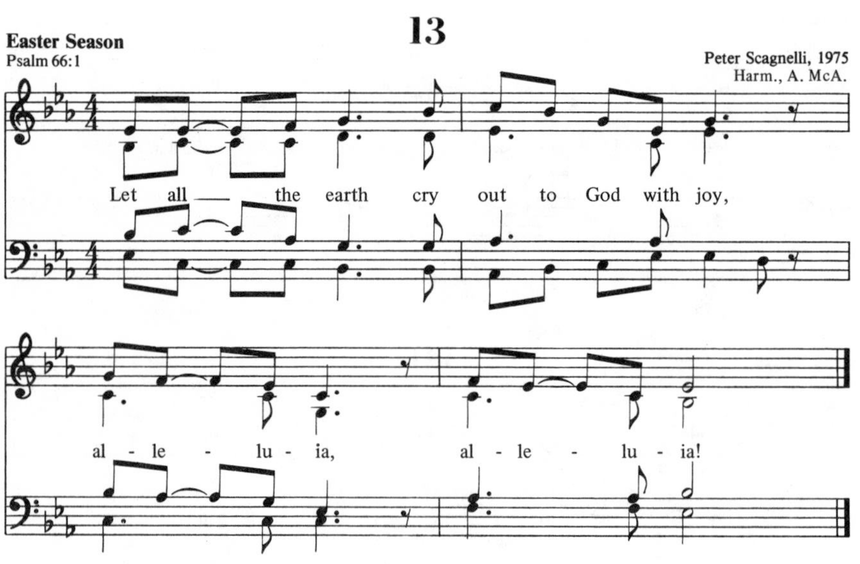
Let all — the earth cry out to God with joy,
al - le - lu - ia, al - le - lu - ia!

14

Easter Season

H. Barrie Cabena, 1972

Al - le - lu - ia, al - le - lu - ia, al - le - lu - ia.

15

Ascension
Psalm 47:6

Peter Scagnelli, 1975
Harm., A. McA.

God mounts his throne to shouts of joy!

16

Pentecost
Psalm 104:30

Peter Scagnelli, 1975
Harm., A. McA.

Lord, send out your Spir - it, and re - new the face of the earth.

17

Ordinary Time
John 6:69

Roger Nachtwey, 1975
Harm., A. McA.

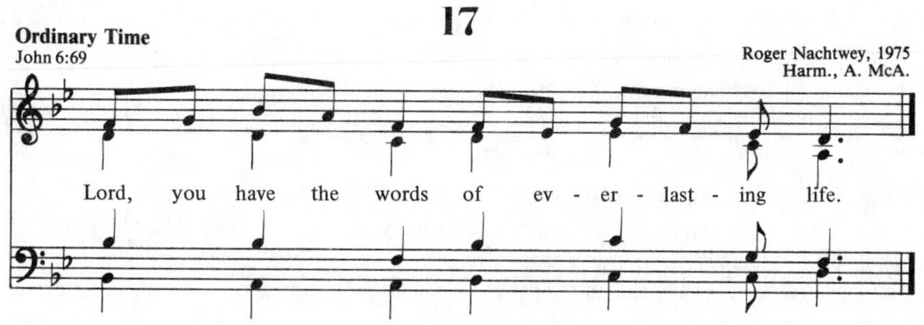
Lord, you have the words of ev - er - last - ing life.

18

Ordinary Time
Psalm 27:1

Peter Scagnelli, 1975
Harm., A. McA.

The Lord is my light and my sal - va - tion.

19

Ordinary Time
Psalm 34:2

Peter Scagnelli, 1975
Harm., A. McA.

I will bless the Lord at all ——— times.

20

Ordinary Time
Psalm 34:9

Peter Scagnelli, 1975
Harm., A. McA.

Taste and see the good - ness of the Lord.

21

Ordinary Time
Psalm 63:2

Peter Scagnelli

My soul is thirst - ing for you, O Lord, my God.

22

Ordinary Time
Psalm 95:8

Thomas McGuire, 1975

If to - day you hear — his voice, hard - en not — your heart.

23

Ordinary Time
Psalm 100:3

Peter Scagnelli, 1975
Harm., A. McA.

We are his peo - ple, the sheep of his flock.

24

Ordinary Time
Psalm 103:8

Roger Nachtwey, 1975
Harm., A. McA.

The Lord is kind and mer - ci - ful.

25

Ordinary Time
Psalm 145:1

Peter Scagnelli, 1975

I will praise your name for - ev - er, O my King and my God.

26

End of the Year
Psalm 122:1

Thomas McGuire, 1975

Let us go re - joic - ing to the house of the Lord.

27

Feasts of Mary
Luke 1:49
Roger Nachtwey, 1975
Harm., A. McA.
The al - might - y has done great things for me,
and ho - ly is his name.

28

Plainsong Melody
Harm., A. McA.
Al - le - lu - ia, al - le - lu - ia, al - le - lu - ia.

29

Plainsong Melody
Harm., A. McA.
Al - le - lu - ia, al - le - lu - ia, al - le - lu - ia.

30[1]
Plainsong Melody
Al - le - lu - ia.
30[2]
Al - le - lu - ia.
31
Plainsong Melody
Al - le - lu - ia.
32
Traditional
Harm., A. McA.
Al - le - lu - ia, al - le - lu - ia, al - le - lu - ia, al - le - lu - ia.
Al - le - lu - ia, al - le - lu - ia, al - le - lu - ia, al - le - lu - ia.

33

C.A. Peloquin
Al - le - lu - ia, Al - le - lu - ia,
last time
Al - le - lu - ia. ia.

34

Elmer Pfeil
Harm., A. McA.
1. Al - le - lu - ia, al - le - lu - ia, Al - le - lu - ia.
2. Praise to you, Lord Je - sus Christ, King of end - less glo - ry!

35

Robert Grogan, 1972
Harm., A. McA.
Praise to you, Lord Je - sus Christ, King of end- less glo - ry!

36

Robert Grogan, 1972
Harm., A. McA.

Praise and hon - or to you, Lord Je - sus Christ!

37

Robert Grogan, 1972
Harm., A. McA.

Glo - ry and praise to you, Lord Je - sus Christ!

38

Robert Grogan, 1972
Harm., A. McA.

Glo - ry to you, Word of God, Lord Je - sus Christ!

39

Thomas McGuire, 1975
Harm., A. McA.

Praise to you Lord Je - sus Christ, King of end - less glo - ry!

40

Thomas McGuire, 1975
Harm., J.S.

Praise and hon - or to you, Lord Je - sus Christ!

41

Thomas McGuire, 1975
Harm., J.S.

Glo - ry and praise to you, Lord Je - sus Christ!

42

Thomas McGuire, 1975
Harm. A. McA.

Glo - ry to you, Word of God, Lord Je - sus Christ!

To be used with the first four acclamations:

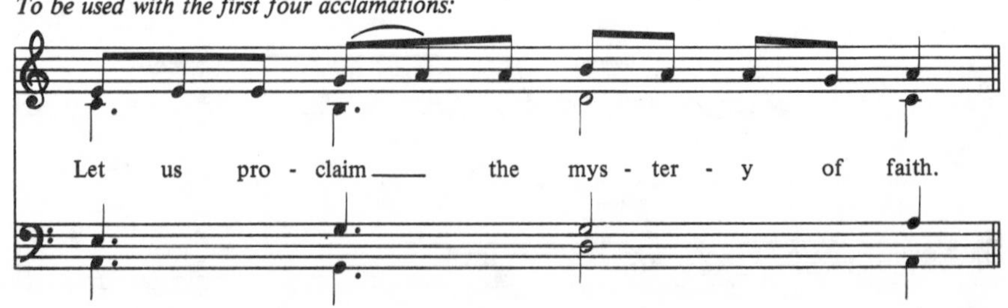
Let us pro - claim the mys - ter - y of faith.

Christ has died, Christ is ris - en, Christ will come ___ a - gain.

44

Dy - ing you de - stroyed our death, ris - ing you re -

stored our life; Lord ___ Je - sus, come in glo - ry.

45

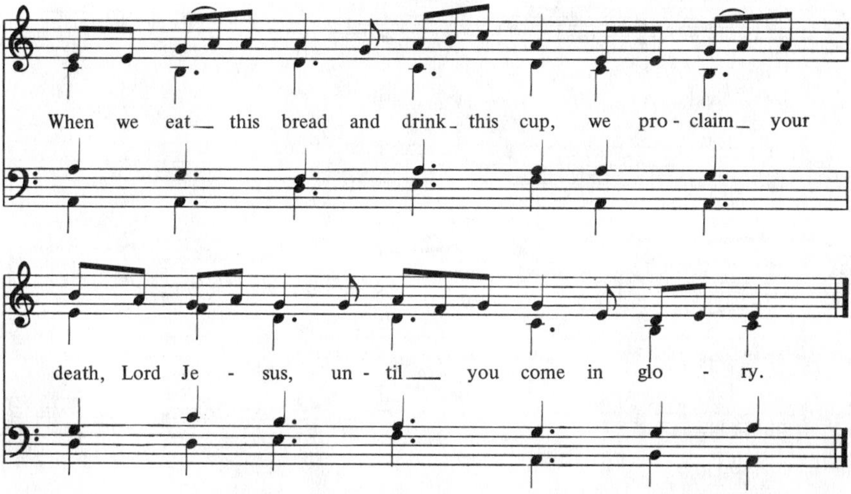

When we eat _ this bread and drink _ this cup, we pro - claim _ your

death, Lord Je - sus, un - til ___ you come in glo - ry.

46
Lord, by your cross and res - ur - rec - tion you have
set us free. You are the Sav - ior of the world.
47
John Lee
Christ has died, Christ is ris - en, Christ will come a - gain.
48
John Lee
Dy - ing you de - stroyed our death, ris - ing you re -
stored our life. Lord Je - sus, come in glo - ry.

49
John Lee
When we eat this bread and drink this cup, we pro-claim your
death, Lord Je - sus, un - til you come in glo - ry.
50
C.A. Peloquin
Christ has died. Christ is ris - en. Christ will come a - gain.
51
C.A. Peloquin
When we eat this bread and drink this cup, we pro - claim your death, Lord Je -
sus, un - til you come in glo - ry.

52

Thomas McGuire, 1969
Harm., J.S.

Let us pro - claim the mys - t'ry of faith.

When we eat this bread and drink this cup, we pro - claim your death, Lord Je - sus,

Un - til you come in glo - ry.

53

Fa - ther, for - ev - er and ev - er.
R. A - men.

54
Roger Nachtwey, 1975
A - men, A - men, A - men.
55
Danish
Harm., J.S.
A - men, A - men, A - men.
56
Greek
Harm., J.S.
A - men, A - men.
57
Tom Parker
A - men, A - men,
A - men!

58

Plainsong Melody
Harm., J.S.
A - men, A - men, A - men.

59

In the name... and of the Ho-ly Spir - it. R. A - men.

60

In the name... and of the Ho - ly Spir - it. R. A - men.

61

Greeting A
The grace of ... be with you all. And al - so with you.

62

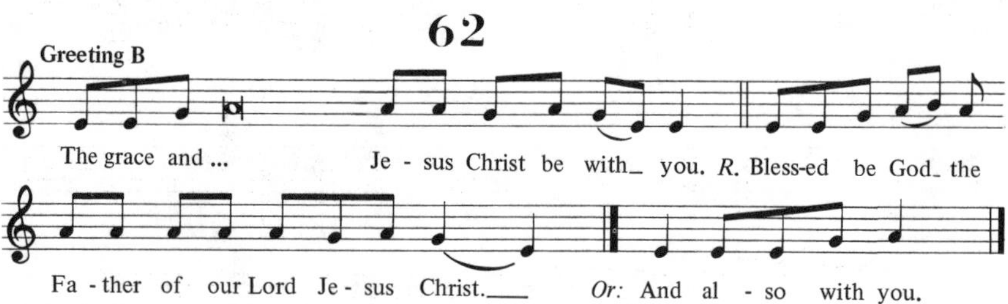
Greeting B
The grace and ... Je - sus Christ be with you. R. Bless-ed be God the
Fa - ther of our Lord Je - sus Christ. Or: And al - so with you.

63

Greeting C
The Lord be with you. R. And al - so with you.

64

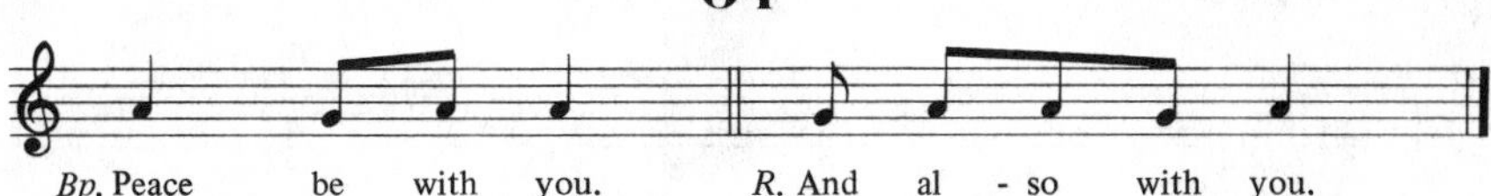
Bp. Peace be with you. R. And al - so with you.

65
Introduction
My broth - ers and sis - ters, to pre - pare our - selves to cel - e -
brate the sa - cred mys - ter - ies, let us call to mind our sins.

66
Penitential Rite A
I con - fess to al - might - y God... Lord our God.

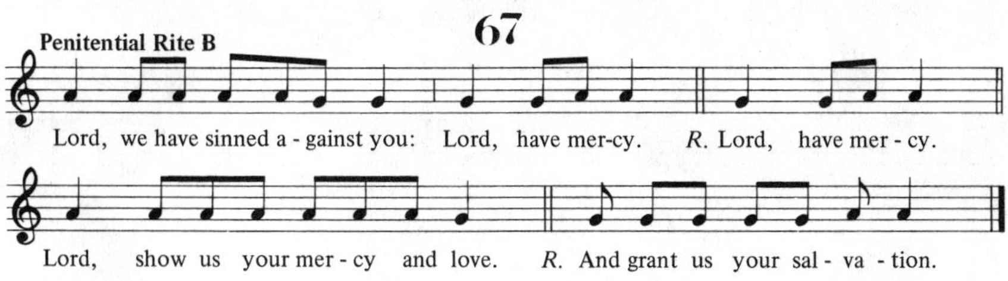
67
Penitential Rite B
Lord, we have sinned a - gainst you: Lord, have mer-cy. R. Lord, have mer - cy.
Lord, show us your mer - cy and love. R. And grant us your sal - va - tion.

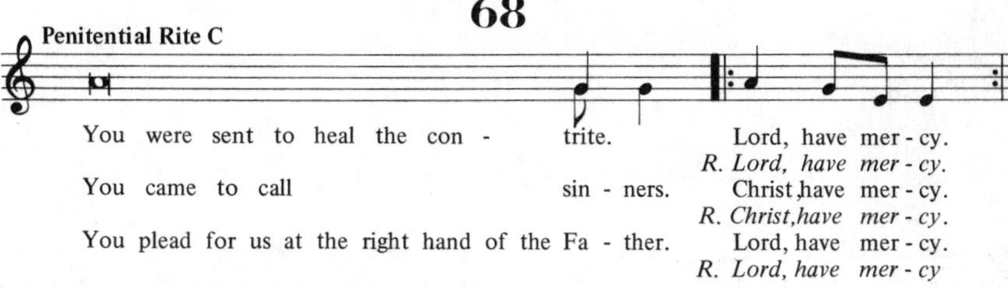
68
Penitential Rite C
You were sent to heal the con - trite. Lord, have mer - cy.
R. Lord, have mer - cy.
You came to call sin - ners. Christ,have mer - cy.
R. Christ,have mer - cy.
You plead for us at the right hand of the Fa - ther. Lord, have mer - cy.
R. Lord, have mer - cy

See successive pages for additional settings of Penitential Rite C.

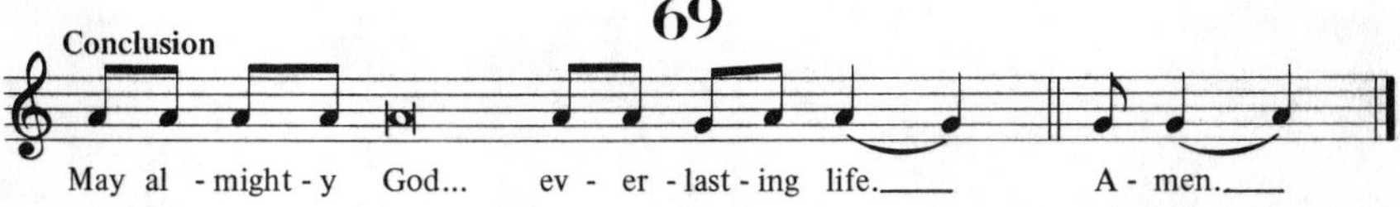
69
Conclusion
May al - might - y God... ev - er - last - ing life.____ A - men.____

70

Plainsong Melody
Harm., J.S.

You were sent to heal the con- trite Lord, have mer - cy.
Ky - ri - e, e - le - i - son.

You came to call sin - ners. Christ, have mer - cy.
Chri - ste, e - le - i - son.

You plead for us at the right hand of the Fa-ther. Lord, have mer - cy.
Ky- ri - e, e - le - i - son.

71

Sacramentary, set vii

Plainsong Melody

Lord, . . . the way to the Fa-ther:
Ky - ri - e,

Lord, have mer - cy.
E - - - le - i - son.
Lord, . . . of the truth: Chri - ste,
Christ, have mer - cy.
E – le - i - son.
Lord, the Good shep-herd: Ky - ri - e,
Lord, have mer - cy.
E – le - i - son.

72
John Merbecke, 1549, adapt., Thomas McGuire, 1975
You . . . con - trite:
Lord, have mer - cy.
Ky - ri - e, e - le - i - son.
You . . . call sin - ners:
Christ, have mer - cy.
Chri - ste, e - le - i - son.
You . . . the Fa - ther:
Lord, have mer - cy.
Ky - ri - e, e - le - i - son.
73
Plainsong Melody
You . . . con - trite:
Lord, have mer - cy.
You . . . call sin - ners:
Christ, have mer - cy.

You . . . the Fa - ther: Lord, have mer - cy.

All of the previous may be used as simple Kyries by omitting the invocations.

74

John H. Olivier

Lord ___ have mer - cy. Lord ___ have mer - cy,
Ky - ri - e, e - le - i - son. Ky - ri - e, e - le - i - son.

Fine

Lord ___ have mer - cy. Christ. have mer - cy,
Ky - ri - e, e - le - i - son. Chri - ste, e - le - i - son.

D.C. al Fine

Christ have mer - cy, Christ have mer - cy.
Chri - ste, e - le - i - son. Chri - ste, e - le - i - son.

75

Healey Willan, 1928

Ky - ri - e, e - le - i - son. Ky - ri - e, e - le - i - son.
Lord, — have — mer - cy. Lord, — have — mer - cy.

Fine

Ky - ri - e, e - le - i - son. Chri - ste, e - le - i - son.
Lord, — have mer - cy. Christ, — have mer - cy.

D.C. al Fine

Chri - ste, e - le - i - son. Chri - ste, e - le - i - son.
Christ, — have mer - cy. Christ, — have mer - cy.

76

Plainsong Melody, 16th cent.

Ky-ri - e, — e - le - i - son *ij*
Chri-ste, — e - le - i - son *ij*

Ky-ri-e, e - le-i-son.
Ky-ri-e,
e - le-i-son.
77
Plainsong melody, adapt. (Vat. ad lib I)
Cleanse us, Lord, from all our sins; wash
us, and we shall be whit-er than snow.

78

Plainsong Melody

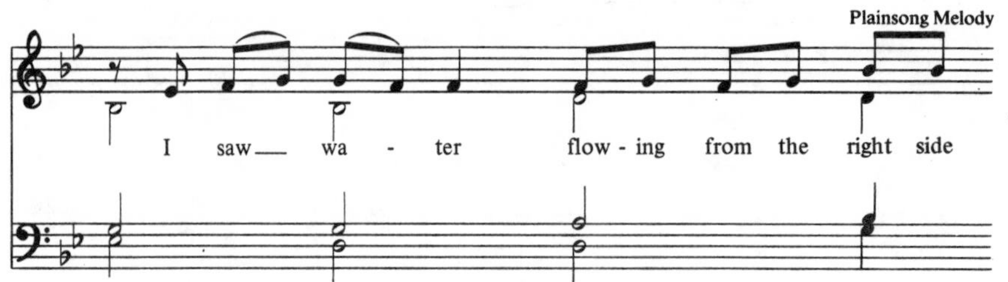
I saw — wa - ter flow - ing from the right side

of the tem - ple, — al - le - lu - ia. It

brought God's life and his sal - va - tion, and — the peo - ple

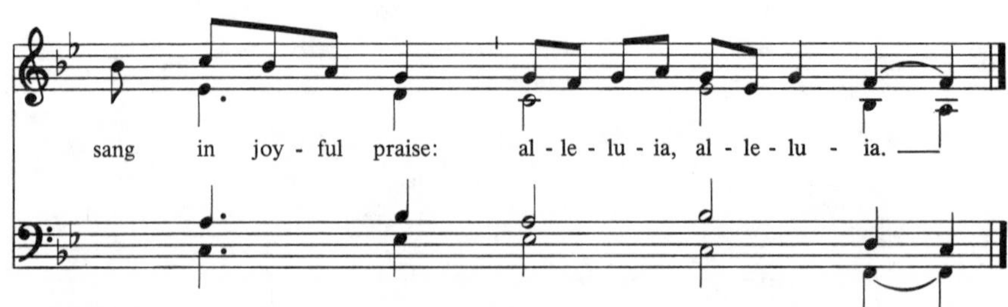
sang in joy - ful praise: al - le - lu - ia, al - le - lu - ia. —

79

Ambrosian Chant

Glo - ry to God in the high - est, and peace to his peo - ple on earth.

Lord God, heav - en - ly King, al - might - y God and Fa -

- - ther, we wor - ship you, we give you thanks,

we praise you for your glo - - - ry.

Lord Je - sus Christ, on - ly Son of the Fa - ther, Lord God,
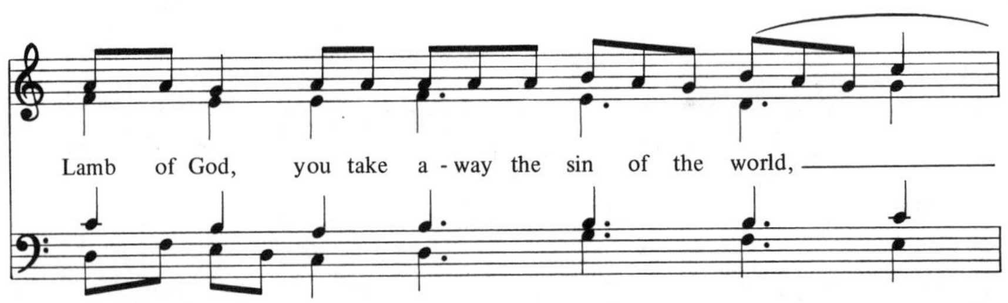
Lamb of God, you take a - way the sin of the world,

have mer - cy on us;

you are seat - ed at the right hand of the Fa - ther: re-ceive our prayer.

For you a - lone are the Ho - ly One, you a - lone are the Lord,
you a - lone are the Most High, Je - sus Christ,
with the Ho - ly Spir - it,
in the glo - ry of God the Fa - ther. A - men.
Or: A - men.

Old Scottish Chant
Glo - ry to God in the high - est, and peace to his peo ple on earth.
Lord God, heav'n-ly King, al - might - y God and Fa - ther,
we wor-ship you, we give you thanks, we praise you for your glo - ry.
Lord Je - sus Christ, on - ly Son of the Fa - ther, Lord God, Lamb of God,

You take a - way the sins of the world: have mer - cy on us;
You are seat - ed on the right hand of the Fa - ther: re - ceive our prayer.
For you a - lone are the Ho - ly One, you a - lone are the Lord,
You a - lone are the Most High, Je - sus Christ, with the Ho - ly
Spir - it, in the glo - ry of God the Fa - ther. A - men.

1st Verse
D.J. Reagan, 1974
Glo-ry to God in the high-est, peace to his peo-ple on earth.
2nd Verse
Lord God, heav-en-ly King, al-might-y God and Fa - ther,
Refrain
Glo-ry to God in the high-est, glo-ry to God in the high-est!

D
3rd Verse
mf
we wor - ship you, we give you thanks, we
mf
we give you thanks, we
mf
D.S. al 4th Verse
praise you for your glo - ry.
praise you glo - ry,
E
4th Verse
Lord Je - sus Christ, on - ly Son of the Fa - ther,
on - ly Son of the Fa - ther,
mf

D.S. 𝄋 al 5th Verse
Lord God, Lamb of God, God,
F
5th Verse
You take-a-way the sin of the world:
have mer-cy on us; you are seat-ed at the

right hand of the Father: receive our prayer.
D.S. al 6th Verse
G
6th Verse
mf
For you a - lone are the Ho - ly
mf
One, You a - lone are the Lord,

D.S. 𝄋 al 7th Verse
H
7th Verse
You a - lone are the
mf
Most High, Je - sus Christ, with the Ho - ly
Spir - it in the glo - ry of God the Fa - ther.
D.S. 𝄋 al 8th Verse

I
8th Verse
A - men, a - men, Glo - ry to God on high!
A - men, a - men, Glo - ry to God on high!

82

Plainsong Melody, 16th cent.
Glo - ri - ia in ex - cel - sis De - o et in ter - ra pax ho - mi - ni - bus
bo - næ vo - lun - ta - tis. Lau - da - mus te. Be - ne - di - ci -
mus te. Ad - o - ra - mus te. Glo - ri - fi - ca - mus te.
Gra - ti - as a - gi - mus ti - bi prop - ter ma - gnam glo - ri - am tu - am.
Do - mi - ne De - us, Rex coe - le - stis, De - us Pa - ter o -

mni - po - tens. Do - mi - ne Fi - li u - ni - ge - ni - te, Je -
su Chri - ste. Do - mi - ne De - us, A - gnus De - i, Fi - li -
us pa - tris. Qui tol - lis pec - ca - ta mun -
di, mi - se - re - re no - bis. Qui tol - lis pec -
ca - ta mun - di, su - sci - pe de - pre - ca - ti - o - nem no -

stram. Qui se - des ad dex - te - ram Pa - tris, mi - se - re - re
no - bis. Quo - ni - am tu so - lus san - ctus. Tu so - lus Do -
mi - nus. Tu so - lus Al - tis - si - mus, Je - su
Chri - ste, Cum San - cto Spi - ri - tu, in glo - ri - a De - i
Pa - tris. A - men.
Ped

83

Plainsong Melody, 11th cent.
Adapted by Roger Nachtwey, 1975

We be-lieve in one God, the Fa-ther, the Al-might-y,

mak-er of heav-en and earth, of all that is seen and

un-seen. We be-lieve in one Lord, Je - sus Christ, the on-ly

Son of God, e - ter-nal-ly be-got-ten of the Fa - ther,

God from God, Light from Light, true God from true God,
be - got - ten, not made, one in Be - ing with the Fa - ther.
Through him all things were made. For us men and for our sal - va - tion
he came down from heav - en: By the pow'r of the Ho - ly Spir - it
he was born of the Vir - gin Mar - y and be - came man.

For our sake he was cru - ci - fied un - der Pon - tius
Pi - late; he suf-fered, died and was bur - ied. On the third day he
rose a - gain in ful - fil - ment of the Scrip - tures;
he as - cend - ed in - to heav - en and is seat - ed at the
right hand of the Fa - ther. He will come a - gain in glo - ry

to judge the living and the dead, and his kingdom will
have no end. We believe in the Holy Spirit, the
Lord, the giver of life, who proceeds from the Father and the Son.
With the Father and the Son he is worshipped and glo-
rified. he has spoken through the Prophets. We be-

lieve in one ho - ly cath - 'lic and ap - os - tol - ic Church.

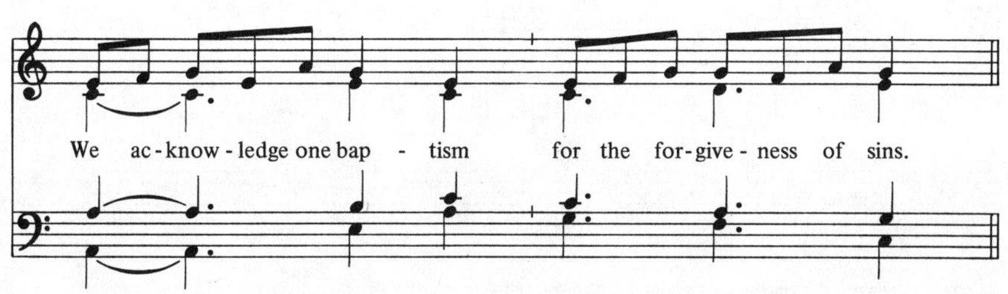
We ac - know - ledge one bap - tism for the for - give - ness of sins.

We look for the res - ur - rec - tion of the dead, and the life of the

world to come. A - men.

84

Old Scottish Chant

We be - lieve in one God, the Fa - ther, the Al - might - y
mak - er of heav'n and earth, of all that is seen and un - seen.
We be - lieve in one Lord, Je - sus Christ, the on - ly Son of God,
e - ter - nal - ly be - got - ten of the Fa - ther, God from God,
Light from Light, true God from true God, be - got - ten, not made,

one in be - ing with the Fa - ther. Through him all things were made.
For us men and for our sal - va - tion he came down from heav-en:
By the pow'r of the Ho - ly Spir - it he was born of the
Vir - gin Mar - y, and be came — man. For our sake he was
cru - ci - fied un - der Pon - tius Pi - late; he suf - fered, died, and was

bur - ied. On the third day he rose a - gain in ful - fil - ment
of the Scrip - tures; he as - cend - ed in - to heav - en and is
seat - ed at the right hand of the Fa - ther. He will come a -
gain in glo - ry to judge the liv - ing and the dead, and his
king - dom will have no end. We be - lieve in the Ho - ly Spir - it, the

Lord, the giv - er of life, who pro-ceeds from the Fa - ther and the Son.
With the Fa - ther and the Son he is wor-shipped and glo - ri - fied.
He has spo - ken through the proph-ets. We be - lieve in one ho - ly
cath - 'lic and ap - os - tol - ic Church. We ac - knowl-edge one bap - tism
for the for - give - ness of sins. We look for the res - ur - rec - tion
of the dead, and the life of the world to come. A - men.

85

Plainsong Melody, 17th cent.

Cre - do in u - num De - um, Pa - trem o - mni - po - ten - tem,
fa - cto - rem cae - li et ter - rae, vi - si - bi - li - um o - mni -
um, et in - vi - si - bi - li - um. Et in u - num Do - mi - num
Je - sum Chri - stum, Fi - li - um De - i u - ni - ge - ni - tum. Et ex
Pa - tre na - tum an - te o - mni - a sae - cu - la.

De - um de De - o, lu - men de lu - mi - ne, De - um ve - rum
de De - o ve - ro. Ge - ni - tum, non fa - ctum, con - sub -
stan - ti - a - lem Pa - tri: per quem o - mni - a fa - cta sunt.
Qui pro - pter nos ho - mi - nes, et pro - pter no - stram sa - lu - tem
de - scen - dit de coe - lis. Et in - car - na - tus est de

Spi - ri - tu San - cto ex Ma - ri - a Vir - gi - ne: Et ho - mo
fa - ctus est. Cru - ci - fi - xus et - i - am pro no -
bis: sub Po - nti - o Pi - la - to pas - sus et se - pul - tus est.
Et re - sur - re - xit ter - ti - a di - e, se - cun - dum Scri - ptu - ras.
Et a - scen - dit in cae - lum: se - det ad de - xte - ram

Pa - tris. et i - te - rum ven - tu - rus est cum glo - ri - a,
ju - di - ca - re vi - vos et mor - tu - os: cu - jus re - gni non e - rit
fi - nis. Et in Spi - ri - tum San - ctum, Do - mi - num, et vi -
vi - fi - can - tem: qui ex Pa - tre Fi - li - o - que pro - ce - dit.
Qui cum Pa - tre et Fi - li - o si - mul ad - o - ra - tur, et

con - glo - ri - fi - ca - tur: qui lo - cu - tus est per Pro - phe - tas.
Et u - nam san - ctam ca - tho - li - cam et a - po - sto - li -
cam Ec - cle - si - am. Con - fi - te - or u - num ba - pti - sma
in re - mis - si - o - nem pec - ca - to - rum. Et ex - spe - cto re - sur -
re - cti - o - nem mor - tu - o - rum. Et vi - tam ven - tu - ri sae - cu - li.
A - - - men.

86

V. Let us pray— to the Lord. R. Lord,— hear our prayer.

87

V. Let us pray to the Lord. R. Lord, hear us, hear our prayer.

88

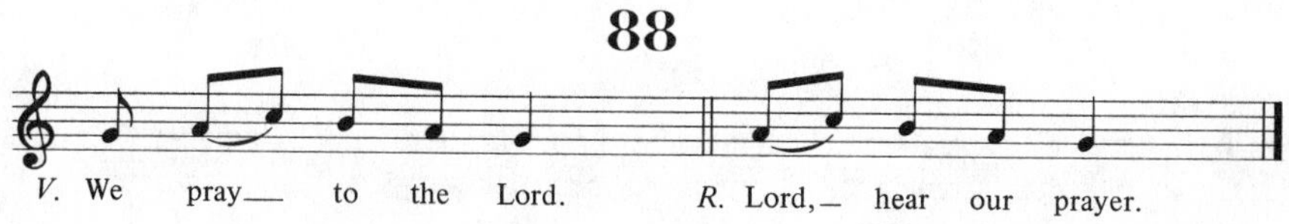
V. We pray— to the Lord. R. Lord,— hear our prayer.

89

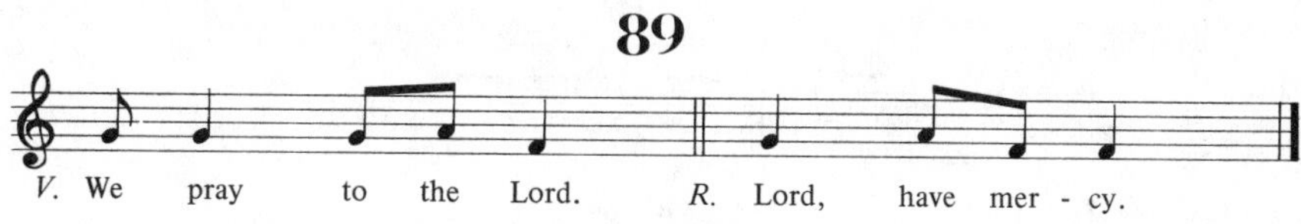
V. We pray to the Lord. R. Lord, have mer - cy.

90

V. Let us pray to the Lord. R. Lord, have mer - cy.

91

V. Let us pray to the Lord.
R. Lord, have mer - cy.
R. Lord, hear our prayer.
R. Hear us, O Lord.

92

V. The Lord be with you. R. And al - so with you.
V. Lift up your hearts R. We lift them
up to the Lord. V. Let us give thanks to the
Lord our God. R. It is right to give him thanks and praise.

93

V. The Lord be with you. R. And al - so
with you. V. Lift up your hearts.
R. We lift them up to the Lord.
V. Let us give thanks to the Lord our God.
R. It is right to give him thanks and praise.

94

Dennis Fitzpatrick, 1963, 1975

V. The Lord be with you. R. And al - so with you.
V. Lift up your hearts. R. We lift them up to the Lord.

V. Let us give thanks to the Lord our God.
V. It is right to give him thanks and praise.

95

Plainsong Melody, 13th cent.

Ho - ly, ho - ly, ho - ly Lord, God of pow'r and might,

heav - en and earth are full of your glo - ry. Ho - san - na

in the high - est. Bless - ed is he who comes in the name

of the Lord. Ho - san - na in the high - est.

96

Thomas McGuire, 1969

Ho - ly, ho - ly, ho - ly Lord, God of pow'r and_ might,
Heav - en and earth are full of your glo - ry. Ho - san - na in the
high - est. Bless - ed is he who comes in the name, who comes in the
name of the Lord. Ho - san - na in the high - est.

97

Plainsong Melody, 12th cent.
Sanc - tus, sanc-tus, sanc - tus Do - mi - nus
De-us Sa - - ba - oth. Ple - ni sunt coe - li
et ter - ra glo - ri - a tu - a. Ho - san - na in ex - cel -
sis. Be - ne - dic - tus qui ve - nit in no-mi-ne Do
mi - ni. Ho - san - na in ex - cel - sis.

98

John H. Olivier
Ho - ly, ho - ly, ho - ly,
Lord God of hosts. Heav - en and earth are filled with your
glo - ry, Ho - san - na in the high - est.
Bless - ed is he who comes in the name of the Lord, Ho -
san - na in the high - est.

99

D.J. Reagan, 1974

Lively 𝅗𝅥 = 84
Ho - ly, ho - ly, ho - ly Lord, God of pow'r and might,
heav - en and earth are full of your glo - ry,
Ho - san - na in the high - est, ho - san - na in the high - est,
Fine
ho - san - na in the high - est, ho - san - na in the high - est.

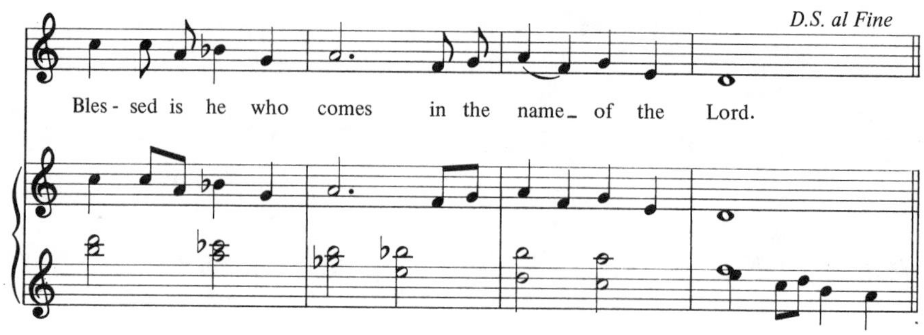
D.S. al Fine
Bles - sed is he who comes in the name of the Lord.

100

Pr: Let us pray . . . in the words our Sav - ior gave us.

Our Fa - ther, who art in heav - en, hal - lowed be thy name;

thy king - dom come; thy will be done on earth as it is in heav - en.

Give us this day our dai - ly bread; and for - give us our tres - pass - es
as we for - give those who tres - pass a - gainst us; and lead us
not in - to temp - ta - tion, but de - liv - er us from e - vil.
Pr: De - liv - er us . . . our Sav - ior Je - sus Christ. All: For the king -
dom, the pow'r and the glo - ry are yours, now and for ev - er.

101

Our Fa - ther in heav - en, ho - ly be your name,
your king - dom come, your will be done on earth as in heav - en.
Give us to - day our dai - ly bread. For - give us our sins,
as we for - give those who sin a - gainst us. Do not bring us
to the test, but de - liv - er us from e - vil.

102

Plainsong Melody

All: Pa - ter no - ster, qui es in cae - lis: san - cti - fi - ce - tur_ no - men tu - um;
ad - ve - ni - at re - gnum tu - um; fi - at vo - lun - tas tu - a, sic - ut in
cae - lo___ et___ in ter - ra. Pa - nem no - strum co - ti - di - a - num da
no - bis ho - di - e; et di - mit - te no - bis de - bi - ta no - stra, sic - ut et
nos di - mit - ti - mus de - bi - to - ri - bus no - stris; et ne nos in - du - cas

in ten - ta - ti - o - nem; sed li - be - ra nos a ma - lo.
Pr: . . . et ad - ven - tum Sal - va - to - ris no-stri Je - su Chri - sti. All: Qui - a
tu - um est re - gnum, et po - te - stas, et glo - ri - a in sae - cu - la.

103

Plainsong Melody, 12th cent.

1,2. Lamb of God, you take a - way the sins of the world:
have mer - cy on us.
3. Lamb of God, you take a - way the sins of the world: grant us peace.

104

John H. Olivier

Lamb of God you take a - way the sins of the
world, have mer - cy on us. Lamb of God, you
take a - way the sins of the world, have mer - cy on
us. Lamb of God you take a -
way the sins of the world, grant us peace.

105

Thomas McGuire

1,2. Lamb of God, you take a - way the sins of ___ the world: have mer - cy on ___ us. 3. Lamb of God, you take a - way the sins of ___ the world: grant us ___ peace.

106

Plainsong Melody, 15th cent.

1,3 A - gnus ___ De - i, qui tol - lis ___ pec - ca -

Fine

ta — mun - di: 1 mi - se - re - re ——— no - bis.
3 do - na no - bis ——— pa - cem.

2 A - gnus — De - i, qui tol - lis pec - ca - ta —

D.C.

mun - di: mi - se - re - re ——— no - bis.

107

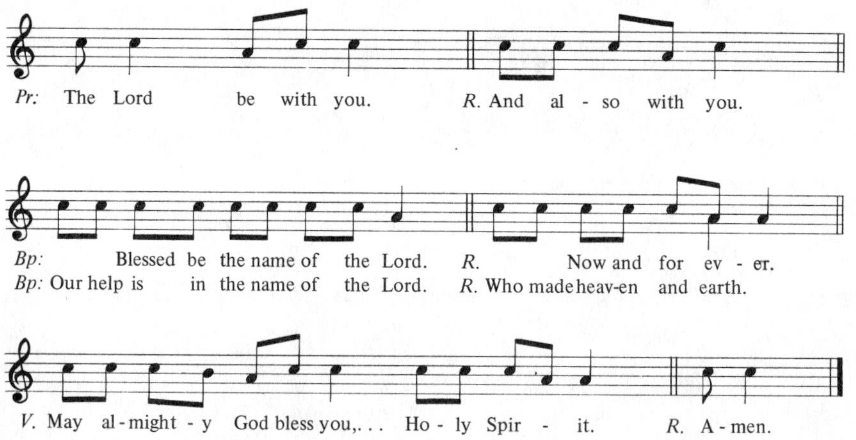
Pr: The Lord be with you. *R.* And al - so with you.
Bp: Blessed be the name of the Lord. *R.* Now and for ev - er.
Bp: Our help is in the name of the Lord. *R.* Who made heav-en and earth.
V. May al-might - y God bless you,. . . Ho - ly Spir - it. *R.* A - men.

108

Pr. The Lord be with you. *R.* And al - so with you.

Bp: Blessed be the name of the Lord. *R.* Now and for ev - er.
Bp: Our help is in the name of the Lord. *R.* Who made heav-en and earth.

V. May al-might-y God bless you, . . . Ho - ly Spir - it. *R.* A - men.

109

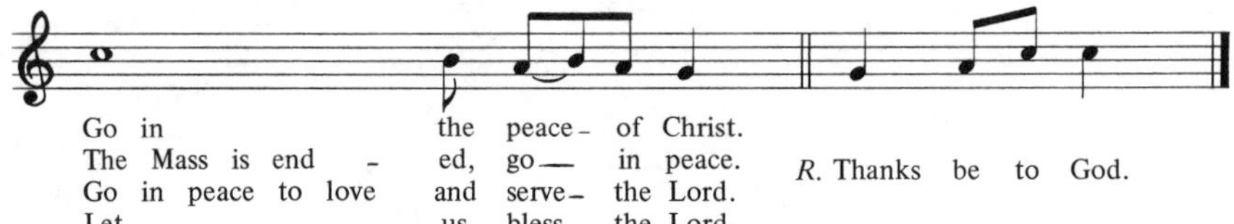
Go in the peace of Christ.
The Mass is end - ed, go in peace.
Go in peace to love and serve the Lord.
Let us bless the Lord.
R. Thanks be to God.

Hymns and Songs

Hymns and Songs

While most of the musical needs for liturgy were well served in the past by Gregorian plainsong and the polyphony provided by trained choirs, the change from Latin into vernacular disclosed a poverty of English language music in the Roman Church in the United States. It is true that we had a small repertoire of devotional hymns and some seasonal selections especially for Christmas and Lent. But, by and large, our use of hymns was primarily extra-liturgical and, not infrequently, songs in the vernacular were banned from liturgical service.

The use of English, the encouragement of congregational participation especially through song, the awkwardness of wedding Gregorian chant to our native vowels and consonants and the absence of a ready collection of native hymns directed our search elsewhere. Other Catholic countries had, indeed, long experienced a rich collection of vernacular hymns as evidenced, for example, in the great diocesan hymnals of Cologne, Speyer, Augsburg. Flanders and France also provided a tradition of "Congregational" singing in the vernacular. In fact, these sources supplied, by way of translation, other English speaking Christian denominations with congregational hymnals for their church services. Indeed, one could say that the first concrete—although not necessarily conscious—expression of ecumenicism manifested itself in song as evidence in the hymnals of the Anglican, Lutheran and Reformed traditions.

The Catholic Liturgy Book contains hymns which have been chosen from various lands, time periods, and traditions. While they reveal a universality and Christian ecumenicism, they have been explicitly chosen and edited to serve our own particular liturgical needs as well as adhering to our tradition of devotional song. For this reason, the user will note that the hymns are chosen primarily as a congregational function to be used throughout the various seasons of the church year and for special moments in the eucharistic liturgy and the celebrations of the sacraments. Particular consideration has been given to selections which will compliment our new lectionary and the biblical orientation of our faith.

Vatican II has repeatedly emphasized that liturgical experience is deepened and made more genuine by the use of song. Consequently, new forms of music for worship will necessarily appear along with revitalized traditional ones. Church musicians should continue and nourish their creative talents by providing new hymns. This on-going process, however, is by nature experimental, slow and often directed to a special or unique occasion or situation. Consequently, even though a particular hymn or composer might be in vogue in this or that part of the country our editorial committee was determined not to be guided by mere popularity but preferred to see how a composition would weather the time.

The hymns of *The Catholic Liturgy Book* should meet all the needs for normal liturgical and extra-liturgical services and, in time, provide the congregation with a rich and varied repertoire. Of equal importance, the hymns should be an expression of the Church's faith. Their texts will prove to be instructive and informative and as such, should provide another medium of Christian education. Truly, music should stir the faithful and elicit an enthusiastic and appropriate response to our call to worship.

200

CONDITOR ALME SIDERUM
7th cent.
Tr., Peter Scagnelli, 1972

CONDITOR ALME SIDERUM
L. M.
Plainsong Melody

1 Creator of the stars of night, Your faithful people's lasting Light: O Christ, Redeemer of us all, Be near and hear us when we call.
2 In sorrow that the ancient curse Should doom to death a universe, You came, urged on by gen'rous love, To be our healing from above.
3 As earth drew near to evening's hour, Your cross became our saving pow'r, And from the loving Virgin's shrine You came, a victim, Lord divine.
4 At your blest name, majestic now, All knees must bend, all hearts must bow; Your awesome pow'r all creatures know On earth and in the depths below.
5 Mankind's great Judge that final day, Be with us as in faith we pray: With gifts of grace your people free And save us from our enemy.
6 Lord Jesus Christ, most loving King, Our grateful praises now we sing. To Father, Son and Spirit be All glory giv'n eternally. Amen.

201

THE KING SHALL COME
From a Greek text
John Brownlie, 1907, alt.

Lower Key at No. 202

ST. STEPHEN
C. M.
William Jones, 1789

1 The King shall come when morn-ing dawns And light tri - umph-ant breaks;
2 Not, as of old, a lit - tle child To suf - fer and to die,
3 The King shall come when morn-ing dawns And earth's dark night is past;
4 And let the end - less bliss be - gin, By wea - ry saints fore - told,

1 When beau - ty gilds the east - ern hills And life to joy a - wakes.
2 But crowned with glo - ry like the sun That lights the morn - ing sky.
3 O haste the ris - ing of that morn Whose day shall ev - er last.
4 When right shall tri - umph o - ver wrong, And truth shall be ex - tolled.

5 The King shall come when morning dawns
And light and beauty brings:
Hail, Christ the Lord! Your people pray:
Come quickly, King of Kings.

202

HARK! THE GLAD SOUND
Phillip Doddridge, 1735, alt.

Higher Key at No. 201

ST. STEPHEN
C. M.
William Jones, 1789

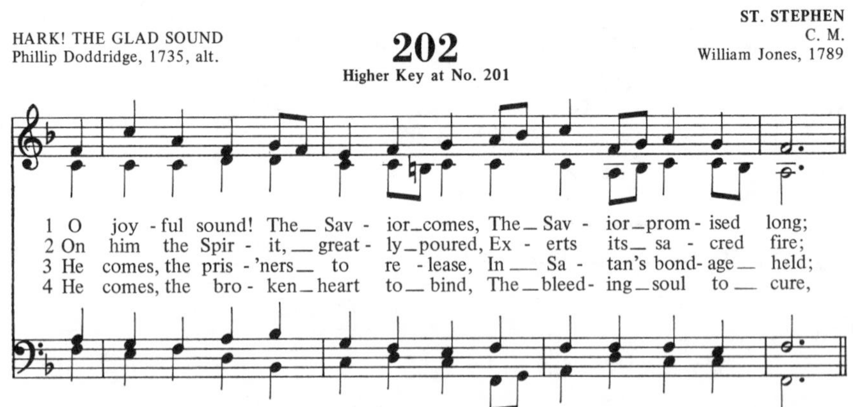
1 O joy - ful sound! The Sav - ior comes, The Sav - ior prom - ised long;
2 On him the Spir - it, great - ly poured, Ex - erts its sa - cred fire;
3 He comes, the pris - 'ners to re - lease, In Sa - tan's bond - age held;
4 He comes, the bro - ken heart to bind, The bleed - ing soul to cure,

1 Let ev - 'ry heart pre - pare a throne, And ev - 'ry voice a song.
2 And wis - dom, might, and zeal, and love His sa - cred heart in - spire.
3 The gates of brass be - fore him burst, The i - ron fet - ters yield.
4 And with the treas - ures of his grace To bless the hum - ble poor.

5 Our glad hosannas, Prince of Peace,
Your welcome shall proclaim,
And heav'n's eternal arches ring
With your belovèd name.

WHEN CAME IN FLESH
J. Anstice, 1808-36

203

SHADDICK
C. M.
Bates G. Burt, 1941

1 When in the flesh came God's own Word, The heed - less world slept on, And
2 When comes the Sav - ior at the last, From east to west shall shine The
3 Lord, who could dare see you de - scend In state, un - less he knew That
4 Dwell in our hearts, O Sav - ior blest; So shall your ad - vent's dawn Be
1 on - ly sim - ple shep - herds heard That God had sent his Son.
2 won - drous pomp, and earth, a - larmed, Shall trem - ble at the sign.
3 you were sor - r'wing sin - ners' friend, The gra - cious and the true?
4 but the veil that hides you, Lord, And by your love with - drawn.

COME, THOU LONG–EXPECTED JESUS
Charles Wesley, 1744, alt.

204

Higher Key at No. 233

STUTTGART
87. 87
Christian Friedrich Witt, 1715

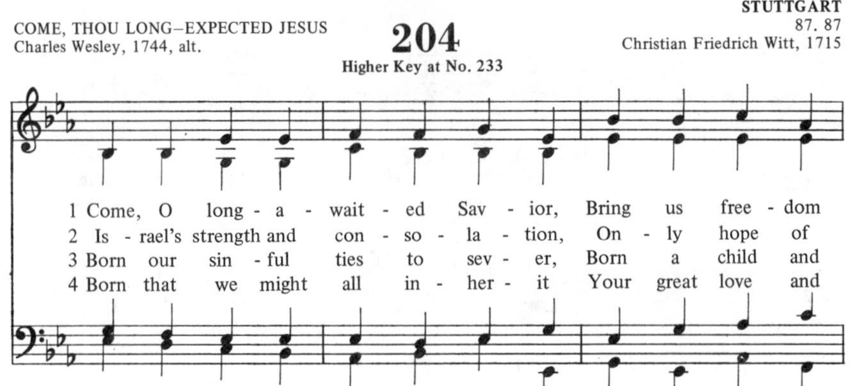
1 Come, O long - a - wait - ed Sav - ior, Bring us free - dom
2 Is - rael's strength and con - so - la - tion, On - ly hope of
3 Born our sin - ful ties to sev - er, Born a child and
4 Born that we might all in - her - it Your great love and

1 from our sin; From our fears and doubts re - lease us;
2 all the earth; Dear de - sire of ev - 'ry na - tion,
3 yet a king, Born to reign in us for - ev - er,
4 life and light, By your all - suf - fi - cient mer - it

1 Give us peace and joy with - in.
2 Come and teach us our true worth.
3 Now your gra - cious king - dom bring.
4 Raise us to your hon - ored right. A - men.

5 Honor, glory, might and blessing
To the Father and the Son,
With the everlasting Spirit,
While unending ages run. Amen.

205

VOX CLARA ECCE INTONAT
ascr. St. Ambrose, c. 397
Tr., Edward Caswall, 1849, alt.

TRUST
87. 87
Felix Mendelssohn, 1840

1 Hark! a thril - ling voice is __ sound - ing! "Christ is near" we hear it __ say, "Cast a - way the works of __ dark - ness, O you __ chil - dren of the __ day."

2 Wak - ened by __ the sol - emn warn - ing, Let __ the earth - bound soul a - rise; Christ, her Sun, all sloth dis - pel - ling, Shines up - on the __ morn - ing __ skies.

3 See, the Lamb, so long ex - pect - ed, Comes with par - don down from heav'n; Let us haste, with tears of __ sor - row, One and __ all, to __ be for - giv'n:

4 That, when next he comes in __ glo - ry And __ the world is wrapped in fear, He may shield us with his __ mer - cy And with __ words of __ love draw near.

A - men.

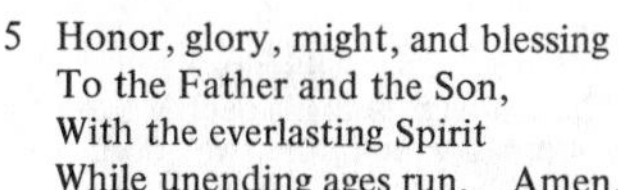

5 Honor, glory, might, and blessing
To the Father and the Son,
With the everlasting Spirit
While unending ages run. Amen.

206

JORDANIS ORAS PRAEVIA
Charles Coffin, 1763
Tr., John Chandler, 1837, alt.

Higher Key at No. 255[2]

WINCHESTER NEW
L. M.
Musikalisches Handbuch, Hamburg, 1690

1 On Jor - dan's bank the Bap - tist's cry An - nounc - es that the
2 Then cleansed be ev - 'ry heart from sin; Make straight the way of
3 For you are our sal - va - tion, Lord, Our ref - uge and our
4 To heal the sick stretch out your hand, And help the fall - en
1 Lord is nigh; A - wake and hark - en, for he brings Glad
2 God with - in; Let each one his own heart pre - pare For
3 great re - ward; Once more up - on your peo - ple shine, And
4 sin - ner stand; Shine forth and let your light re - store Earth's
1 tid - ings of the King of kings.
2 Christ to come and en - ter there.
3 fill the world with love di - vine.
4 own true love - li - ness once more. A - men.

5 To God the Son all glory be,
Whose advent sets his people free,
Whom with the Father we adore
And Holy Spirit evermore, Amen.

207

Based on Psalm 24
MACHT HOCH DIE TÜR
George Weissel, 1642
Tr., Catherine Winkworth, alt.

Higher Key at No. 502

TRURO
L. M.
Psalmodia Evangelica, 1789

1 Lift up your heads, O migh - ty gates, Be-
2 O blest the land, the ci - ty blest, Where
3 Fling wide the por - tals of your heart; Make
4 Re - deem-er, come! We o - pen wide Our
1 hold, the King of glo - ry waits! The
2 Christ, the rul - er, is con - fessed! O
3 it a tem - ple set a - part From
4 hearts to you; here, Lord, a - bide! Let
1 King of kings is draw - ing near; The
2 hap - py hearts and hap - py homes To
3 sel - fish use for his em - ploy, A-
4 us your in - ner pre - sence feel; Your
1 Sav - ior of the world is here!
2 which this King in tri - umph comes!
3 dorned with prayer and love and joy.
4 grace and love in us re - veal.

5 So come, Redeemer; enter in!
Let new and nobler life begin;
May God the Spirit guide us on
Until the glorious crown is won.

208

Based on Isaiah 40
COMFORT MY PEOPLE
St. Joseph's Abbey, 1967

CONSOLAMINI
10 10. 10 10
F. V. Strahan, 1972
Harm. by Jerry R. Brubaker

1 Com - fort my peo - ple and qui - et her fear;
2 Say to the cit - ies of Ju - dah: "Be - hold!
3 Moun - tains and hills shall be - come like a plain.
1 Tell her the time of sal - va - tion draws near.
2 Gen - tle, yet might - y, the arm of the Lord
3 Van - ished are mourn - ing and hun - ger and pain;
1 Tell her I come to re - move all her shame;
2 Res - cues the cap - tives of dark - ness and sin,
3 Nev - er a - gain shall these war a - gainst you;
1 "She that is pit - ied" shall be her new name.
2 Bring - ing them jus - tice and joy with - out end."
3 "See, he comes quick - ly to make all things new!"

209

INSTANTIS ADVENTUM DEI
Charles Coffin, 1736
Tr., Roger Nachtwey, 1974

Lower Key at No. 435

WILLIAMS (ST. THOMAS)
S. M.
Aaron Williams, 1763

1 The com - ing of our God We seek in
2 The ev - er - last - ing Son Comes down to
3 O Zi - on, rise in haste To meet the
4 As Judge, on glis - t'ning clouds, The Vic - tor
1 ar - dent prayer; In joy we'll meet him
2 Mar - y's womb; He bears our hu - man
3 meek and mild; Throw wide your arms; em-
4 comes a - gain To take his mem - bers
1 on the way And sing our prais - es there.
2 serv - i - tude To save us from our doom.
3 brace the peace Brought by this ho - ly child.
4 back in joy With him to heav - en then.

5 Let dark and evil deeds
Retreat before his dawn;
Our new life must advance in grace;
The old one must be gone.

6 We praise your Father blest;
Your Spirit, too, we praise;
Emancipator, Christ, our Lord,
We'll praise you all our days!

210

VENI, VENI, EMMANUEL
9th cent.
Tr., Thomas Helmore, 1854, alt.

VENI, EMMANUEL
L. M. with Chorus
Melody adapted from plainsong, Mode I,
By Thomas Helmore, 1854

1 O come, O come, Em - man - u - el, And ran - som cap - tive
2 O come, O Wis - dom from on high, And or - der all things
3 O come, O come, O Lord of might, Who to your tribes on
4 O come, O Rod of Jes - se's stem, From ev - 'ry foe de-
5 O Key of Da - vid, come once more, And op - en wide the
6 O come, O Day - spring from on high, And cheer us by your
7 O come De - sire of na - tions, bind All peo - ples in one
1 Is - ra - el That mourns in lone - ly ex - ile here
2 far and nigh; To us the path of knowl - edge show
3 Si - nai's height In an - cient times be - stowed the law
4 liv - er them Who trust your migh - ty pow'r to save,
5 heav'n - ly door; Make safe the way that leads on high,
6 draw - ing nigh; Dis - perse the gloom - y clouds of night
7 heart and mind; Bid en - vy, strife, and quar - rels cease,
1 Un - til the Son of God ap - pear.
2 And cause us in her way to go.
3 In cloud and ma - jes - ty and awe.
4 And give them vict 'ry o'er the grave.
5 That we no more have cause to sigh.
6 And death's dark shad - ow put to flight.
7 And fill the world with heav en's peace.
Refrain
Re - joice! re - joice!

O Is - ra - el! To you shall come E - man - u - el.

REGENT SQUARE
87. 87. 87

211

ANGELS FROM THE REALMS OF GLORY
James Montgomery, 1816, 1825, alt.

Henry Smart, 1867

Lower Key at No. 473 (Second Tune)

1 An - gels, from the realms of glo - ry, Wing your flight o'er all the earth;
2 Shep-herds, in the fields a - bid - ing, Watch - ing o'er your flocks by night,
3 Sag - es, leave your con - tem-pla-tions, Bright-er Vi - sions beam a - far;
4 Saints, be - fore the al - tar bend-ing, Watch - ing long in hope and fear,

1 As you sang cre - a - tion's sto - ry, Now pro - claim Mes - si - ah's birth:
2 God with man is_ now re - sid - ing, Yon - der shines the_ in - fant Light:
3 Seek the great De - sire of na - tions; You have seen his_ na - tal star:
4 Sud - den - ly the_ Lord, de - scend - ing, In his tem - ple_ shall ap - pear:

Come and wor - ship, come and wor - ship, Wor - ship Christ, the_ new - born King!

212

VENI, REDEMPTOR GENITUM
ascr. St. Ambrose, c. 397
Paraphrased by Martin Luther, 1524
Tr., William M. Reynolds, 1850, alt.

Lower Key at No. 267

NUN KOMM, DER HEIDEN HEILAND
77. 77
After a plainsong melody
Eyn Enchiridion, Erfurt, 1524

213

SING O SING THIS BLESSED MORN
Christopher Wordsworth, 1862, alt.

ENGLAND'S LANE
77. 77. 77
Traditional English Melody
Adapted by Geoffrey Shaw, 1919

1 Sav - ior of the na - tions, come;
2 From the Fa - ther forth __ he came,
3 You, the Fa - ther's on - ly Son,
4 Bright - ly does your man - ger shine;
1 Vir - gin's Son, make here your home. Mar - vel now, __ O
2 And __ re - turns un - to the same, Cap - tive lead - ing
3 Have __ o'er sin the vic - t'ry won. Bound-less shall __ your
4 Glo - rious is its light di - vine. Let not sin __ o'er
1 heav'n and earth, That the Lord chose such __ a birth.
2 death and hell. High the song of tri - umph swell!
3 king - dom be; When shall we its glo - ries see?
4 cloud this light; Ev - er be our faith __ thus bright.
1 Sing, O __ sing, this bless - ed morn, Un - to us a __ child is born
2 God of __ God, and Light of Light, Comes with mer - cies __ that he might
3 God with us, Em - man - u - el, Deigns for - ev - er __ now to dwell;
4 God comes down that man may rise, Lift - ed by him __ to the skies;

1 Un - to us a son is giv'n, God him - self comes down from heav'n.
2 Join now in a won - drous plan Heav'n to earth and God to man.
3 He on Ad - am's fall - en race Sheds the full - ness of his grace.
4 Christ is Son of man that we Sons of God in him may be.
Sing, O sing, this bless - ed morn, Je - sus Christ to - day is born.

5 O renew us, Lord, we pray,
With your Spirit day by day,
That we ever may be true
To the Father and to you.

Luke 2:8-15
WHILE SHEPHERDS WATCHED
Nahum Tate, 1700, alt.

214[1]
Higher Key

WINCHESTER OLD
C. M.
Thomas Est's *Whole Book of Psalmes,* 1592

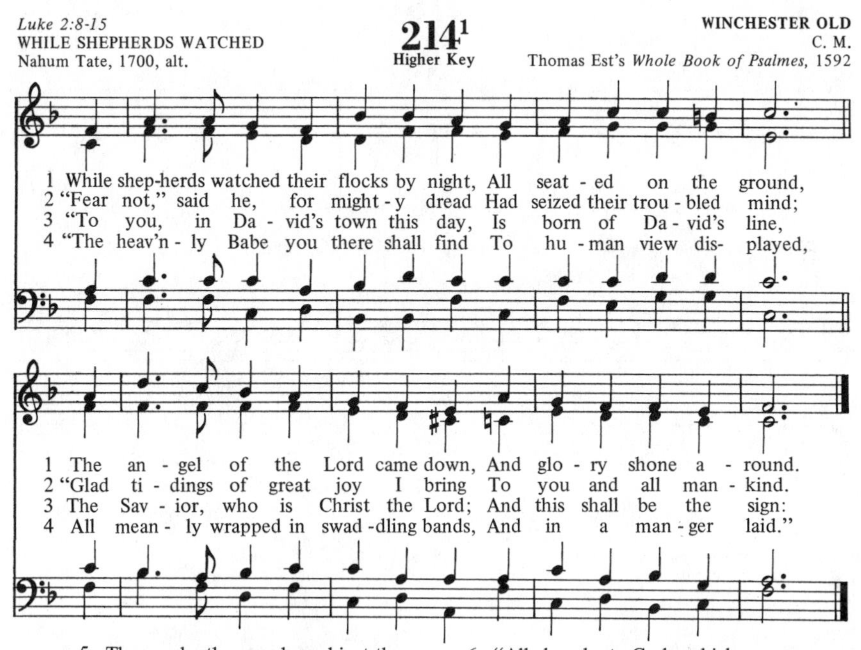
1 While shep-herds watched their flocks by night, All seat - ed on the ground,
2 "Fear not," said he, for might - y dread Had seized their trou - bled mind;
3 "To you, in Da - vid's town this day, Is born of Da - vid's line,
4 "The heav'n - ly Babe you there shall find To hu - man view dis- played,
1 The an - gel of the Lord came down, And glo - ry shone a - round.
2 "Glad ti - dings of great joy I bring To you and all man - kind.
3 The Sav - ior, who is Christ the Lord; And this shall be the sign:
4 All mean - ly wrapped in swad - dling bands, And in a man - ger laid."

5 Thus spoke the seraph, and just then
Appeared a shining throng
Of angels praising God, who thus
Addressed their joyful song:

6 "All glory be to God on high,
And on the earth be peace;
Good will hence forth from heav'n to men
Begin and never cease."

214[2]

Lower Key

CHRISTIANS, AWAKE
John Byrom, 1749, alt.

215

Lower Key at No. 522

YORKSHIRE (STOCKPORT)
10 10. 10 10. 10 10
John Wainwright, 1750

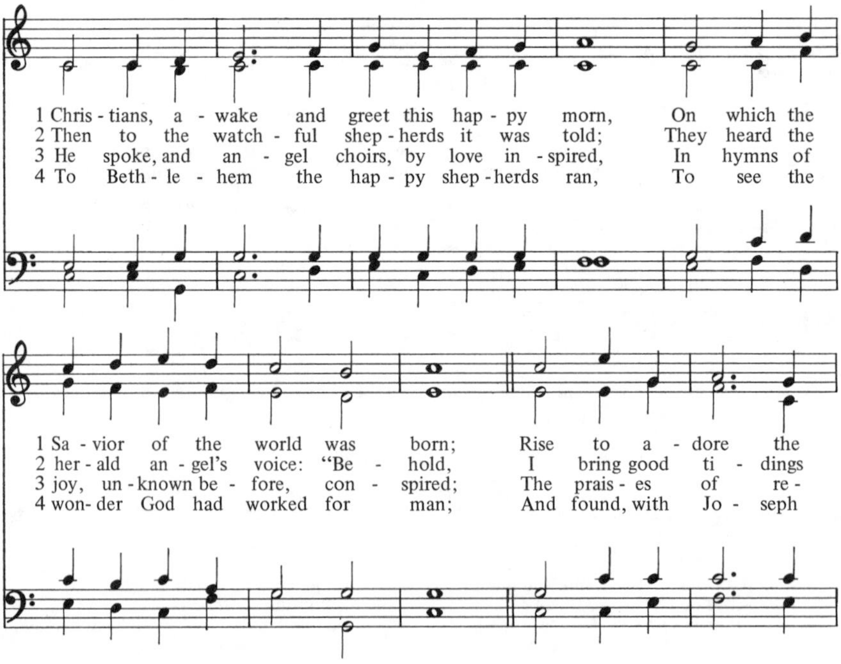

1 Chris - tians, a - wake and greet this hap - py morn, On which the
2 Then to the watch - ful shep - herds it was told; They heard the
3 He spoke, and an - gel choirs, by love in - spired, In hymns of
4 To Beth - le - hem the hap - py shep - herds ran, To see the

1 Sa - vior of the world was born; Rise to a - dore the
2 her - ald an - gel's voice: "Be - hold, I bring good ti - dings
3 joy, un - known be - fore, con - spired; The prais - es of re -
4 won - der God had worked for man; And found, with Jo - seph

1 mys - ter - y of love, Which hosts of an - gels chant - ed
2 of a Sa - vior's birth To you and all the na - tions
3 deem- ing love they sang, And all the heav'ns with al - le -
4 and the bless - ed maid, Her Son, the Sa - vior, in a
1 from a - bove; With them the joy - ful ti - dings first be -
2 on the earth: This day has God ful - filled his prom - ised
3 lu - ias rang; God's high - est glo - ry was their an - them
4 man - ger laid; Grate - ful, the won - drous sto - ry they pro -
1 gan Of Vir - gin's Son, our Sa - vior, God and Man.
2 word, This day is born a Sa - vior, Christ the Lord."
3 still, Peace on the earth, and un - to men good will.
4 claim, The first great her - alds of the Sa - vior's name.

5 Let us, like Mary ponder in our mind
God's wondrous love in saving lost mankind;
Trace we the Babe, who has retrieved our loss,
From his poor manger to his bitter cross;
Treading his steps, assisted by his grace,
Till man's first heav'nly state again takes place.

6 Then may we hope, with all the angel throng,
To sing, redeemed, a glad triumphal song;
He that was born upon this joyful day
Around us all his glory shall display;
Saved by his love, incessant we shall sing
Eternal praise to heav'n's Almighty King.

O LITTLE TOWN OF BETHLEHEM
Phillips Brooks, 1867
216
ST. LOUIS
86. 86. 76. 86.
Louis H. Redner, 1868
1 O lit - tle town of Beth - le - hem, How
2 For Christ is born of Mar - y; And
3 How si - lent - ly, how si - lent - ly The
4 O ho - ly Child of Beth - le - hem, De-
1 still we see thee lie; A-
2 gath - ered all a - bove, While
3 won - drous gift is giv'n! So
4 scend to us, we pray; Cast
1 bove thy deep and dream - less sleep The
2 mor - tals sleep, the an - gels keep Their
3 God im - parts to hu - man hearts The
4 out our sin and en - ter in, Be
1 si - lent stars go by. Yet
2 watch of won - d'ring love. O
3 bless - ings of his heav'n. No
4 born in us to - day. We

CHRISTMAS

1 in thy dark streets shin - eth The
2 morn - ing stars, to - geth - er Pro-
3 ear may hear his com - ing, But
4 hear the Christ - mas an - gels The
1 ev - er - last - ing Light; The
2 claim the ho - ly birth; And
3 in this world of sin, Where
4 great glad ti - dings tell; O
1 hopes and fears of all the years Are
2 prais - es sing to God the King, And
3 meek souls will re - ceive him, still The
4 come to us, a - bide with us, Our
1 met in thee to - night.
2 peace to men on earth.
3 dear Christ en - ters in.
4 Lord, Em - man - u - el! A - men!

217

Based on Psalm 98:5-9
JOY TO THE WORLD
Isaac Watts, 1719

ANTIOCH
C. M.
Attr. to George Frederick Handel, 1742
Mason's *The Modern Psalmist,* 1839
Arr. by Robert Carwithen, 1972

1 Joy to the world! the Lord is come; Let
2 Joy to the world! the Sav - ior reigns; Let
3 No more let sins and sor - rows grow, Nor
4 He rules the world with truth and grace, And

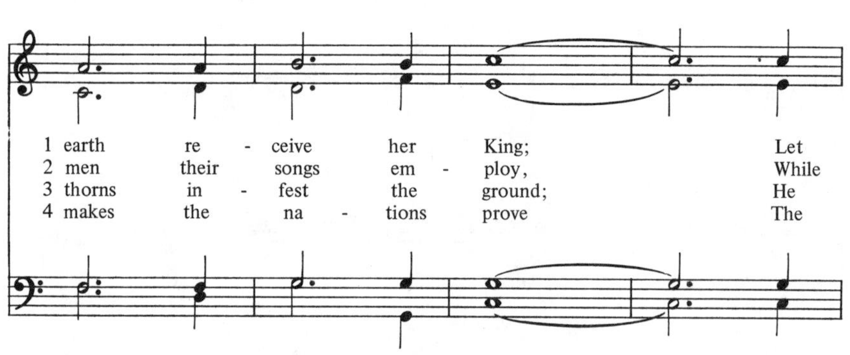
1 earth re - ceive her King; Let
2 men their songs em - ploy, While
3 thorns in - fest the ground; He
4 makes the na - tions prove The

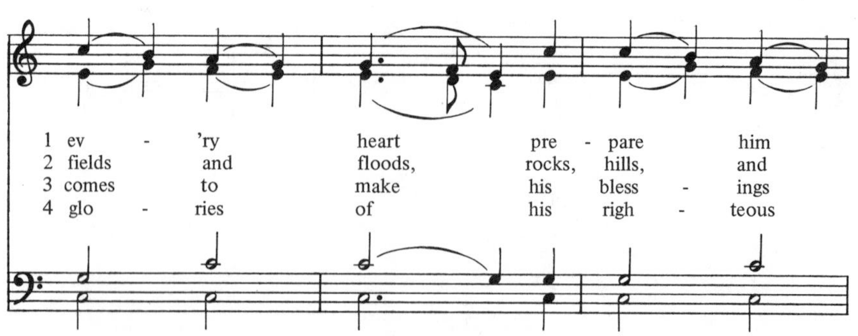
1 ev - 'ry heart pre - pare him
2 fields and floods, rocks, hills, and
3 comes to make his bless - ings
4 glo - ries of his righ - teous

CHRISTMAS

1 room, And heav'n and na - ture sing, And
2 plains Re - peat the sound - ing joy, Re -
3 flow Far as the curse is found, Far
4 ness, And won - ders of his love, And
And heav'n and na - ture
Re - peat the sound-ing
Far as the curse is
And won-ders of his

1 heav'n and na - ture sing, And heav'n and
2 peat the sound - ing joy, Re - peat, re-
3 as the curse is found, Far as, far
4 won - ders of his love, And won - ders,
sing, And heav'n and na - ture sing, And
joy, Re - peat the sound - ing joy, Re-
found, Far as the curse is found, Far
love, And won - ders of his love, And

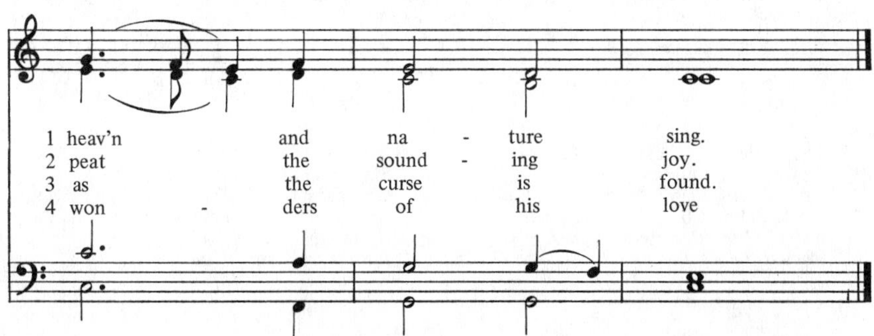
1 heav'n and na - ture sing.
2 peat the sound - ing joy.
3 as the curse is found.
4 won - ders of his love

THE FIRST NOWELL
Old English Carol

218

THE FIRST NOWELL
Traditional Melody, pub. 1833

1 The first Now - ell the an - gel did say was to cer - tain poor
2 They look - ed up and saw a star shin-ing in the
3 And by the light of that same star, Three Wise Men
4 This star drew nigh to the north - west, o'er Beth - le -
1 shep - herds in fields as they lay, In fields where they lay
2 east be - yond them far, And to the earth it
3 came from coun - try far, To seek for a king was
4 hem it took its rest, And there it did both
1 keep-ing their sheep, on a cold win - ter's night that was so deep. *Now -*
2 gave great light, and so it con - tin - ued both day and night. *Now -*
3 their in - tent, and to fol - low the star wher - ev - er it went. *Now -*
4 stop and stay, right o - ver the place where Je - sus lay. *Now -*
ell, Now - ell, Now - ell, Now - ell, Born is the King of Is - ra - el! A-men.

5 Then entered in those Wise Men three,
Fell rev'rently upon their knee,
And offered there in his presence their
Gold, and myrrh, and frankincense.
Nowell, Nowell, Nowell, Nowell,
Born is the King of Israel!

6 Then let us all with one accord
Sing praises to our heav'nly Lord,
Who has made heav'n and earth of naught,
And with his blood mankind has bought.
Nowell, Nowell, Nowell, Nowell,
Born is the King of Israel!

219

STILLE NACHT
Joseph Mohr, 1818
Tr., John Freeman Young, c. 1863

STILLE NACHT
Irregular
Franz Grüber, 1818

1 Si - lent night, ho - ly night! All is calm, all is bright
Stil - le Nacht, heil - i - ge Nacht! Al - les schlaft, ein - sam wacht
2 Si - lent night, ho - ly night! Shep-herds quake at the sight;
Stil - le Nacht, heil - i - ge Nacht! Hir - ten erst kund - ge - macht
1 Round yon vir - gin - moth-er and Child. Ho - ly In -fant so ten - der and mild,
Nur das trau - te, hoch - heil - i - ge Paar. Hold- er Kna - be im lock - i - gen Haar,
2 Glo - ries stream from hea - ven a - far, Heav'n - ly hosts sing "Al - le - lu - ia!"
Durch der En - gel "Al - le - lu - ia," Tont es laut von fern und nah:

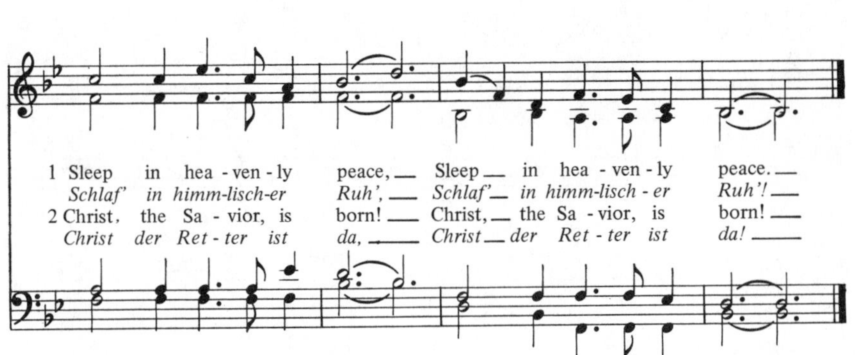
1 Sleep in hea - ven - ly peace, Sleep in hea - ven - ly peace.
Schlaf' in himm-lisch-er Ruh', Schlaf' in himm-lisch - er Ruh'!
2 Christ, the Sa - vior, is born! Christ, the Sa - vior, is born!
Christ der Ret - ter ist da, Christ der Ret - ter ist da!

3 Silent night, holy night!
Son of God, love's pure light
Radiant beams from thy holy face
With the dawn of redeeming grace,
Jesus, Lord, at thy birth,
Jesus, Lord, at thy birth.

3 Stille Nacht, heilige Nacht!
Gottes Sohn, o wie lacht
Lieb' aus deinem göttlichen Mund,
Da uns schlägt die rettende Stund':
Christ, in deiner Geburt,
Christ, in deiner Geburt!

IT CAME UPON THE MIDNIGHT CLEAR
Edmund Hamilton Sears, alt.
220
CAROL
C.M.D.
Richard Storrs Willis, 1850
1 It came up - on the mid - night clear, That
2 Still through the clo - ven skies they come With
3 Yet with the woes of sin and strife The
4 And ye, be - neath life's crush - ing load, Whose
1 glo - rious song of old, From
2 peace - ful wings un - furled, And
3 world has suf - fered long; Be -
4 forms are bend - ing low, Who
1 an - gels bend - ing near the earth To
2 still their heav - 'nly mu - sic floats O'er
3 neath the heav - 'nly strain have rolled Two
4 toil a - long the climb - ing way With
1 touch their harps of gold: "Peace
2 all the wear - y world; A -
3 thou - sand years of wrong; And
4 pain - ful steps and slow, Look

CHRISTMAS
1 on the earth good will to men From heav'n's all gracious King." The world in solemn stillness lay To hear the angels sing.
2 bove its sad and lowly plains They bend on hov'ring wing, And ever o'er its Babel sounds The blessed angels sing.
3 man, at war with man, hears not The tidings which they bring; O hush the noise, ye men of strife, And hear the angels sing!
4 now! for glad and golden hours Come swiftly on the wing; O rest beside the weary road And hear the angels sing!

5 For lo! the days are hast'ning on,
By prophets seen of old,
When with the ever-circling years
Shall come the time foretold,

When peace shall over all the earth
Its ancient splendors fling,
And all the world give back the song
Which now the angels sing.

FRÖLICH SOLL MEIN HERZE SPRINGEN
Paulus Gerhardt, 1653
Tr., Catherine Winkworth, 1858, alt.

221

WARUM SOLLT ICH (EBELING) (BONN)
83. 36. D.
Johann Georg Ebeling, 1666

1 All my heart this day re - joic - es, As I hear,
2 Hark! a voice from yon - der man - ger, Soft and sweet,
3 Come, then, let us has - ten yon - der; Here let all,
4 You, dear Lord, with heed I'll cher - ish; Live to you,
1 Far and near, Sweet - est an - gel voic - es:
2 Does en - treat: "Flee from woe and dan - ger;
3 Great and small, Kneel in awe and won - der;
4 And, with you Dy - ing, shall not per - ish;
1 "Christ is born," their choirs are sing - ing, Till the air,
2 Broth - ers, come; from all that grieves you You are freed;
3 Love him, who with love is yearn - ing; Hail the star
4 But shall dwell with you for - ev - er, Far on high,
1 Ev - 'ry - where, Now with joy is ring - ing.
2 All you need I will sure - ly give you."
3 That from far Bright with hope is burn - ing!
4 In the joy That shall al - ter nev - er.

222

NOW YIELD WE THANKS
Howard Chandler Robbins, 1929, alt.

DARMSTADT
67. 67. 66. 66
Asasuerus Fritch, 1679
Arr. and Harm. by J. S. Bach

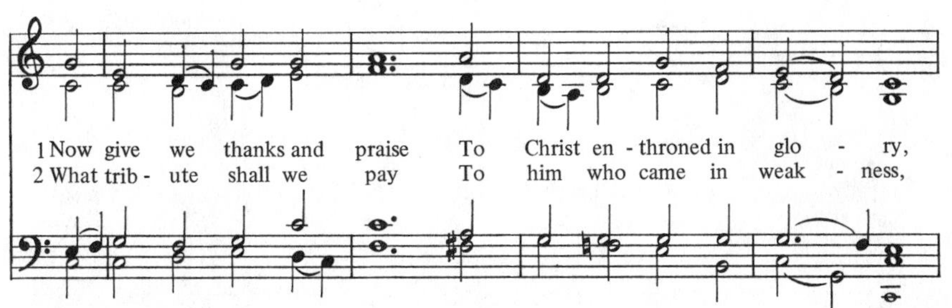
1 Now give we thanks and praise To Christ en - throned in glo - ry,
2 What trib - ute shall we pay To him who came in weak - ness,

1 And on this day of days Tell out re - demp - tions sto - ry,
2 And in a man-ger lay To teach his peo - ple meek - ness?

1 Who tru - ly have be - lieved That on this bless - ed morn,
2 Let ev - 'ry house be bright; Let prais - es nev - er cease:

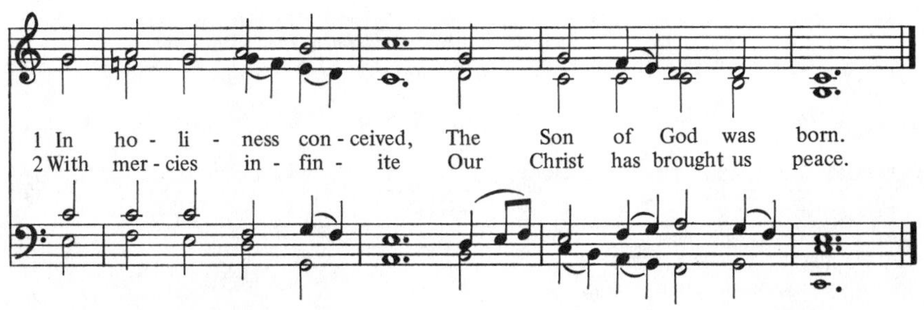
1 In ho - li - ness con - ceived, The Son of God was born.
2 With mer - cies in - fin - ite Our Christ has brought us peace.

Alternative Tune: "NUN DANKET."

223

BORN IN THE NIGHT
Geoffrey Ainger, 1964

MARY'S CHILD
Irregular
Geoffery Ainger, 1964
Harm. by Richard D. Wetzel, 1972

G
Em
Am
Cm6
1 Born in the night, Mar - y's Child, A
2 Clear shin - ing light, Mar - y's Child, Your
3 Truth of our life, Mar - y's Child, You
4 Hope of the world, Mar - y's Child, You're

G
Em
Am
D7
G
G+
1 long way from your home; Com - ing in need,
2 face lights up our way; Light of the world,
3 tell us God is good; Prove it is true,
4 com - ing soon to reign; King of the earth,

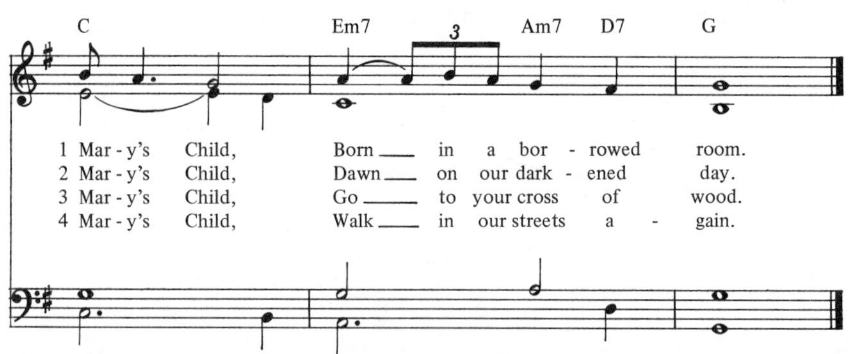
C
Em7
Am7
D7
G
1 Mar - y's Child, Born in a bor - rowed room.
2 Mar - y's Child, Dawn on our dark - ened day.
3 Mar - y's Child, Go to your cross of wood.
4 Mar - y's Child, Walk in our streets a - gain.

LES ANGES DANS NOS COMPAGNES
Anonymous, 18th cent.
Tr., in *Crown of Jesus,* 1862, alt.
224
GLORIA
77. 77, with Chorus
French carol
As in *Pilgrim Hymnal,* 1958
1 An - gels we have heard on high, Sweet - ly sing - ing o'er the plains,
2 Shep - herds, why this ju - bi - lee? Why your joy - ous strains pro - long?
3 Come to Beth - le - hem and see Him whose birth the an - gels sing;
4 See him in a man - ger laid Whom the an - gels praise a - bove;
1 And the moun - tains in re - ply Ech - o still their joy - ous strains.
2 Say what may the ti - dings be, Which in - spire your heav'n - ly song?
3 Come, a - dore on bend - ed knee Christ, the Lord, the new - born King.
4 Mar - y, Jo - seph, lend your aid, While we raise our hearts in love.
Glo - - - - - ri - a
in ex - cel - sis De - o,
Glo - - - - - - - - - - ri - a
in ex - cel - sis De - o.
A - men.

225

HARK HOW ALL THE WELKIN RINGS
Charles Wesley, 1739, alt.

MENDELSSOHN
77. 77. D, with Refrain
Felix Mendelssohn, 1840
Arr. by William H. Cummings, 1855

1 Hark! the her - ald an - gels sing, "Glo - ry to the new - born King;
2 Christ, by high - est heav'n a - dored; Christ, the ev - er - last - ing Lord!
3 Hail, the heav'n-born Prince of Peace! Hail the Sun of Right-eous-ness!
1 Peace on earth, and mer - cy mild, God and sin - ners rec - on - ciled!"
2 Late in time be - hold him come, Off - spring of the Vir - gin's womb:
3 Light and life to all he brings, Ris'n with heal - ing in his wings.
1 Joy - ful, all ye na - tions, rise, Join the tri - umph of the skies;
2 Veiled in flesh the God - head see; Hail th'in - car - nate De - i - ty,
3 Mild he lays his glo - ry by, Born that man no more may die,
1 With th'an - gel - ic host pro - claim: "Christ is born in Beth - le - hem!"
2 Pleased as man with men to dwell, Je - sus, our Em - man - u - el.
3 Born to raise the sons of earth, Born to give them sec - ond birth.
Hark! the her - ald an - gels sing, "Glo - ry to the new - born King!"

226

ONCE IN ROYAL DAVID'S CITY
Cecil Frances Alexander, 1848, alt.

IRBY
87. 87. 87
Henry J. Gauntlett, 1849

1 Once in roy - al Da - vid's cit - y Stood a low - ly
2 He came down to earth from heav - en Who is God and
3 Je - sus is our child - hood's pat - tern, Day by day like
4 And our eyes at last shall see him, Thru his own re -
1 cat - tle shed, Where a moth - er laid her ba - by
2 Lord of all And his shel - ter was a sta - ble
3 us he grew; He was lit - tle, weak, and help - less
4 deem - ing love; For that child so dear and gen - tle
1 In a man - ger for his bed: Mar - y was that
2 And his cra - dle was a stall: With the poor, and
3 Tears and smiles like us he knew: And he com - forts
4 Is our Lord in heav'n a - bove, And he leads his
1 moth - er mild, Je - sus Christ, her lit - tle child.
2 mean and low - ly, Lived on earth our Sav - ior ho - ly.
3 us in sad - ness, And he shares in all our glad - ness.
4 chil - dren on To the place where he has gone.

227

ADESTE, FIDELES
John F. Wade, 1711-86
Tr., Frederick Oakley, 1802-80. et al.

ADESTE, FIDELES
Irregular with Chorus
J. F. Wade's
Cantus Diversi, 1751

1 O come all ye faith - ful, Joy - ful and Tri -
A - des - te fi - de - les, Lae - ti tri - um -
2 Sing choirs of an - gels, Sing in ex - ul -
Can - tet nunc, "I - o!" Cho - rus an - gel -

1 um - phant O come, ye, O come, ye, To
phan - tes, Ve - ni - te, Ve - ni - te In
2 ta - tion, Sing, all ye cit - ti - zens Of
or - um; Can - tet nunc au - la Cae -

1 Beth - le - hem. Come and be -
Beth - le - hem. Na - tum vi -
2 heav'n a - bove: Glo - ry to
les - ti - um. Glo - ri - a

1 hold him Born, the King of an - gels.
de - te Re - gem an - gel - or - um.
2 God Glo - ry in the high - est!
glo - ria In ex - cel - sis De - o!
Refrain
O come, let us a - dore him, O come, let us a - dore him,
Ve ni - te, a - do - re - mus, Ve - ni - te, a - do - re - mus,
O come, let us a - dore him, Christ, the Lord!
Ve - ni - te, a - do - re - mus Do - mi - num!

3 Then tenderly greet him,
For our sakes made needy,
Homeless this night and in a
Manger laid.
Love so unsparing!
Who would not return it?
O come, let us adore him.

4 Yea, Lord, we greet thee,
Born this happy morning;
Jesus, to thee be
All glory giv'n;
Word of the Father,
Now in flesh appearing.
O come, let us adore him.

3 Pro nobis egenum
Et fœno cubantem
Piis foveamus
Amplexibus.
Sic nos amentem
Quis non redamaret?
Venite, adoremus.

4 Ergo, qui natus
Die hodierna,
Jesu, tibi
Sit gloria:
Patris æterni
Verbum caro factum!
Venite, adoremus.

GOOD CHRISTIAN MEN, REJOICE
Based on a medieval carol
John Mason Neale, 1853

228

IN DULCI JUBILO
66. 77. 78. 55
ascr. Henry Suso, d. 1366

1 Good Chris-tian men, re - joice __ With heart and soul and voice! __
2 Good Chris-tian men, re - joice __ With heart and soul and voice! __
3 Good Chris-tian men, re - joice __ With heart and soul and voice! __
1 Give ye heed to what we say: Je - sus Christ is born _ to - day.
2 Now ye hear of end - less bliss; Je - sus Christ was born _ for this!
3 Now ye need not fear the grave; Je - sus Christ was born _ to save!
1 Ox and ass be - fore him bow, And he is in _ the man - ger now.
2 He has oped the heav'n-ly door, And man is bless-ed ev - er - more.
3 Calls you one and calls you all To gain his ev - er - last - ing hall.
1 Christ is born to - day! __ Christ is born to - day! __
2 Christ was born for this! __ Christ was born for this! __
3 Christ was born to save! __ Christ was born to save! __

Based on Luke 2:15
VON HIMMEL HOCH
Martin Luther, 1535
Tr., Winfred Douglas, 1939

229

VON HIMMEL HOCH
L. M.
Geistliche Lieder, Leipzig, 1539

1 "From heav - en high I come to you; I bring you ti - dings
2 "For you a lit - tle child is born Of God's own cho - sen
3 "Lo, he is Christ, the Lord in - deed, Our God, to guide you
5 We sing the praise and glo - ry due, O Je - sus, vir - gin

1 good and new, Good ti - dings of great joy I bring: There -
2 maid, this morn: A fair and ten - der ba - by bright, To
3 in your need: And he will be your Sav - ior, strong To
5 born, to you; The Fa - ther, too, do we a - dore And

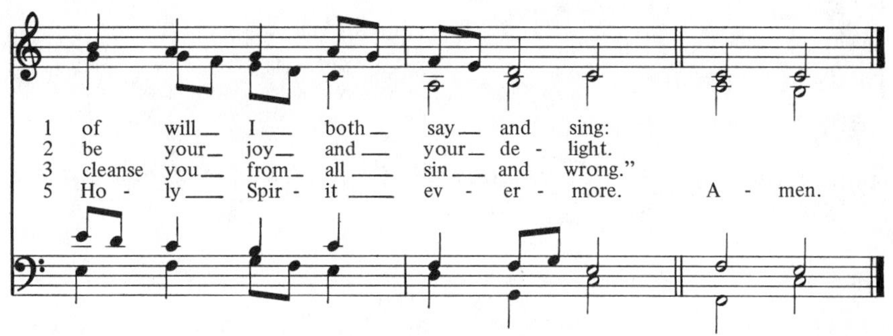
1 of will I both say and sing:
2 be your joy and your de - light.
3 cleanse you from all sin and wrong."
5 Ho - ly Spir - it ev - er - more. A - men.

4 Praise God above on his high throne,
Who gave his sole-begotten Son.
The angel hosts rejoice in bliss
To chant a glad New Year like this. Amen

230

RING OUT, WILD BELLS
Alfred Lord Tennyson, 1809-1892

PALMARUM
L. M.
J. Fred. Wolle, 1923

1 Ring out wild bells, to the wild sky, The flying cloud, the frosty light: The year is dying in the night; Ring out, wild bells, and let him die.
2 Ring out the old, ring in the new, Ring, happy bells, across the snow! The year is going, let him go; Ring out the false, ring in the true.
3 Ring out the grief that saps the mind, For those that here we see no more; Ring out the feud of rich and poor; Ring in redress to all mankind.
4 Ring out false pride in place and blood, The civic slander and the spite; Ring in the love of truth and right; Ring in the common love of good.

5 Ring in the valiant man and free,
The larger heart, the kindlier hand;
Ring out the darkness of the land;
Ring in the Christ that is to be.

Alternative Tunes: VON HIMMEL HOCH, No. 229
and DEUS TUORUM MILITUM, No. 231

231

GREAT GOD, WE SING
Philip Doddridge, 1702-1751

DEUS TUORUM MILITUM
L. M.
Grenoble Church Melody

1 Great God, we sing that might - y hand By
2 By day, by night, at home, a - broad, Still
3 With grate - ful hearts the past we own; The
4 In scenes ex - alt - ed or de - pressed, You
1 which sup - port - ed still we stand; The
2 are we guard - ed by our God: By
3 fu - ture, all to us un - known, We
4 are our joy, you are our rest; Your
1 o - p'ning year your mer - cy shows; That
2 his in - ces - sant boun - ty fed, By
3 to your guard - ing care com - mit To
4 good - ness all our hopes shall raise, A -
1 mer - cy crowns it till it close.
2 his un - err - ing coun - sel led.
3 do with, Lord, as you see fit.
4 dored through all our chang - ing days.

Alternative Tunes: VON HIMMEL HOCH, No. 229
and PALMARUM, No. 230

SONGS OF THANKSGIVING
Christopher Wordsworth, 1862, alt.
St. 3, Irvin Udulutsch, 1957

232

Higher Key at No. 275

SALZBURG
77. 77. D.
Jakob Hintze, 1678, alt.

1 Songs of thank - ful - ness and praise, Je - sus, Lord, to you we raise,
2 Man - i - fest at Jor - dan's stream, Proph - et, Priest, and King su - preme;
3 Grant us, Lord, your gifts of grace, Faith to see your sa - cred face,
4 Grant us grace to see you, Lord, Mir - rored in your ho - ly word;
1 Man - i - fest - ed by the star To the Ma - gi from a - far;
2 And at Ca - na, wed - ding guests, In your God-head man - i - fest;
3 Still re - vealed in your true Church, Giv - ing life to those who search;
4 May we im - i - tate you here, Live as men who know no fear;
1 Branch of roy - al Da - vid's stem, In your birth at Beth - le - hem.
2 Man - i - fest in pow'r di - vine, Chang - ing wa - ter in - to wine.
3 That same face which we shall see In that great E - piph - a - ny,
4 That we like to you may be At your great E - piph - a - ny;
1 May we praise you, ev - er - blest, God in man made man - i - fest!
2 May we praise you, ev - er - blest, God in man made man - i - fest!
3 When we praise you, ev - er - blest, God in man made man - i - fest!
4 And may praise you, ev - er blest, God in man made man - i - fest!

233

O SOLA MAGNARUM URBIUM
Aurelius Clemens Prudentius, 348-413
Tr., Edward Caswall, 1849, alt.

Lower Key at No. 204

STUTTGART
87. 87
C. F. Witt's *Psalmodia Sacra*, 1715

1 Earth has man - y no - ble cit - ies; Beth - le - hem, you
2 Fair - er than the sun at morn - ing Was the star that
3 East - ern sa - ges at his cra - dle Make their of - f'rings
4 Sa - cred gifts of mys - tic mean - ing: In - cense does their
1 do ex - cell; Out of you the Lord from heav - en
2 told his birth, To the world its God an - nounc - ing,
3 rich and rare; See them give in deep de - vo - tion
4 God dis - close, Gold pro - claims him King for - ev - er,
1 Came to rule his Is - ra - el.
2 Seen in hu - man form on earth.
3 Gold and frank - in - cense and myrrh.
4 Myrrh his sep - ul - chre fore - shows.
A - men.

5 Jesus, whom the gentiles worshipped
At your glad Epiphany,
Unto you, with God the Father
And the Spirit ever be. Amen.

DIX (TREUER HEILAND)
77. 77. 77
AS WITH GLADNESS
William Chatterton Dix, 1860, alt.
234
Lower Key at No. 315
Konrad Kocher, 1838
Abreviated by William Henry Monk, 1861
1 As with glad - ness men of old Did the guid - ing
2 As with joy - ful steps they sped To the Christ Child's
3 As they of - fered gifts most rare At the man - ger
4 Ho - ly Je - sus, ev - 'ry day Keep us in thy
1 star be - hold; As with joy they hailed its light,
2 low - ly bed, There to bend the knee be - fore
3 rude and bare, So may we with ho - ly joy,
4 ho - ly way; And, when earth - ly things are past,
1 lead - ing on - ward, beam - ing bright; So, most gra - cious
2 Him whom heav'n and earth a - dore, So, may we with
3 Pure, and free from sin's al - loy, All our cost - liest
4 Bring our ran - somed souls at last Where they need no
1 Lord, may we Ev - er - more be led to thee.
2 ea - ger pace Ev - er seek the Fount of grace.
3 treas - ures bring, Christ, to thee, our heav'n - ly King.
4 star to guide, Where no clouds thy glo - ry hide.

GEHE AUF, DU TROST DER HEIDEN
Hermann Fick, d. 1885
Tr., Composite
235
ALLELUIA
87. 87 D
Samuel S. Wesley, 1868
1 Rise, O Light of Gen - tile na - tions, Je - sus, bright and Morn -ing Star;
2 See the blind -ness of the na - tions, Stran - gers to your glo - rious light,
3 Lord, if you had not had mer - cy And not saved us from this plight,
4 Know-ing you and your sal - va - tion, Grate - ful love can nev - er cease
1 Let your Word, the joy - ous ti - dings, Ring out loud - ly near and far,
2 Stray - ing_hope- less till they find you, Wand-'ring aim - less in the night.
3 In like_dark - ness we would lan - guish, Hope - less, help - less, in sin's night.
4 To pro - claim your gra - cious mer - cies, Lov - ing Lord, your heav'n-ly_peace.
1 Bring-ing free - dom to the cap - tives, Peace and com - fort to the slave,
2 See their pit - i - ful con - di - tion; See, great dark - ness cov - ers all,
3 With great love, O Lord, you sought us In the beau - ty of your grace;
4 We will spread the Gos - pel ti - dings To the earth's re - mot - est bound:
1 That all na - tions, free from bond-age, May pro - claim your pow'r to save.
2 And no ray of hope re - fresh - es Nor dis - pells the dread-ful pall.
3 Now with joy we free - ly_serve you, We, your bles - sed, cho - sen race.
4 That the sin - ner has been par - doned And for - give - ness can be found.

5 Savior, shine in all your glory
On the nations near and far;
From the highways and the byways
Call them, bright and Morning Star,

Guide those whom your grace has chosen
From a life of self and sin
To the mansions of your Father;
There is room for all therein.

Isaiah 60:1-6
BRICH AUF UND WERDE LICHTE
Martin Opitz, 1628
Tr., Sts. 1-5, Gerhard Gieschen, 1937
Tr., St. 6, Emmanuel Cronewett, 1880

236

INNSBRUCK
776. 778
ascr. Heinrich Isaak, c. 1490
Adapted by J. S. Bach, 1685-1750

1 A - rise and shine in splen - dor, Let_ night_to_ day_sur -
2 See earth in dark-ness ly - ing, The_ hea - then_na - tions
3 The world's re - mot-est rac - es, Up - on_whose wea - ry
4 Lift up your eyes_in won - der; See,_ na - tions_gath - er
1 ren - der; Your light is draw - ing near. A -
2 dy - ing In hope - less gloom and night. To
3 fac - es The sun looks from_the sky, Shall
4 yon - der, They all come un - to you. The
1 bove you day_is beam - ing, In_ match - less_beau - ty
2 you the Lord of heav - en Your_ life, your_hope has
3 run with zeal_un - tir - ing, With_ joy your_light de -
4 world has heard your sto - ry, Your_ sons come_to your
1 gleam - ing; The glo - ry_ of_ the_ Lord is here.
2 giv - en Great glo - ry,_ hon - or,_ and de - light.
3 sir - ing That breaks up - on_ them_ from on high.
4 glo - ry, And daugh-ters_ haste_ your_ light to view.

5 Your heart will leap for gladness
When from the realms of sadness
They come o'er sea and land.
Your eyes will wake from slumber
When people without number
Come thronging, in your light to stand.

6 There are glad delegations
From Epha and far nations
And crowds from Midian;
With gold shall Sheba cheer you
And incense. All those near you
Shall sing and praise the Holy One.

237

WE THREE KINGS
John Henry Hopkins, Jr. 1857

THREE KINGS OF ORIENT
88. 446, with Refrain
John Henry Hopkins, Jr., 1857

1 We three kings of O - ri - ent are, Bear - ing gifts we tra-verse a - far,
2 Born a King on Beth - le - hem's plain, Gold I bring to crown him a - gain,
3 Frank - in - cense to of - fer have I, In - cense owns a De - i - ty nigh,
4 Myrrh is mine; its bit - ter per - fume Breathes a life of gath - er-ing gloom;
5 Glo - rious now be - hold him a - rise, King, and God, and Sac - ri - fice;
1 Field and foun - tain, Moor and moun - tain, Fol - low - ing yon - der star.
2 King for - ev - er, Ceas - ing nev - ver O - ver us all to reign.
3 Prayer and prais - ing, All men rais - ing, Wor - ship him, God on high.
4 Sor - rowing, sigh - ing, Bleed - ing dy - ing, Sealed in the stone-cold tomb.
5 Heav'n sings "Al - le - lu - ia;" "Al - le - lu - ia," the earth re - plies.
O star of won - der, star of night, Star with roy - al beau - ty bright
West - ward lead - ing, Still pro-ceed - ing, Guide us to thy per - fect light!

HOSTIS HERODES IMPIE
Cœlius Sedulius, c. 450
Tr., John Mason Neale, 1852, alt.

238

DUKE STREET
L. M.
John Hatton, 1793

1 The star proclaims the King is here;
2 The wiser Magi see from far
3 Within the Jordan's crystal flood
4 At Cana first his pow'r is shown;
1 But, Herod, why this senseless fear?
2 And follow on his guiding star;
3 In meekness stands the lamb of God,
4 His might the blushing waters own
1 He takes no realms of earth away;
2 And, led by light, to Light they press,
3 And, sinless, sanctifies the wave,
4 And, changing as he speaks the word,
1 He gives the realms of heav'nly day.
2 And by their gifts their God confess.
3 Mankind from sin to cleanse and save.
4 Flow wine, obedient to their Lord. Amen

5 O Jesus, Lord, all glory be
For this your glad epiphany,
Whom with the Father we adore,
And Holy Spirit evermore. Amen

Based on Isaiah 9:2-4, 6-7
THE PEOPLE THAT IN DARKNESS SAT
John Morrison, 1770, alt.

239

GERONTIUS
C. M.
John Dykes, 1868

1 The peo - ple that in dark - ness sat A glo - rious
2 To praise you, Sun of Right - eous - ness, The gath - 'ring
3 Their bur - den you a - lone re - move And break the
4 For un - to us a Child is born, To us a

1 light have seen; The light has shone on
2 na - tions come; Re - joic - ing as when
3 ty - rant's rod, As on the day when
4 Son is giv'n, And on his shoul - der

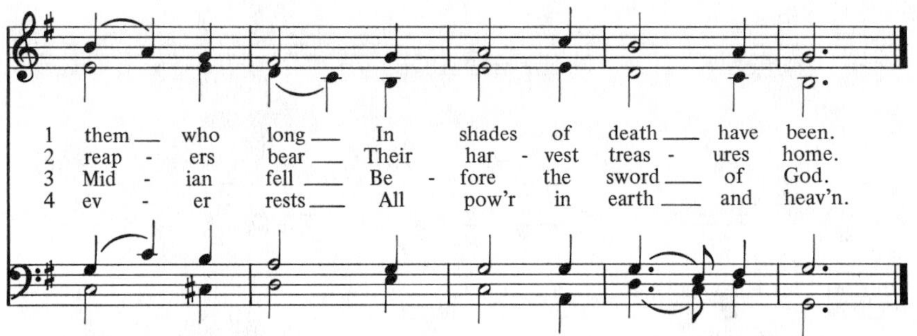
1 them who long In shades of death have been.
2 reap - ers bear Their har - vest treas - ures home.
3 Mid - ian fell Be - fore the sword of God.
4 ev - er rests All pow'r in earth and heav'n.

5 His name shall be the Prince of Peace,
The Everlasting Lord,
The Wonderful, the Counselor,
The God by all adored.

6 His righteous government and pow'r
Shall over all extend;
On judgement and on justice based,
His reign shall have no end.

HAIL, THOU SOURCE
Basil Woodd, c. 1810, alt.
240
Higher Key at No. 437
BEECHER
87. 87. D
John Zundel, 1870
1 Hail, O Source of ev - 'ry_bless - ing, Sov - ereign Fa - ther of man-kind!
2 Once far off, but now in - vit - ed, We ap - proach your sa - cred_throne;
3 Hail, O un - i - ver - sal_Sav- ior! Gen - tiles now their off - 'rings bring;
1 Gen - tiles now, your grace pos - ses - sing In your courts ad - mis - sion_find.
2 In your cov - e - nant u - nit - ed, Re - con - ciled, re - deemed, made one.
3 In your tem - ples seek your fa - vor, Je - sus Christ, our Lord and_King.
1 Grate - ful now we hear the_sto - ry, In your Church ob - tain a_place,
2 Now re - vealed to East - ern_Sa - ges, See the star of mer - cy_shine:
3 May we, bo - dy, soul, and_spir - it, Life de - vot - ed to your praise,
1 Now by faith be - hold your glo - ry, Praise your truth, a - dore your grace.
2 Myst - 'ry hid in form - er_a - ges, Myst - 'ry great of love di - vine.
3 Glo - rious realms of bliss in - her - it, Grate - ful an - thems ev - er_raise!

ATTENDE, DOMINE
Paris Processional, 1824
Vv. based on an ancient Mozarabic litany
Tr., Irvin Udulutsch, 1956

241

ATTENDE, DOMINE
11. 11. 11, with Refrain
Paris Processional, 1824
Harm., Roger Nachtwey

Hear our en - treat-ies, Lord, and show us mer-cy, For we are sin-ners be - fore you.
At - ten - de, Do - mi - ne, et mi - se - re - re, Qui - a pec - ca - vi - mus ti - bi.
1 King high ex - alt - ed, all the world's Re - deem - er, To you your chil - dren
Ad te Rex sum - me, o - mni - um Re - demp - tor, O - cu - los no - stros
2 Right hand of God - head, head-stone of the cor - ner, Path of sal - va - tion,
Dex - te - ra Pa - tris, la - pis an - gu - la - ris, Vi - a sa - lu - tis,
1 lift their eyes with weep - ing; Christ, we im-plore you, hear our sup - pli - ca - tion.
sub - le - va - mus flen - tes: Ex - au - di, Chri - ste, sup - pli - can - tum pre - ces.
2 gate of heav - en's king - dom, Lord, cleanse your peo - ple, stained with much trans-gres - sion.
ja - nu - a cæ - le - stis, Ab - lu - e no - stri ma - cu - las de - li - cti.

3 We, your eternal majesty entreating,
Make lamentation in your holy hearing:
Graciously grant, Lord, to our sins indulgence.

4 Humbly confessing all our sins against you,
All our misdoings, hidden now no longer;
Lord, our Redeemer, by your love grant pardon.

5 Led away captive, guiltless, unresisting,
Brought by false witness unto death for sinners,
Christ, Jesus, keep us whom your blood has ransomed.

Rogamus, Deus, tuam majestatem:
Auribus sacris gemitus exaudi:
Crimina nostra placidus indulge.

Tibi fatemur crimina admissa:
Contrito corde pandimus occulta:
Tua, Redempter, pietas ignoscat.

Innocens captus, nec repugnans ductus;
Testibus falsis pro impiis damnatus;
Quos redemisti, tu conserva, Christe.

HERZLIEBSTER JESU
11 11. 11 5
Johan Crüger, 1640
Adapted by J. S. Bach, 1685-1750
Harmony based on Bach

242

AURES AD NOSTRAS
Ante-Tridentine Breviary
Tr., Alan G. McDougal, alt.

Higher Key at No. 265

1 O God of pit - y, turn to us, your chil - dren;
2 Look down in mer - cy from your throne in glo - ry;
3 Free us from sin by might of your great lov - ing,
4 O Christ, true light and good - ness, life of all things,

1 Bend down your ear in your great lov - ing -
2 Pour on our souls the ra - diance of your
3 And cleanse the sor - did, loose the fet - tered
4 Joy of the whole world, in - fin - ite in

1 kind - ness. And, as your peo - ple's song is now as -
2 pres - ence; Drive from our wea - ry hearts the shades of
3 spir - it. Spare ev - 'ry sin - ner; raise with your own
4 kind - ness, Who by the crim - son flow - ing of your

1 cend - ing, We beg you, hear us.
2 dark - ness; Our foot - steps light - en.
3 right hand All who have fal - len.
4 life - blood To life re - store us.

5 All praise to God the Father everlasting,
All praise forever to the sole begotten,
With whom the Holy Spirit, with them equal,
Reigns thru the ages.

243

HEINLEIN
77. 77
ascr. M. Herbst, 1654-81
Nürnbergisches Gesangbuch, 1676

FORTY DAYS AND FORTY NIGHTS
George Hunt Smyttan, 1856, alt.

1 For - ty days and for - ty nights
2 Shall not we your sor - row share
3 Then, if Sa - tan on us press,
4 Keep, O keep us, Sav - ior dear,
1 You were fast - ing in the wild;
2 And from world - ly joys ab - stain,
3 Flesh or spir - it to as - sail,
4 Ev - er con - stant at your side,
1 For - ty days and for - ty nights
2 Fast - ing with un - ceas - ing prayer,
3 Vic - tor in the wil - der - ness,
4 That with you we may ap - pear
1 Tempt - ed and yet un - de - filed.
2 Strong with you to suf - fer pain?
3 Grant we may not faint or fail!
4 At the e - ter - nal East - er - tide.

SUMMI LARGITOR PRAEMII
Sarum Breviary
Tr., Alan G. McDougal, alt.

244

Higher Key at No. 292

ST. BONIFACE
L. M.
Mainz Gesangbuch, 1833
Harm., A. Gregory Murray

1 Sole hope of all the world, and Lord, Be - stow - er of the
2 And, though our con - scienc - es pro - claim Our deep trans - gres - sion
3 Our sins re - mem - ber now no more; For - give; your mer - cy
4 Ac - cept, O Lord, this Lent - en tide. This fast which you have

1 great re - ward, Re - ceive the prayers your serv - ants raise; Ac -
2 and our shame, Cleanse us, O God, we hum - bly plead, From
3 can re - store; So, Lord, take on your - self our care, That
4 sanc - ti - fied, That we, Through sac - ra - men - tal ways, May

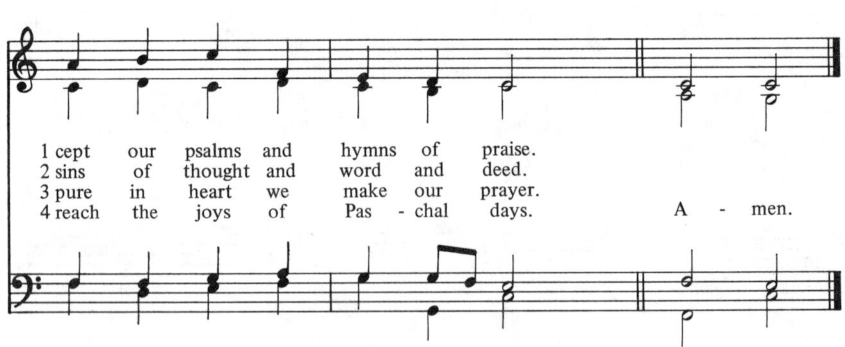
1 cept our psalms and hymns of praise.
2 sins of thought and word and deed.
3 pure in heart we make our prayer.
4 reach the joys of Pas - chal days.
A - men.

245

JAM CHRISTE SOL JUSTITIAE
6th cent.
Tr., Peter Scagnelli, 1973

JAM CHRISTE SOL JUSTITIAE
L. M.
Plainsong Melody
Harm., Roger Nachtwey

1 O Sun_ of jus - tice, Je - sus Christ, Dis - pel the dark - ness
2 In this_ our "time_ ac - cept - a - ble" Touch ev - 'ry heart with
3 The day,_ your day,_ in beau - ty dawns When in your light earth
4 O lov - ing Trin - i - ty,_ our God, To you we bow thru
1 of_ our hearts, Till your_ blest light_ makes night time flee_ And
2 sor - row, Lord, That, turned_ from sin,_ re - newed by grace,_ We
3 blooms_ a - new; Led back_ a - gain_ to life's true way,_ May
4 end - less days, And in_ your grace_ new - born we sing_ New
1 brings_ the joys_ your day_ im - parts.
2 may_ press on_ toward love's_ re - ward.
3 we,_ for - giv'n,_ re - joice_ in you.
4 hymns_ of grat - i tude_ and praise. A - men.

Alternative Tune: ST. BONIFACE, No. 244

LORD, WHO THROUGHOUT THESE FORTY DAYS
Claudia F. Hernaman, 1838-98, alt.

246

ST. FLAVIAN
C. M.
John Day's Psalter, 1562

1 Through - out these for - ty days, O Lord, With
2 Through - out these days of pen - i - tence, Thru
3 Do not a - ban - don us, O Lord, But
4 A - bide with us that, when this course Of

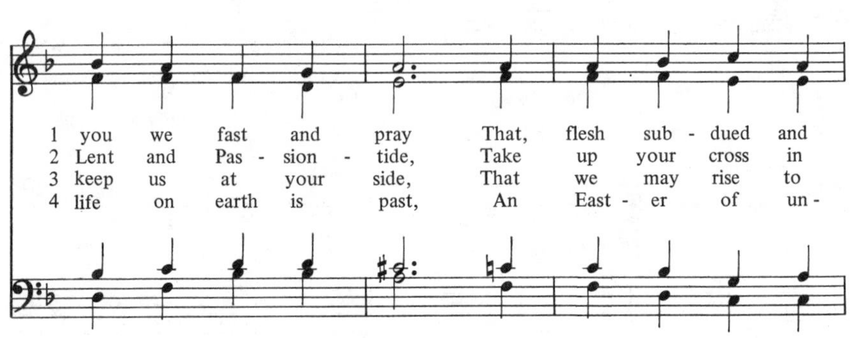
1 you we fast and pray That, flesh sub - dued and
2 Lent and Pas - sion - tide, Take up your cross in
3 keep us at your side, That we may rise to
4 life on earth is past, An East - er of un -

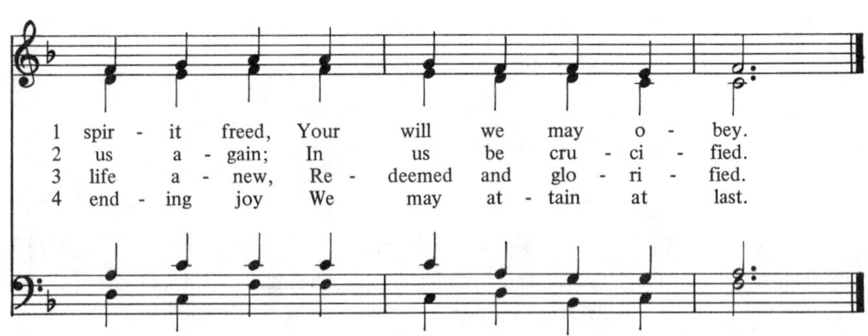
1 spir - it freed, Your will we may o - bey.
2 us a - gain; In us be cru - ci - fied.
3 life a - new, Re - deemed and glo - ri - fied.
4 end - ing joy We may at - tain at last.

247

CLARUM DECUS JEJUNII
6th cent.
Tr., Maurice F. Bell, 1906, alt.

Lower Key at No. 521

ERHALT' UNS HERR (SPIRES)
L. M.
J. Klug's *Geistliche Lieder,* 1543
Harm., J. S. Bach, 1685-1750

1 The glo - ry of these for - ty days We cel - e - brate with songs of praise; For Christ, by whom all things were made, Him - self has fast - ed and has prayed.
2 A - lone and fast - ing Mo - ses saw The lov - ing God who gave the law; And to E - li - jah, fast - ing, came The steeds and char - i - ots of flame.
3 So Dan - iel trained his mys - tic sight, De - liv - ered from the li - ons might; And John, the Bride-groom's friend be - came The her - ald of Mes - si - ah's name.
4 Then grant us, Lord, like them to do Such things as bring great praise to you; Our spir - its strength-en with your grace, And give us joy to see your face.

5 O Father, Son, and Spirit blest,
To you be ev'ry prayer addressed,
Who are by all mankind adored,
From age to age, the only Lord.

248

AUDI, BENIGNE CONDITOR
St. Gregory the Great, 540-604
Tr., Composite, 1974

SAXONY
L. M.
Christliches Gesangbüchlein, 1568
Harm., A. Gregory Murray

1 O mer - ci - ful Cre - a - tor, hear; In kind - ness turn to us your ear; Con - trite, our prayers and hymns we raise In this our fast of for - ty days
2 Kind judge of hearts, look now with - in; Be - hold our weak - ness and our sin. Give us your par - don and your grace As we re - turn to seek your face.
3 Our sins are man - y, this we know; As we con - fess, your mer - cy show. Your name we'll praise through all our ills If you but strength - en our weak wills.
4 Give us the self - con - trol that springs From dis - ci - pline in out - ward things, That from each stain and spot of sin Our souls may keep the fast with - in.
A - men.

5 Grant, O most blessed Trinity,
Grant, O essential Unity,
That this our fast of forty days
May work our merit and your praise. Amen.

Alternative Tune: SPIRES, No. 247.

249

EX MORE DOCTI MYSTICO
ascr., Gregory the Great, D. 604
Tr., Peter Scagnelli, 1973

AUDI, BENIGNE CONDITOR
L. M.
Plainsong Melody
Harm., Roger Nachtwey

1 A - gain we __ keep this __ sol - emn __ fast,
2 The __ law and __ proph - ets __ from of __ old
3 More __ spar - ing, __ there - fore, __ let us __ make
4 Let __ us a - void each __ harm - ful __ way
1 A __ gift __ of __ faith from a - ges __ past,
2 In __ fig - ured __ ways this lent __ fore __ told,
3 The __ words __ we __ speak, the food __ we __ take,
4 That __ lures __ the __ care - less mind __ a - stray;
1 This lent which binds __ us lov - ing - ly
2 Which Christ, all a - ges' King and __ Guide,
3 Our sleep, our laugh - ter, ev - 'ry __ sense;
4 By watch - ful prayer __ our spir - its __ free
1 To __ faith __ and hope __ and char - i - ty.
2 In __ these __ last days __ has sanc - ti - fied.
3 Learn __ peace __ thru ho - ly pen - i - tence.
4 From __ schem - ing of __ the En - e - my.
A - men.

5 We pray, O blessed Three - in - One,
Our God while endless ages run,
That this, our lent of forty days,
May bring us growth and give you praise. Amen.

Alternative Tunes: ERHALT UNS HERR (SPIRES) No. 247
and SAXONY, No. 248

Based on Isaiah 58:5-9
ATTEND AND KEEP
Roger Ruston, 1970
250
TRANMERE
C.M.D.
W. Hayes, 1706-77
1 At - tend and keep this hap - py _ fast I preach to you this day.
2 But is this not the fast I _ choose, That shares the heav- y load;
3 Then like the dawn your light will break; To life you will _ be raised.
1 Is this the fast that pleas - es me That takes your joy a - way?
2 That seeks to bring the poor man in Who's wea - ry of the road;
3 And men will praise the Lord for you; Be hap - py in your days.
1 Do I de - light in sor - row's dress, Says God, who reigns a - bove
2 That gives the hun - gry bread to eat, To stran - gers gives a home;
3 The glo - ry of the Lord will shine, And in your steps his grace.
1 The hang - ing head, the dis - mal look, Will they at - tract my love?
2 That does not let you hide your face From your own flesh and bone?
3 And when you call he'll an - swer you; He will not _ hide his face.

251

Psalm 130
FROM THE DEEP
Luke Connaughton, 1969

GOTTES LAMM RUFT (GLORIFICATION)
75. 75. D.
Adapted from Grossner's *Choralbuch*
Leipzig, 1832

1 From the deep I lift my voice; Hear my cry, O God.
2 Night and day my spir - it waits, Longs to see my God,
1 Lis - ten, Lord, to my ap - peal; None but you can help.
2 Like a watch-man, wea - ry, cold, Wait - ing for the dawn.
1 If you count our griev - ous sins. No man will be spared,
2 O - pen - hand - ed is the Lord, Swift to par - don us:
1 But your mer - cy still for - gives; In your love we trust.
2 He will lead his peo - ple free, Clean from all their sins.

252

Psalm 130
I CRY TO YOU FROM DEPTHS
C.J. Marivoet

I CRY TO YOU
10.11.10
L. de Vocht

1. I cry to you from depths of sor - row, Lord;
2. My plead - ings speak with force - ful voice, O Lord;
3. Man's faults! If you re - mem - ber them, O Lord,
4. For - give - ness comes from you for - ev - er Lord;
1. To you I cry for help, for you can save me.
2. Your ear, O lend to them, give ear in pa - tience.
3. What man could stand, O Lord, what man could face you?
4. With thanks we ren - der you our hum - ble ser - vice.
Your peo - ple wait for your sal - va - tion, Lord!

5. My lasting trust I place in you, my Lord;
   Your word brings peace to me, for you are loyal.

6. Much more than watchmen wait for daybreak, Lord,
   Your people look to you with hopeful longing.

7. All mercy has its source in you, O Lord;
   Redemption comes from you in all its fullness.

8. You'll bring salvation to your people, Lord,
   And, though our sins abound, your grace is richer.

GLORIA LAUS ET HONOR
St. Theodolph of Orleans, c. 820
Tr., Anthony G. Petti, 1971
253[1]
Higher Key
ST. THEODULPH
76. 76. D.
Melchior Teschner, 1615
All glo - ry, praise and hon - or To you, _ Re - deem - er, King!
For whom the lips of chil - dren Made loud _ ho - san - nas ring.
1 For you are _ King of _ Is - ra - el, Of Da - vid's roy - al line;
2 The mul - ti - tudes of _ an - gels A - dore _ you from on high,
3 The He - brews ran to _ greet _ you With ol - ives and with palms,
4 Be - fore your _ bit - ter pas - sion They paved your way with praise,
5 Their hom - age _ you ac - cept - ed: Re - ceive the prayers we bring,
1 From God you came to save _ us In maj - es - ty di - vine.
2 And here all earth - ly crea - tures With prais - es fill the sky.
3 And now to you in heav - en We sing our hymns and psalms.
4 And now to you tri - umph - ant Our hum - ble songs we raise.
5 For you are good and gra - cious, Dear Christ, our Lord and King!

253[2]

Lower Key

ELLACOMBE (AVE MARIA KLARER)
76. 76. D.
Gesangbuch der Herzogl. Wirtembergischen Katolischen Hofkapelle, 1784

HOSANNA, LOUD HOSANNA
Jennette Threfall, 1873

254

Lower Key at No. 316

1 Ho - san - na, loud ho - san - na, The lit - tle chil - dren sang;
2 From Ol - i - vet they fol - lowed Mid that ex - ult - ant crowd,
3 "Ho - san - na in the high - est!" That glo-rious song we sing,

1 Through pil - lared court and tem - ple The lov - ly an - them rang;
2 The vic - tor palm branch wav - ing, And chant- ing clear and loud;
3 For Christ is our Re - deem - er, The Lord of heav'n, our King.

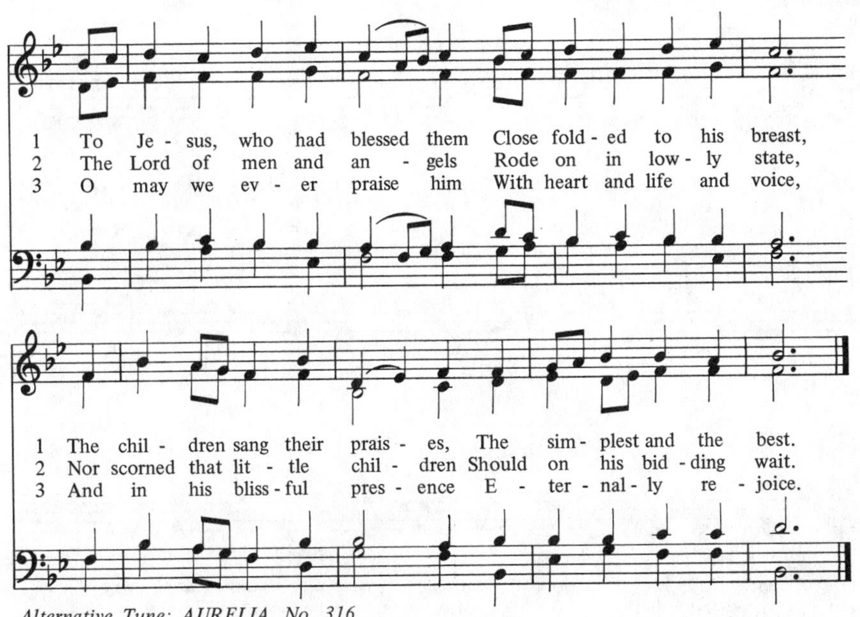
1 To Je - sus, who had blessed them Close fold - ed to his breast,
2 The Lord of men and an - gels Rode on in low - ly state,
3 O may we ev - er praise him With heart and life and voice,
1 The chil - dren sang their prais - es, The sim - plest and the best.
2 Nor scorned that lit - tle chil - dren Should on his bid - ding wait.
3 And in his bliss - ful pres - ence E - ter - nal - ly re - joice.

Alternative Tune: AURELIA, No. 316

255[1]

THE KING'S MAJESTY
L. M.

RIDE ON! RIDE ON IN MAJESTY
Henry Hart Milman, 1827, alt.

Lower Key at No. 258

Graham George, 1940

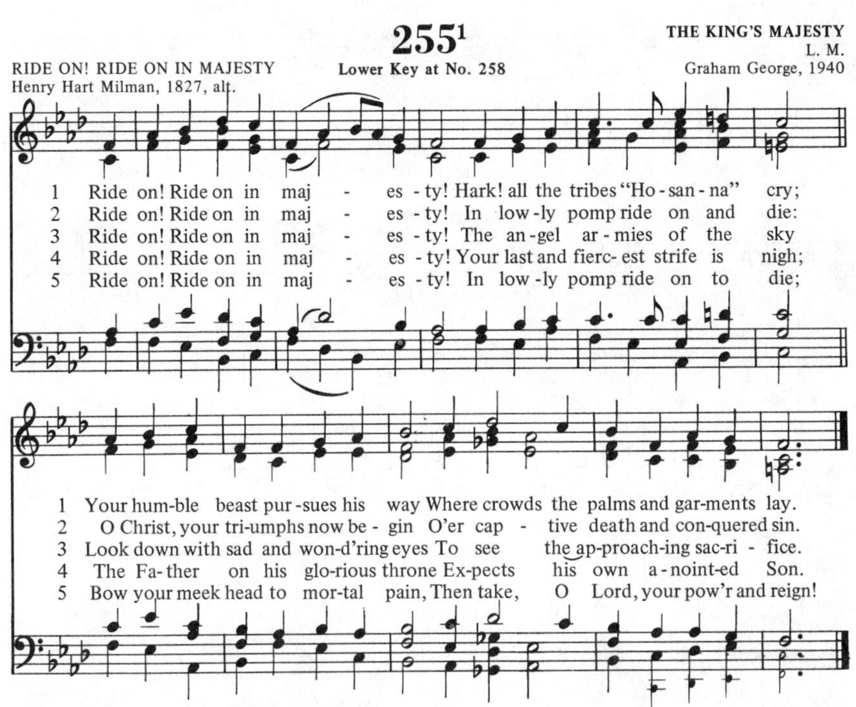
1 Ride on! Ride on in maj - es - ty! Hark! all the tribes "Ho - san - na" cry;
2 Ride on! Ride on in maj - es - ty! In low - ly pomp ride on and die:
3 Ride on! Ride on in maj - es - ty! The an - gel ar - mies of the sky
4 Ride on! Ride on in maj - es - ty! Your last and fierc - est strife is nigh;
5 Ride on! Ride on in maj - es - ty! In low - ly pomp ride on to die;
1 Your hum - ble beast pur - sues his way Where crowds the palms and gar - ments lay.
2 O Christ, your tri - umphs now be - gin O'er cap - tive death and con - quered sin.
3 Look down with sad and won - d'ring eyes To see the ap - proach - ing sac - ri - fice.
4 The Fa - ther on his glo - rious throne Ex - pects his own a - noint - ed Son.
5 Bow your meek head to mor - tal pain, Then take, O Lord, your pow'r and reign!

RIDE ON! RIDE ON IN MAJESTY
Henry Hart Milman, 1827, alt.

255[2]

Lower Key at No. 206

WINCHESTER NEW
L. M.
Musikalisches Handbuch, Hamburg, 1690

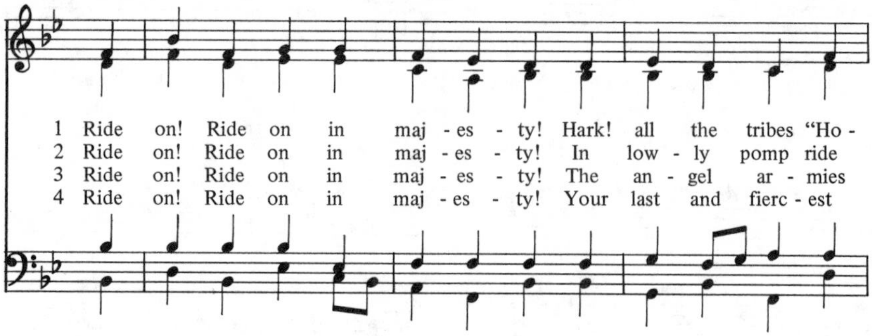

1 Ride on! Ride on in maj - es - ty! Hark! all the tribes "Ho -
2 Ride on! Ride on in maj - es - ty! In low - ly pomp ride
3 Ride on! Ride on in maj - es - ty! The an - gel ar - mies
4 Ride on! Ride on in maj - es - ty! Your last and fierc - est

1 san - na" cry; Your hum - ble beast pur - sues his way Where
2 on and die: O Christ, your tri - umphs now be - gin O'er
3 of the sky Look down with sad and won - d'ring eyes To
4 strife is nigh; The Fa - ther on his glo - rious throne Ex -

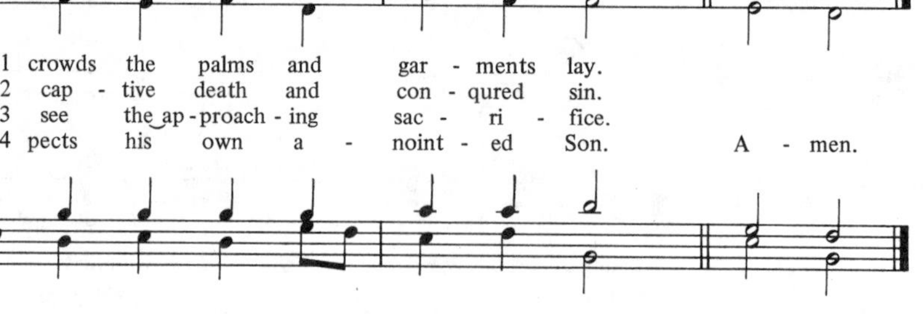

1 crowds the palms and gar - ments lay.
2 cap - tive death and con - qured sin.
3 see the ap - proach - ing sac - ri - fice.
4 pects his own a - noint - ed Son.
A - men.

5 Ride on! Ride on in majesty!
In lowly pomp ride on to die;
Bow your meek head to mortal pain,
Then take, O Lord, your pow'r and reign! Amen.

ARBOR FETA ALMA LUCE
Anonymous
Tr., Roger Nachtwey &
David Crosby, 1966, 1974

256

Lower Key at No. 446

ST. NICHOLAS (ELLIS)
87. 87. 87
W. Ellis, 1868-1947

1 Sun - light makes the ol - ive fruit - ful; From the fruit the
2 In your kind - ness, King im - mor - tal, Con - se - crate this
3 May all peo - ple, men and wom - en, Through this chris - m
4 When our minds are cleansed by wa - ter, Let our sins be
1 oil is pressed; Sav - ior of the gen - er - a - tions,
2 ol - ive oil; May it be a sign and safe - guard,
3 be made new, That the wound to their first glo - ry
4 put to flight; When our fore - heads are a - noint - ed,
1 Now we bring it to be blessed.
2 And the schemes of Sa - tan foil.
3 May be healed, O Lord, by you.
4 May we share your Spir - it's might.
O Re - deem - er,
hear our sing - ing As we praise you with one voice!

5 Born of love of God the Father,
Dwelling in the Virgin's womb,
Give us light, who share this chrism;
Close the door of death's dark tomb.

6 May we keep this feast forever
As a holy day of days;
May our hearts grow never weary
As we sing its fitting praise.

257

'TWAS ON THAT DARK, THAT DOLEFUL NIGHT
Isaac Watts, 1709, cento

Lower Key at No. 262 (Second Tune)

ANDERNACH
L. M.
Andernach Gesangbuch, 1608
Harm., A. Gregory Murray

1 'Twas on that dark, dis - tress - ing night When powr's of
2 Be - fore the mourn-ful scene be - gan, He took the
3 "This is my bod - y, broke for sin; Re - ceive and
4 "Do this," he said, "till time shall end In mem - 'ry
1 earth and hell a - rose A - gainst the Son of God's de -
2 bread and blessed and broke. What love through all his ac - tions
3 eat the liv - ing food": Then took the cup and blessed the
4 of your dy - ing Friend; Meet at my ta - ble and re -
1 light And friends be - trayed him to his foes.
2 ran! What won - drous words of grace he spoke!
3 wine: "It's the new cov - 'nant in my blood."
4 cord The love of your de - part - ed Lord."

5 O Lord, your feast we celebrate;
We show your death, we sing your name,
Till you return and we shall eat
The Marriage supper of the Lamb.

258

BEHOLD A WONDROUS MYSTERY
Matthias Loy, 1880, alt.

THE KING'S MAJESTY
L. M.
Graham George, 1940

Higher Key at No. 255

In unison
1 Be - hold a won - drous mys - t'ry here To chal - lange
2 All can be love - less, but a - bove What won - drous
3 In con - se - crat - ed wine and bread No eye per -
4 How dull are all the pow'rs of sense Em - ployed on
1 faith and wak - en fear: The Sav - ior comes as food di -
2 bound - less - ness of love! The King of glo - ry stoops to
3 ceives the mys - t'ry dread; But Je - sus' words are strong and
4 proofs of love im - mense! The rich - est food re - mains un -
1 vine, Con - cealed in earth - ly bread and wine.
2 me, My spir - it's life and strength to be.
3 clear: "My bod - y and my blood are here."
4 seen, And high - est gifts ap - pear how mean!

5 But here we have no boon on earth,
And faith alone discerns its worth;
The Word, not sense, must be our guide,
And faith assure, since sight's denied.

6 Lord, show us still that you are good
And give us evermore this food.
Give faith to ev'ry wav'ring soul
And make each wounded spirit whole.

Alternative Tune: ANDERNACH' No. 257

259

LOVE IS HIS WORD
Luke Connaughton, 1970

CRESSWELL
44 44. 54 7, with Chorus
Anthony Milner, 1970

1 Love is his word, love is his way, feast - ing with men, fast - ing a - lone,
2 Love is his way, love is his mark, shar - ing his last Pass - o - ver feast,
3 Love is his mark, love is his sign, bread for our strength, wine for our joy,
4 Love is his sign, love is his news, "Do this," he said, "lest you for-get
1 Liv - ing and dy - ing, ris - ing a -gain, Love, on - ly love, is his way.
2 Christ at his ta - ble, host to the twelve, Love, on - ly love, is his mark.
3 "This is my bod - y, this is my blood," Love, on - ly love, is his sign.
4 All my deep sor - row, all my dear blood." Love, on - ly love, is his news.
Rich - er than gold is the love of my Lord: Bet - ter than splen - dor and wealth!

5 Love is his news, love is his name,
We are his own, chosen and called,
Family, brethren, cousins and kin.
Love, only love, is his name.

6 Love is his name, love is his law.
Hear his command, all who are his:
"Love one another, I have loved you."
Love, only love, is his law.

7 Love is his law, love is his word:
Love of the Lord, Father and Word,
Love of the Spirit, God ever one.
Love, only love, is his word.

260

SALVE CAPUT CRUENTATUM
ascr. St. Bernard of Clairvaux, d. 1153
Tr., Anthony G. Petti, 1971

Lower Key at No. 487

HERZLICH TUT MICH
(O HAUPT VOLL BLUDT)
76. 76. D.
Hans Leo Hassler, 1601
Adapt. & Harm., J. S. Bach

1 Dear face with pain trans - fig - ured, Which pierc-ing thorns have scarred,
2 With strength and vig - or fail - ing, Your bod - y wracked with pain,
3 Good Shep-herd, by your pas - sion, Your grief and mis - er - y,

1 Your head with blows dis - fig - ured, Your coun-te - nance so marred:
2 The mark of death pre - vail - ing, Life ebbs from ev - 'ry vein;
3 Thru kind-ness and com - pas - sion, From sin you set us free.

1 How pale those looks so ten - der, Your fea - tures bruised and sore;
2 En - dur - ing des - e - cra - tion, You die for love of me,
3 In all your bound-less giv - ing, Grant us our last re - quest,

1 How dimmed the king - ly splen - dor Which heav'n-ly hosts a - dore.
2 In all your des - o - la - tion Re - lieve my mis - er - y.
3 That with you ev - er liv - ing We dwell a - mong the blest.

SOLUS AD VICTIMAM PROCEDIS
Peter Abelard, 1079-1142
Tr., F. Bland Tucker, 1938, 1972

261[1]

Lower Key at No. 388

BANGOR
C. M.
William Tans'ur, 1734

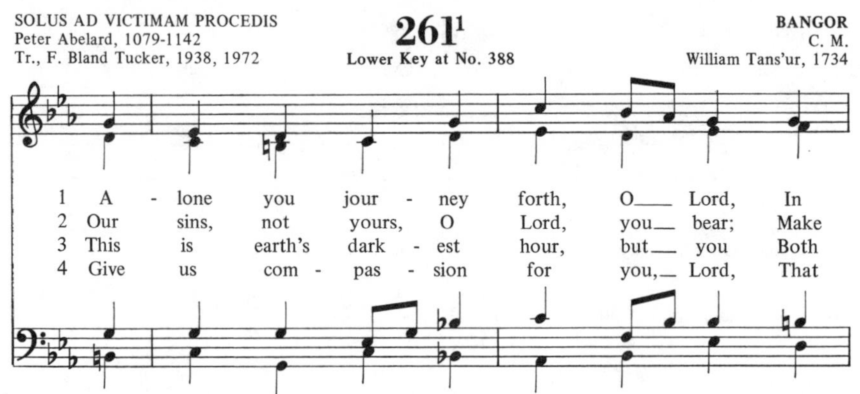
1 A - lone you jour - ney forth, O___ Lord, In
2 Our sins, not yours, O Lord, you___ bear; Make
3 This is earth's dark - est hour, but___ you Both
4 Give us com - pas - sion for you,___ Lord, That

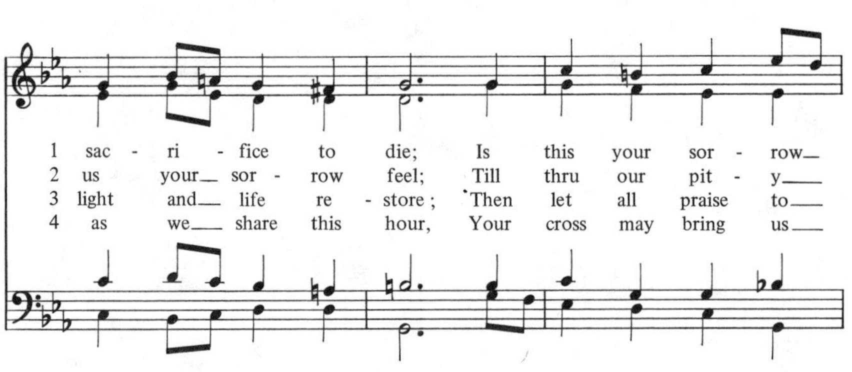
1 sac - ri - fice to die; Is this your sor - row___
2 us your___ sor - row feel; Till thru our pit - y___
3 light and___ life re - store; Then let all praise to___
4 as we___ share this hour, Your cross may bring us___

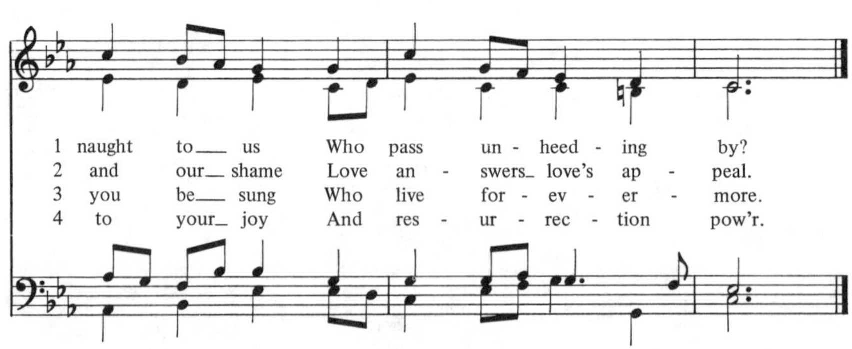
1 naught to___ us Who pass un - heed - ing by?
2 and our___ shame Love an - swers___ love's ap - peal.
3 you be___ sung Who live for - ev - er - more.
4 to your___ joy And res - ur - rec - tion pow'r.

SOLUS AD VICTIMAM PROCEDIS
Peter Abelard, 1079-1142
Tr., F. Bland Tucker, 1938, 1972

261[2]

Second Tune

CHALVEY
C. M.
Richard Runciman Terry, 1865-1938

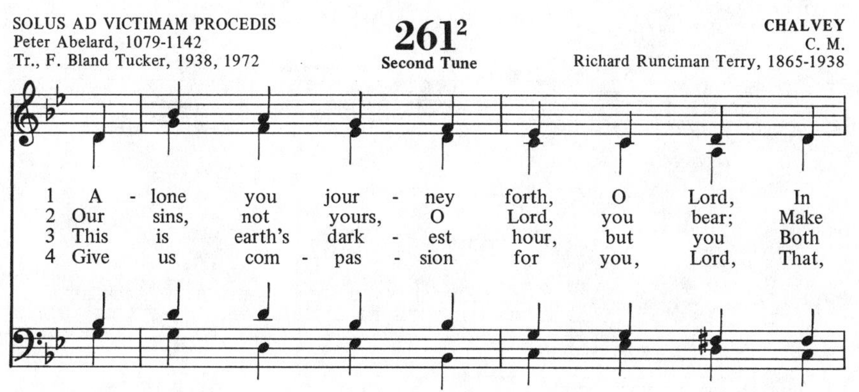
1 A - lone you jour - ney forth, O Lord, In
2 Our sins, not yours, O Lord, you bear; Make
3 This is earth's dark - est hour, but you Both
4 Give us com - pas - sion for you, Lord, That,

1 sac - ri - fice to die; Is this your sor - row
2 us your sor - row feel; Till through our pit - y
3 light and life re - store; Then let all praise to
4 as we share this hour, Your cross may bring us

1 naught to us Who pass un - heed - ing by?
2 and our shame Love an - swers love's ap - peal.
3 you be sung Who live for - ev - er - more.
4 to your joy And res - ur - rec - tion pow'r.

VEXILLA REGIS PRODEUNT
Venantius Fortunatus, 569
Tr., Composite, 1974

262[1]

First Tune

VEXILLA REGIS
L. M.
Plainsong Melody
Harm., Roger Nachtwey

1 The roy - al ban - ners for - ward go, The
2 There, while he hung his sa - cred side By
3 Ful - filled is all that Da - vid told In
4 O love - ly and re - splend - ent tree, A-
1 cross shines forth in mys - tic glow Where he, as
2 sol - dier's spear was o - pened wide, To cleanse us
3 true pro - phet - ic song of old: "O'er all the
4 dorned with pur - ple maj - es - ty, Your wood was
1 man, who gave man breath, Now bows be-
2 in the pre - cious flood Of wa - ter
3 na - tions God," says he, "Has reigned and
4 cho - sen as the best On which his
1 neath the yoke of death.
2 min - gled with his blood.
3 tri - umphed from a tree.
4 sa - cred limbs might rest.
A - men.

5 On whose strong arms, so widely flung,
The price of this world's ransom hung,
The beam on which his body lay
To steal from hell its destined prey.

6 O cross, our one reliance, hail!
Still may your pow'r with us avail
More good for righteous souls to win
And save the sinner from his sin.

7 O Trinity, our praise we sing
To you, from whom all graces spring;
The triumph of the cross bestow;
Reward your faithful here below. Amen.

VEXILLA REGIS PRODEUNT
Venantius Fortunatus, 569
Tr., Composite, 1974

262[2]

Second Tune
Higher Key at No. 257

ANDERNACH
L. M.
Andernach Gesangbuch, 1608
Harm., A. Gregory Murray

1 The royal banners forward go, The cross shines forth in mystic glow Where he, as man who gave man breath, Now bows beneath the yoke of death.
2 There, while he hung, his sacred side By soldier's spear was opened wide, To cleanse us in the precious flood Of water mingled with his blood.
3 Fulfilled is all that David told In true prophetic song of old: "O'er all the nations God," says he, "Has reigned and triumphed from a tree.
4 O lovely and resplendent tree, Adorned with purple majesty, Your wood was chosen as the best On which his sacred limbs might rest: Amen.

5 On whose strong arms, so widely flung,
The price of this world's ransom hung,
The beam on which his body lay
To steal from hell its destined prey.

6 O cross, our one reliance, hail!
Still may your pow'r with us avail
More good for righteous to win
And save the sinner from his sin.

7 O Trinity, our praise we sing
To you, from whom all graces spring;
The triumph of the cross bestow;
Reward your people here below. Amen.

ARFON
77. 77. 77
THRONED UPON THE AWFUL TREE
John Ellerton, 1875, alt.
263[1]
Higher Key
Welsh variant of old French Noel
O vous dont les tendres ans
1 Throned up - on the aw - ful tree, Lamb of God, your grief we see.
2 Si - lent through those dread - ful hours, Wres - tling with the e - vil pow'rs,
3 Hear the cry that ech - oes loud Up - ward through the whelm-ing cloud!
4 Lord, should fear and an - guish roll Dark - ly o'er our sin - ful soul,
1 Dark - ness veils your an - guished face; None its lines of woe can trace.
2 Left a - lone with hu - man sin, Gloom a - round you and with - in,
3 You, the Fa - ther's on - ly Son, You, his own a - noint - ed one,
4 You, who once were thus be - reft So your own might not be left,
1 None can tell what pangs un - known Hold you si - lent and a - lone.
2 Till th'ap - point - ed time is nigh, Till the Lamb of God may die.
3 You are ask - ing can it be? "Why have you for - sak - en me?"
4 Teach us by that bit - ter cry In the gloom to know you nigh.
263[2]
Lower Key

WERE YOU THERE
Black Spiritual

264

WERE YOU THERE
Irregular

1 Were you there when they cru - ci - fied my Lord? Were you
2 Were you there when they nailed him to the tree? Were you
3 Were you there when they pierced him in the side? Were you
4 Were you there when the sun re - fused to shine? Were you
5 Were you there when they laid him in the tomb? Were you
6 Were you there when he rose from out the tomb? Were you
1 there when they cru - ci - fied my Lord?
2 there when they nailed him to the tree?
3 there when they pierced him in the side?
4 there when the sun re - fused to shine?
5 there when they laid him in the tomb?
6 there when he rose from out the tomb?
Oh!
Some - times it caus - es me to trem - ble, trem - ble, trem - ble.
1 Were you there when they cru - ci - fied my Lord?
2 Were you there when they nailed him to the tree?
3 Were you there when they pierced him in the side?
4 Were you there when the sun re - fused to shine?
5 Were you there when they laid him in the tomb?
6 Were you there when he rose from out the tomb?

HERZLIEBSTER JESU
Johann Heermann, 1630
Tr., Anthony G. Petti, 1972
After Robert Bridges, 1899

265

Lower Key at No. 242

HERZLIEBSTER JESU
11 11. 11 5
Johan Crüger, 1640
Adapted by J. S. Bach, 1685-1750

1 My lov - ing Sav - ior, how have you of - fend - ed,
2 It was my guilt brought all these things up - on you,
3 So now the Shep - herd for the sheep is of - ered,
4 For us, dear Je - sus, was your in - car - na - tion,
1 That such a hate in man on you de -
2 Through all my sins was this in - jus - tice
3 Man - kind is guilt - y, but the Son has
4 Your bit - ter death and shame - ful cru - ci -
1 scend - ed? Both mocked and scorned, you suf - fered our re -
2 done you. Lord Je - sus, it was I that did de -
3 suf - fered. For man's a - tone - ment, which man nev - er
4 fix - ion, Your bur - ial and your glo - rious res - ur -
1 jec - tion In deep af - flic - tion.
2 ny you And cru - ci - fy you.
3 heed - ed, God in - ter - ced - ed.
4 rec - tion: For our sal - va - tion.

5 Although, good Jesus, we cannot repay you,
We shall adore you and shall ever praise you.
For all your kindness and your love unswerving,
Not our deserving.

MAN OF SORROWS
Matthew Bridges, 1800-94
Adapted by Anthony Petti
& Geoffrey Laycock, 1972

266

TICHFIELD
77. 77. D.
John Richardson, 1816-79

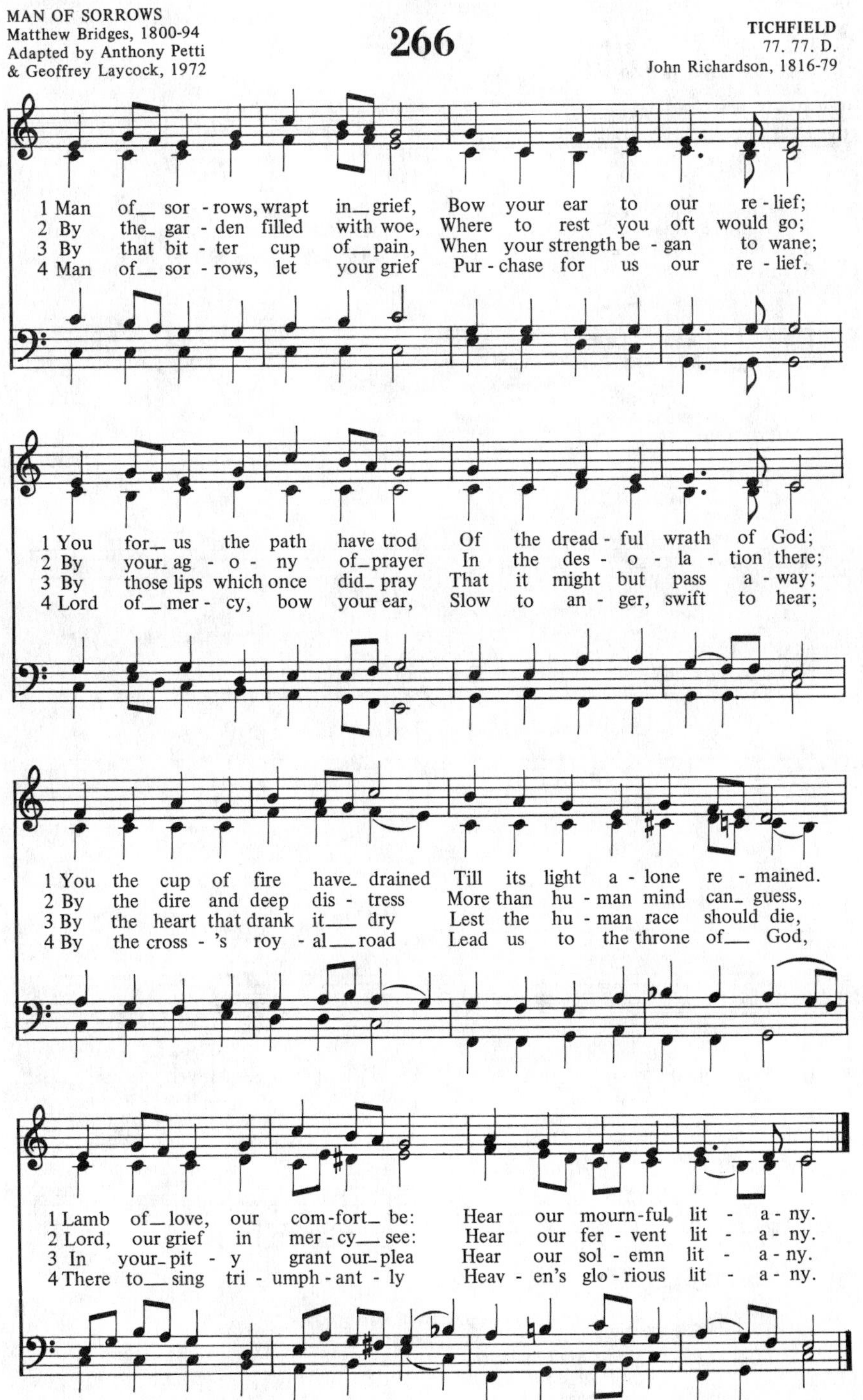
1 Man of_ sor - rows, wrapt in_ grief, Bow your ear to our re - lief;
2 By the_ gar - den filled with woe, Where to rest you oft would go;
3 By that bit - ter cup of_ pain, When your strength be - gan to wane;
4 Man of_ sor - rows, let your grief Pur - chase for us our re - lief.
1 You for_ us the path have trod Of the dread - ful wrath of God;
2 By your_ ag - o - ny of_ prayer In the des - o - la - tion there;
3 By those lips which once did_ pray That it might but pass a - way;
4 Lord of_ mer - cy, bow your ear, Slow to an - ger, swift to hear;
1 You the cup of fire have_ drained Till its light a - lone re - mained.
2 By the dire and deep dis - tress More than hu - man mind can_ guess,
3 By the heart that drank it_ dry Lest the hu - man race should die,
4 By the cross - 's roy - al_ road Lead us to the throne of_ God,
1 Lamb of_ love, our com - fort_ be: Hear our mourn - ful lit - a - ny.
2 Lord, our grief in mer - cy_ see: Hear our fer - vent lit - a - ny.
3 In your_ pit - y grant our_ plea Hear our sol - emn lit - a - ny.
4 There to_ sing tri - umph - ant - ly Heav - en's glo - rious lit - a - ny.

IN PASSIONE DOMINI
St. Bonaventure, 1221-74
Tr., Frederick Oakeley, 1802-80, et al.

267

Higher Key at No. 212

NUN KOMM, DER HEIDEN HEILAND
77. 77
After a plainsong melody
Eyn Enchiridion, Erfurt, 1524
Harm., Roger Nachtwey

1 In the Lord's a - ton - ing grief
2 Thorns and cross and nails and spear,
3 May these all our spir - its fill,
4 Cru - ci - fied, we you a - dore

1 Be our rest and sweet re - lief; Deep with - in our
2 Wounds that faith - ful hearts re - vere. Vin - e - gar and
3 And with love in - flame our will; Plant in us con -
4 And with all our love im - plore; With the saints our

1 hearts we'll store Those dear pains and wrongs he bore.
2 gall and reed, And the pang his soul that freed.
3 tri - tion's root, Rip - en there its sav - ing fruit.
4 souls u - nite In the realms of heav'n - ly light.

5 Christ, by coward hands betrayed,
Christ, for us a captive made,
Christ, upon the bitter tree,
Slain for man, all praises be!

268

VICTIMAE PASCHALI LAUDES
ascr. Wipo of Burgundy, c. 1030
Tr., Jane E. Leeson, 1851, alt.

Higher Key at No. 295

VICTIMAE PASCHALI LAUDES
77. 77. D.
Traditional Melody

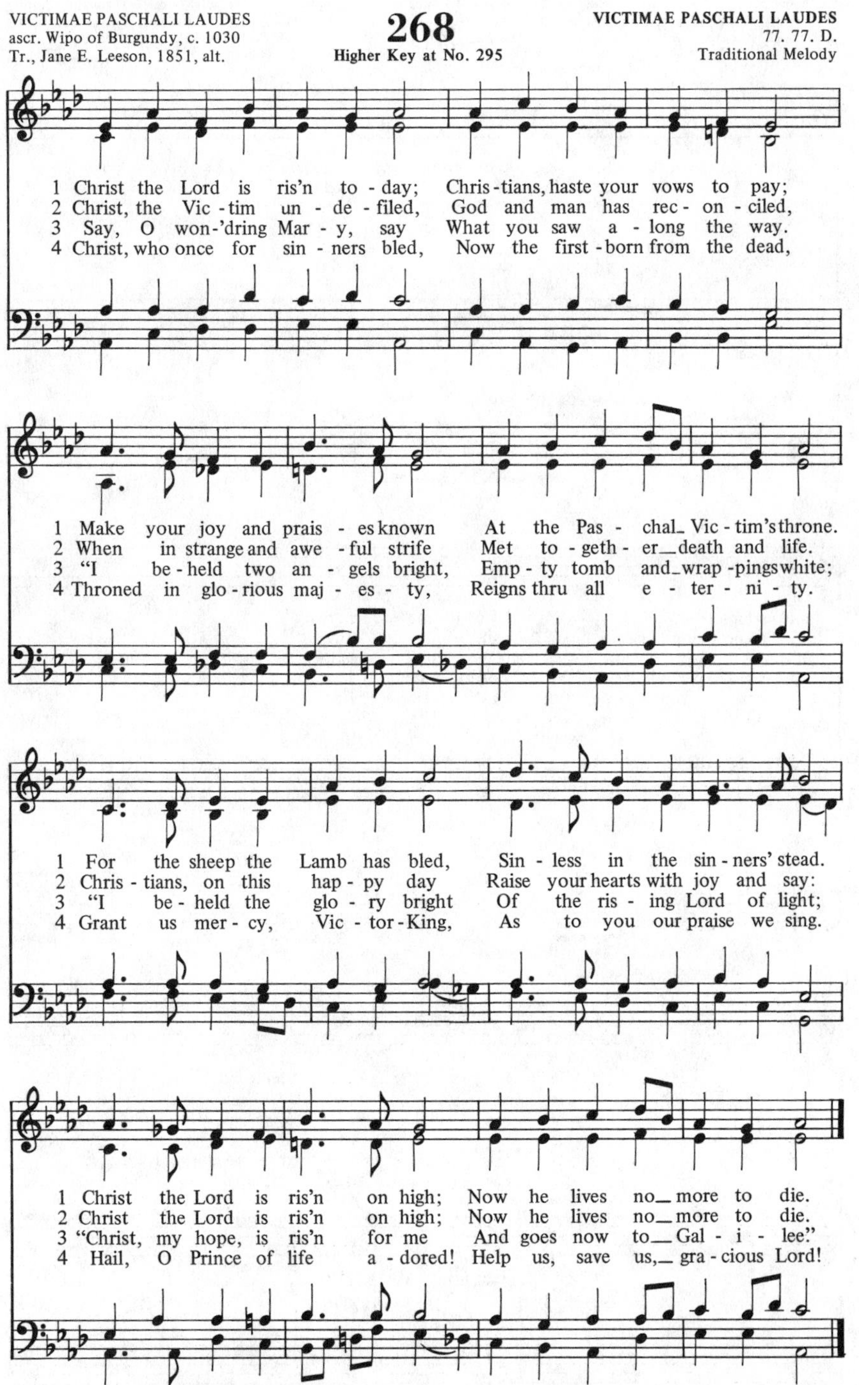
1 Christ the Lord is ris'n to - day; Chris - tians, haste your vows to pay;
2 Christ, the Vic - tim un - de - filed, God and man has rec - on - ciled,
3 Say, O won-'dring Mar - y, say What you saw a - long the way.
4 Christ, who once for sin - ners bled, Now the first - born from the dead,
1 Make your joy and prais - es known At the Pas - chal_ Vic - tim's throne.
2 When in strange and awe - ful strife Met to - geth - er_ death and life.
3 "I be - held two an - gels bright, Emp - ty tomb and_ wrap - pings white;
4 Throned in glo - rious maj - es - ty, Reigns thru all e - ter - ni - ty.
1 For the sheep the Lamb has bled, Sin - less in the sin - ners' stead.
2 Chris - tians, on this hap - py day Raise your hearts with joy and say:
3 "I be - held the glo - ry bright Of the ris - ing Lord of light;
4 Grant us mer - cy, Vic - tor - King, As to you our praise we sing.
1 Christ the Lord is ris'n on high; Now he lives no_ more to die.
2 Christ the Lord is ris'n on high; Now he lives no_ more to die.
3 "Christ, my hope, is ris'n for me And goes now to_ Gal - i - lee."
4 Hail, O Prince of life a - dored! Help us, save us,_ gra - cious Lord!

LASST UNS ERFREUEN
L. M. with Alleluias
Ausserlesne Katolische Geistliche Kirchengesänge
Cologne, 1623

AURORA LUCIS RUTILAT
4th or 5th cent.
Tr., John Mason Neale, 1851, alt.

269

Lower Key at No. 288

1 Morn fills the sky with crim - son light; Glad
2 While he the King, the might - y King, De -
3 His tomb just then had been well barred By
4 The days of mourn - ing now are past, The
5 O Lord of all, with us a - bide In
6 To God the Fa - ther let us sing, To
1 songs go ech - oing thru the height: Al - le -
2 spoil - ing death of all its sting, Al - le -
3 stone and seal and heav - y guard; Al - le -
4 pains of hell are loosed at last; Al - le -
5 this our joy - ful East - er - tide; Al - le -
6 God the Son, our ris - en King; Al - le -
1 lu - ia! Al - le - lu - ia! The glad earth shouts her tri - umph
2 lu - ia! Al - le - lu - ia! And, tram - pling down the pow'rs of
3 lu - ia! Al - le - lu - ia! But now, in pomp and ju - bi -
4 lu - ia! Al - le - lu - ia! An an - gel robed in light has
5 lu - ia! Al - le - lu - ia! Your own re - deemed for - ev - er
6 lu - ia! Al - le - lu - ia! And e - qual - ly let us a -

1 high, And groan - ing hell makes wild re - ply.
2 night, Brings forth his ran - somed saints to light.
3 lee, He comes from death to vic - to - ry.
4 said: "The Lord is ris - en from the dead."
5 shield From ev - 'ry weap - on death can wield.
6 dore The Ho - ly Spir - it ev - er - more.
Al - le - lu - ia! Al - le - lu - ia! Al - le-
lu - ia! Al - le - lu - ia! Al - le - lu - ia!

270

CLARO PASCHALI GAUDIO
4th or 5th cent.
Tr., John Mason Neale, 1851, alt.

PUER NOBIS
L. M.
Adapted by Michael Praetorius, 1609
Harm. by George R. Woodward, 1904

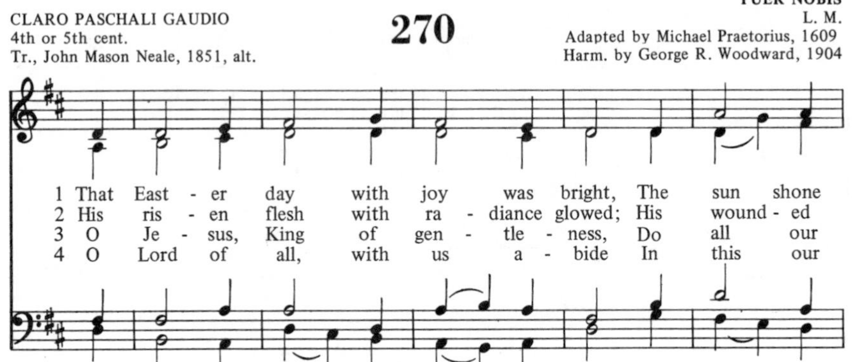
1 That East - er day with joy was bright, The sun shone
2 His ris - en flesh with ra - diance glowed; His wound - ed
3 O Je - sus, King of gen - tle - ness, Do all our
4 O Lord of all, with us a - bide In this our

1 out with fair - er light, When, to their long - ing eyes re -
2 hands and feet he showed; Those scars their sol - emn wit - ness
3 in - most hearts pos - sess, And we to you will ev - er
4 joy - ful East - er - tide; Your own re - deemed for - ev - er

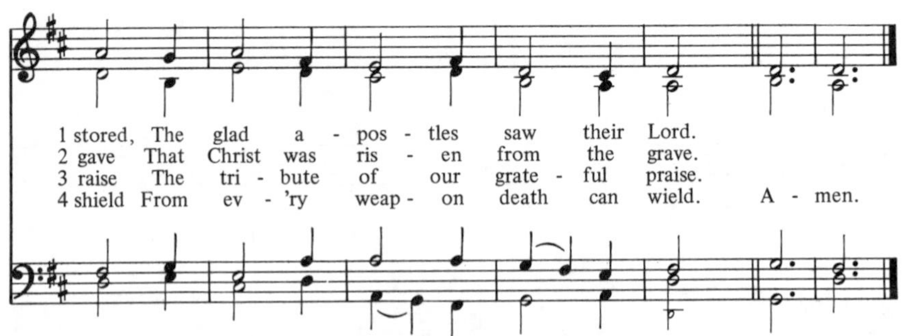
1 stored, The glad a - pos - tles saw their Lord.
2 gave That Christ was ris - en from the grave.
3 raise The tri - bute of our grate - ful praise.
4 shield From ev - 'ry weap - on death can wield. A - men.

5 To God the Father let us sing,
To God the Son, our risen King,
And equally let us adore
The Holy Spirit evermore. Amen.

THROUGH THE RED SEA
Ronald A. Knox, 1939
271[1]
Higher Key
STRAF MICH NICHT
77. 337, with Alleluias
Hundert Arien, Dresden, 1694
1 Through the_Red Sea brought at last, al - le - lu - ia,
2 Like the_cloud that o - ver - head, al - le - lu - ia,
3 In that_cloud and in that sea, al - le - lu - ia,
4 Then, de - ceit - ful world, *a - dieu,* al - le - lu - ia,
1 E - gypt's chains be - hind we cast, al - le - lu - ia.
2 Through the_bil - lows Is - rael led, al - le - lu - ia.
3 Bur - ied_and bap - tized were we, al - le - lu - ia.
4 E - gypt's land in dis - tant view, al - le - lu - ia.
1 Deep and wide Flows the tide Sev - 'ring us_from
2 By his tomb Christ makes room, Souls re - stor - ing
3 Earth - ly night Brought us light Which is ours_ e -
4 Christ our love Draws a - bove, Dead with him_ and
1 bond - age past, al - le - lu - ia!
2 from the dead, al - le - lu - ia!
3 ter - nal - ly, al - le - lu - ia!
4 ris'n a - new, al - le - lu - ia!

271²

Lower Key

SURREXIT CHRISTUS HODIE
Tr., in *Lyra Davidica,* 1708, alt.
Sts. 2, 3, *The Compleat Psalmodist,* 1749, alt.
St. 4, William Reynolds, 1860

272

EASTER HYMN
77. 77, with Alleluias
Lyra Davidica, London, 1708
Alt. in *The Compleat Psalmodist,* 1749

1 Je - sus Christ is ris'n to - day,
2 Hymns of praise then let us sing,
3 But the pains which he en - dured,
4 Praise to God the Fa - ther sing,
Al - le - lu - ia!

EASTER

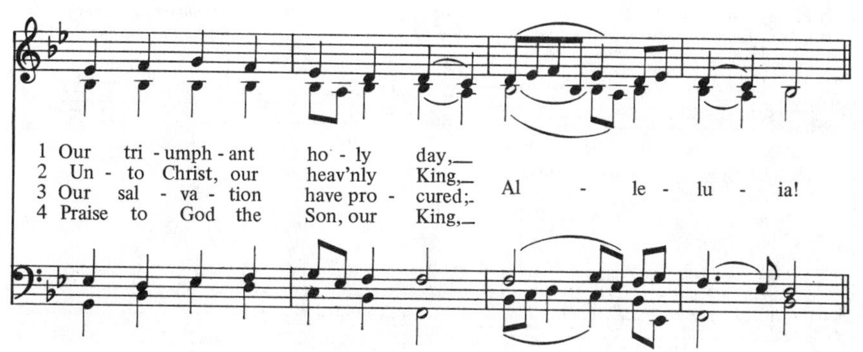
1 Our tri - umph - ant ho - ly day,
2 Un - to Christ, our heav'nly King,
3 Our sal - va - tion have pro - cured;
4 Praise to God the Son, our King,
Al - le - lu - ia!

1 Who did once up - on the cross,
2 Who en - dured the cross and grave,
3 Now a - bove the sky he's King,
4 Praise to God the Spir - it be,
Al - le - lu - ia!

1 Suf - fer to re - deem our loss.
2 Sin - ners to re - deem and save.
3 Where the an - gels ev - er sing.
4 Now and through e - ter - ni - ty.
Al - le - lu - ia!

273

GOOD CHRISTIAN MEN
Cyril A. Alington, 1931, alt.

GELOBT SEI GOTT
8.8.8. with Alleluias
Attr. to Melchior Vulpius, 1609
As in *Pilgrim Hymnal*, 1958

1 Good Chris - tian men, re - joice and sing!
2 The Lord of life is ris'n to - day!
3 Praise we in songs of vic - to - ry
4 Your name we bless, O ris - en Lord,
1 Now is the tri - umph of our King!
2 Sing songs of praise a - long his way;
3 That love, that life which can - not die,
4 And sing to - day with one ac - cord
1 To all the world glad news we bring:
2 Let all man - kind re - joice and say:
3 And sing with hearts up - lift - ed high:
4 The life laid down, the life re - stored:
Al - le - lu - ia! Al - le - lu - ia! Al - le - lu - ia!

274
ALLELUIA! LET THE HOLY ANTHEM
E. Caswall, 1814-78
HOLY ANTHEM
87. 87. D.
Traditional Melody
Harm. by Jerry R. Brubaker
1. Al - le - lu - ia! Al - le - lu - ia! Let the ho - ly an-them rise, And the
2. Al - le - lu - ia! Al - le - lu - ia! He en-dured the knot-ted whips, And the
3. Al - le - lu - ia! Al - le - lu - ia! Like the sun from out the wave He has
4. Al - le - lu - ia! Al - le - lu - ia! He has burst our pris - on bars; He has
1. choirs of heav - en chant it in the tem - ple of the skies; Let the
2. jeer - ing of the rab - ble, and the scorn of mock-ing lips, And the
3. ris - en up in tri - umph from the dark - ness of the grave. He's the
4. lift - ed up the por - tals of our home be - yond the stars; He has
1. moun - tains skip with glad - ness and the joy - ful val - leys ring With ho -
2. ter - rors of the gib - bet up - on which he would be slain, But his
3. splen - dor of the na - tions; He's the lamp of end - less day; He's the
4. won for us our free - dom–'neath his feet our foes are trod; He has
1. san - nas in the high - est to our Sav - ior and our King!
2. death was on - ly slum - ber; he is ris - en up a - gain!
3. ver - y Lord of glo - ry who is ris - en up to - day!
4. pur - chased back our birth-right to the king - dom of our God!

5 Alleluia! Alleluia! Blessed Jesus, make us rise
From the life of this corruption to the life that never dies.
May we share with you your glory when the days of time are past,
And the dead shall be awakened by the trumpet's mighty blast!

275

AD REGIAS AGNI DAPES
ascr. St Ambrose, 333-397
Tr., Robert Campbell, 1848, alt.

Lower Key at No. 232

SALZBURG
77. 77. D.
Jakob Hintze, 1678, alt.

1 At the Lamb's high feast we sing Praise to— our vic - to -rious King;
2 Where the Pas - chal blood is poured, Death's dark an -gel sheathes his sword;
3 Might - y— Vic - tim— from— on high, Pow'rs of— hell now van-quished lie;
4 East - er— tri - umph, East - er joy Sin a - lone can this de - stroy;
1 He has cleansed us— in the tide Flow - ing— from his o - pen side.
2 God's tri - umph - ant— peo - ple go Through the— sea that drowns the foe.
3 Sin is— con - quered— in the fight; You have brought us life and light.
4 Souls from sin and— death set free Glo - ry in their lib - er - ty.
1 Praise to him whose love di - vine Gives his sa - cred blood for wine,
2 Praise to Christ whose blood was shed, Christ our vic - tim, Christ our bread;
3 Your tri - umph - ant ban - ners wave; You have ris - en— from the grave;
4 Hymns of glo - ry, hymns of praise, Fa - ther, un - to— you we raise;
1 Gives his bod - y for— the feast, Christ the— vic - tim, Christ the priest.
2 Let us feast with faith and love On this— man - na from a - bove.
3 You have o - pened par - a - dise, And in— you all men shall rise.
4 Ris - en Lord, to you we sing: Let our hymns thru heav - en— ring!

276[1]

'Αναστάσεως ἡμέρα
St. John of Damascus, 8th cent.
Tr., John Mason Neale, 1859, alt.

Higher Key

AVE VIRGO VIRGINUM (GAUDEAMUS PARITER)
76. 76. D.
Johan Horn, 1544

1 Come, O faith - ful, sing the hymn Of tri - umph - ant glad - ness;
2 'Tis the spring of souls to - day; Christ has burst his pris - on
3 Now the queen of sea - sons, bright With the day of splen - dor,
4 Neith - er could the gates of death, Nor the tomb's dark por - tal,
1 God has brought his Is - ra - el In - to joy from sad - ness;
2 And from three days' sleep in death As a sun has ris - en;
3 With the roy - al feast of feasts, Comes its joy to ren - der;
4 Nor the watch - ers, nor the seal, Hold you as a mor - tal:
1 Loosed from Phar - oah's bit - ter yoke Ja - cob's sons_ and daugh - ters;
2 All the win - ter of our sins, Long and dark_ is fly - ing
3 Comes to glad Je - ru - sa - lem, Who with true_ af - fec - tion
4 But to - day a - mid your own You have stood_ be - stow - ing
1 Led them all com - plete - ly dry Through the Red Sea wa - ters.
2 From his light, to whom we give Song and praise un - dy - ing.
3 Wel - comes with un - tir - ing praise Je - sus' re - sur - rec - tion.
4 Your own peace which ev - er - more Pass - es hu - man know - ing.

Alternative Tune: TEMPUS ADEST FLORIDUM, No. 283

276[2]
Lower Key
CHRIST THE LORD IS RISEN TODAY
Sts. 1, 2, 3, 4, Charles Wesley, 1739, alt.
St. 5, Compilers
277
Lower Key at No. 289
LLANFAIR
77. 77, with Alleluias
Robert Williams, 1817
1 "Christ the Lord is ris'n to - day,"
2 Lives a - gain our glo - rious King;
3 Love's re - deem - ing work is — done,
4 Soar we now where Christ has — led,
Al - le - lu - ia!

1 Sons of men and an - gels say;
2 Where, O death, is now your sting?
3 Fought the fight, the bat - tle won.
4 Fol - low - ing our ris - en Head;
Al - le - lu - ia!
1 Raise your joys and tri - umphs high;
2 Once he died, our souls to save;
3 Death in vain for - bids him rise;
4 Made like him, like him we rise;
Al - le - lu - ia!
1 Sing, O heav'ns, and earth re - ply,
2 Where's your vic - t'ry now, O grave?
3 Christ has o - pened par - a - dise.
4 Ours the cross, the grave, the skies.
Al - le - lu - ia!

5 Hail the Lord of heav'n and earth!
Praise the Lord for our rebirth!
Let us all forever sing,
Praises to our risen King. Alleluia!

278

FINITA JAM SUNT PROELIA
Symphonia Sirenum Selectarum, Cologne, 1695
Tr., Francis Pott, 1861, alt.

VICTORY
888, with Alleluias
Palestrina, 1588
Adapted by William H. Monk, 1861

Al - le - lu - ia! Al - le - lu - ia! Al - le - lu - ia!
1 The strife is o'er, the bat - tle done; The vic - to - ry of life is won; The song of tri - umph has be - gun. Al - le - lu - ia!
2 The pow'rs of death have done their worst, But Christ their le - gions has dis - persed: Let shouts of ho - ly joy out - burst! Al - le - lu - ia!
3 The three sad days have quick - ly sped; He ri - ses glo - rious from the dead: All glo - ry to our ris - en Head! Al - le - lu - ia!
4 He closed the yawn - ing gates of hell; The bars from heav'n's high port - al fell: Let hymns of praise his tri - umph tell. Al - le - lu - ia!

5 Lord, by your wounds on Calvary
From death's dread sting your servants free,
That we may live eternally.
Alleluia!

Alternative Tune: O FILII ET FILIAE, No. 279

O FILII ET FILIAE
Jean Tisserand, d. 1494
Tr., E. Caswall, J. M. Neale, et al., alt.

279

O FILII ET FILIAE
8 8 8, with Alleluia
French, 15th cent.; Solesmes Version, Mode II

Al - le - lu - ia! Al - le - lu - ia! Al - le - lu - ia!
1 O sons and daugh-ters of the Lord, The King of glo - ry, King a - dored, From death to life has been re - stored. Al-le-lu-ia!
2 On Sun - day morn at break of day The sad dis - ci - ples went their way To see the tomb where Je - sus lay. Al-le-lu-ia!
3 Not Mag - da - len, not Sa - lo - me, Nor James' own moth- er then de - lay Em - balm - ing Je - sus' corpse that day. Al-le-lu-ia!
4 An an - gel clothed in white they see; He said, "You seek the Lord, but he Is ris'n and gone to Gal - i - lee." Al-le-lu-ia!

5 The dear belov'd apostle John
Could faster than St. Peter run,
Arriving first before the tomb.
Alleluia! *Refrain*

6 While the disciples hid in fear,
Their Christ among them did appear;
He said, "My peace be with you here."
Alleluia! *Refrain*

7 When Thomas heard what had been said,
That Christ was risen from the dead,
It entered not his heart or head.
Alleluia! *Refrain*

8 "O Thomas, see my side," said he;
"My hands, my feet, my body see.
No longer doubt; believe in me."
Alleluia! *Refrain*

9 When Thomas saw the wounded side,
The truth no longer he denied;
"You are my Lord and God," he cried.
Alleluia! *Refrain*

10 "Oh, blest are they who do not see
Their Lord, but yet believe in me:
Life shall be theirs eternally."
Alleluia! *Refrain*

11 On this most holy feast let's raise
Our hearts to God in hymns of praise,
And let us bless the Lord always.
Alleluia *Refrain*

12 Our humble thanks to God let's show
And fitting praise on him bestow
For Paschal blessings here below!
Alleluia! *Refrain*

Ἄισωμεν, πάντες λαοί
St. John of Damascus, c. 750
Tr., John Mason Neale, 1862, alt
280[1]
Higher Key
Higher Key at No. 529
LANCASHIRE
76. 76. D.
Henry Smart, 1836
1 The day of re - sur - rec - tion! Earth, tell it out a - broad! The Pass - o - ver of glad - ness, The Pass - o - ver of God. From death to life e - ter - nal, From this world to the sky,
2 Our hearts be pure from e - vil, That we may see a - right The Lord in rays e - ter - nal Of re - sur - rec - tion light, And list - 'ning to his ac - cents, May hear so calm and clear
3 Now let the heav'ns be joy - ful, Let earth its song be - gin, Let all the world keep tri - umph And all that is there - in; Let all things seen and un - seen Their notes of glad - ness blend,

1 Our Christ has brought us o - ver With vic - t'ry hymns on high.
2 His own "All hail" and, hear - ing, Re - peat for all to hear.
3 For Christ the Lord has ris - en, Our joy that has no end.

Alternative Tune: ZOAN, No. 480

280[2]

Lower Key

Based on Luke 24:28-35
DAYLIGHT FADES
Peter Scagnelli, 1973

281

DOMHNACH TRIONOIDE
87. 87. D.
Janet Stuart, 1914

1 Day - light fades in days when death - less Light has robbed earth's night of
2 Won - drous mys - t'ry of love's giv - ing! Our for - giv - ing Fa - ther's
3 O Lord Je - sus, ris - en Sa - vior, Hear our joy - ful hymn of
1 fear: On the edge of all our twi - lights East - er's an - gel shall ap -
2 Son, Crushed in sor - row, raised to glo - ry Death had con - quered; life has
3 praise; Grant a sea - son of sal - va - tion, Peace, and joy these East - er
1 pear; When hearts bro - ken by be - liev - ing Count their faith and hope as
2 won! Once in si - lence he sub - mit - ted, Now earth sings to him, our
3 days. To our Fa - ther and the Spir - it E - qual prais - es ev - er
1 dead, Christ will greet them in each oth - er And in break - ing of the bread.
2 King; Fear will ev - er flee de - feat - ed When a heart in love can sing!
3 be; Born a - gain, we sing God's good - ness Now and through e - ter - ni - ty.

282

CHRIST LAG IN TODESBANDEN
Martin Luther, 1524
Richard Massie, 1854, alt.

CHRIST LAG IN TODESBANDEN
87. 87. 78. 74.
Geistliches Gesangbuchlein, Wittenburg, 1524
Adapted by J. S. Bach, 1685-1750

1 Christ Je - sus_ lay in death's strong bands, For our of - fens- es_ giv - en,
2 It was a_ strange and dread - ful strife, When life and death con - tend - ed;
3 Here the true Pas - chal Lamb we see, Whom God so free - ly_ gave_ us;
4 So let us_ keep the fes - ti - val To which the Lord in - vites_ us.
5 Then let us_ feast this East - er day On Christ, the bread of_ heav - en;
1 But now at_ God's right hand he stands And brings us life from heav - en;
2 The vic - to - ry re - mained with life; The reign of death was_ end - ed.
3 He died on_ that ac - curs - ed tree So strong his love to_ save_ us.
4 Christ is him - self the joy of all, The Sun that warms and_ lights_ us;
5 The word of_ grace has purged a - way The old and wick - ed_ leav - en.
1 There - fore let us_ joy - ful be And sing to God right thank - ful - ly
2 Stripped of pow'r, death no more reigns; An emp - ty form a - lone re - mains;
3 See_ his blood now marks our door. Faith points to it; death pas - es o'er,
4 By_ his grace he_ does im - part E - ter - nal sun - shine to the heart;
5 Christ a - lone our_ souls will feed; He is our meat and_ drink in - deed;
Al - le - lu - ia.
1 Loud songs of_ "Al - le - lu - ia!"
2 His sting is_ lost for - ev - er.
3 And Sa - tan_ can - not harm_ us.
4 The night of_ sin is end - ed.
5 Faith lives up - on no oth - er.
Al - le - lu - ia.
Al - le - lu - ia.
Al - le - lu - ia.

283

TEMPUS ADEST FLORIDUM
Piæ Cantiones, 1582
Tr. in Oxford Book of Carols, 1928

TEMPUS ADEST FLORIDUM
76. 76. D.
Piæ Cantiones, 1582

1 Spring has now un-wrapped the flow'rs, Day is fast re-viv-ing;
2 Herb and plant that, win-ter long, Slum-bered at their leis-ure,
3 Thru each won-der of fair days God him-self ex-press-es;
4 Earth puts on her dress of glee; Flow'rs and grass-es hide her;
1 Life in all her grow-ing pow'rs Toward the light is striv-ing:
2 Now a-wak-'ning, green and strong, Find in growth their pleas-ure:
3 Beau-ty fol-lows all his ways, As the world he bless-es:
4 We go forth in char-i-ty, Broth-ers all be-side her;
1 Gone the i-ron touch of cold, Win-ter time and frost time;
2 All the world with beau-ty fills, Gold the green en-hanc-ing;
3 So, as he re-news the earth, Art-ist with-out ri-val,
4 For, as man this glo-ry sees In the wak-'ning sea-son,
1 Seed-lings, work-ing thru the mould, Now make up for lost time.
2 Flow'rs make glee a-mong the hills; Set the mead-ows danc-ing.
3 In his grace of glad new birth We must seek re-vi-val.
4 Rea-son learns the heart's de-crees; Hearts are led by rea-son.

5 Praise the Maker, all you saints;
He with glory girt you,
He who skies and meadows paints
Fashioned all your virtue;
Praise him, prophets, heroes, kings,
Heralds of perfection;
Brothers, praise him, for he brings
All to resurrection.

284

HIC EST DIES
St. Ambrose, d. 397
Tr., Peter Scagnelli, 1973

DE HEER IS WAARLIJK OPGESTAAN
84 84. 77 84
Wim ter Burg, b. 1914

1 This day of God de - stroys the night, Al - le - lu - ia!
2 What could sur - pass this vic - to - ry? Al - le - lu - ia!
3 Lord Je - sus, ris - en ev - er - more, Al - le - lu - ia!
1 Ser - ene and blest God's ho - ly light, Al - le - lu - ia!
2 Grace con - quers sin e - ter - nal - ly, Al - le - lu - ia!
3 Where sor - row rules, your joy re - store, Al - le - lu - ia!
1 Death and hate had sealed life's grave, Con - quered by the love he gave:
2 Love now reigns where fear brought strife; Death yields gift of last - ing life;
3 In the peace of Eas - ter days, Born a - gain we sing your praise,
1 This is the day the Lord has made, Al - le - lu - ia!
2 Christ in our midst a - live a - gain, Al - le - lu - ia!
3 To Fa - ther, Son, and Spir - it blest, Al - le - lu - ia!

285

NOW THE GREEN BLADE RISETH
John M. C. Crum, 1872-1958

NOEL NOUVELET
11 11. 10 11
Provencal Noel

1 Now the green blade ris - es from the_ bur - ied grain,
2 In the grave they laid him, Love whom men had slain,
3 Forth he came at East - er, like the_ ris - en grain,
4 When our hearts are win - try, griev - ing,_ or in pain,
1 Wheat that in the dark earth man - y_ days has lain;
2 Think - ing that he nev - er would a - wake a - gain,
3 Je - sus, who for three days in the_ grave had lain,
4 Your dear touch can call us back to_ life a - gain;
1 Love lives a - gain that with the dead has been:
2 Laid in the earth like grain that sleeps un - seen:
3 Live from the dead my ris - en Lord is seen:
4 Fields of our hearts that dead and bare have been:
Love is come a - gain, like wheat that_ springs up green.

286

O THRONED, O CROWNED
Edward White Benson, 1860, alt.

MATERNA
C. M. D.
Samuel A. Ward, 1882

Higher Key at No. 321

1 O Jesus crowned with all renown, Since you the earth have trod,
You're reigning, and by you come down Henceforth the gifts of God.
Yours is the health and yours the wealth That in our land abound,
And yours the beauty and the joy With which the years are crowned.

2 Lord, in their change, let frost and heat, And winds and dews be giv'n;
All fost'ring pow'r, all influence sweet, breathe from the gracious heav'n.
And temper fair with gentle air The sunshine and the rain,
That kindly earth with timely birth May yield her fruits again:

3 That we may feed the poor aright, And, gath'ring round your throne,
Here, in the holy angels' sight, Repay you of your own:
That we may praise you all our days, And with the Father's Name,
And with the Holy Spirit's gifts, Our Savior's love proclaim.

287

LORD, IN THY NAME
J. Keble, 1792-1866, alt.

MARTYRS
C. M.
Scottish Psalter, 1615

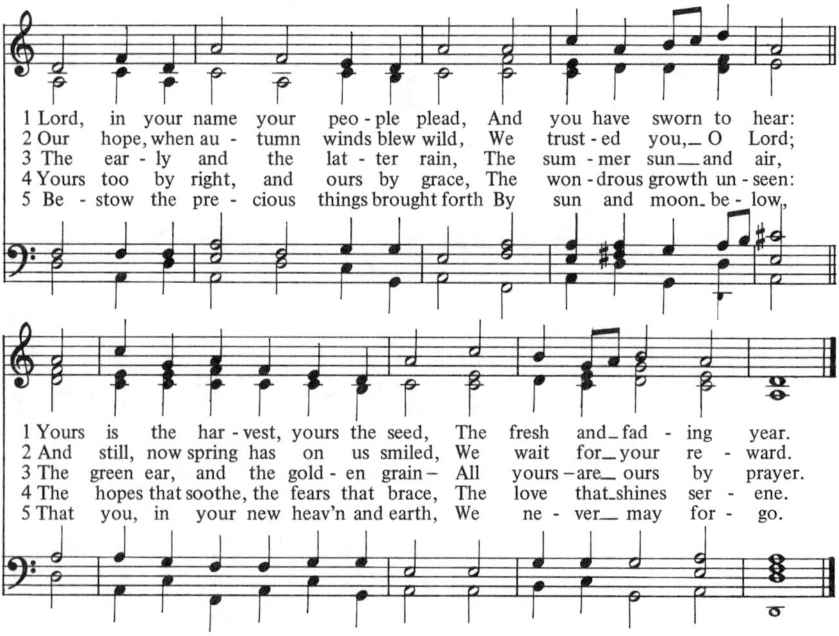

1 Lord, in your name your people plead, And you have sworn to hear:
Yours is the harvest, yours the seed, The fresh and fading year.

2 Our hope, when autumn winds blew wild, We trusted you, O Lord;
And still, now spring has on us smiled, We wait for your reward.

3 The early and the latter rain, The summer sun and air,
The green ear, and the golden grain– All yours–are ours by prayer.

4 Yours too by right, and ours by grace, The wondrous growth unseen:
The hopes that soothe, the fears that brace, The love that shines serene.

5 Bestow the precious things brought forth By sun and moon below,
That you, in your new heav'n and earth, We never may forgo.

288

HYMNUM CANAMUS GLORIAE
The Venerable Bede, 673-735
Tr., Benjamin Webb, 1854, alt.

Higher Key at No. 269

LASST UNS ERFREUEN
L. M. with Alleluias
Ausserlesne Katolische Geistliche Kirchengesänge
Cologne, 1623

1 A hymn of glory let us sing; New songs thruout the world shall
2 In won-d'ring awe his faithful band Upon the mount of olives
3 Then spoke the angel, drawing nigh, "Why stand and gaze upon the
4 May we who rose thru his great love, Keep our desires and thoughts a-
5 O risen Christ, ascended Lord, All praise to you let earth ac-

ASCENSION

1 ring.
2 stand,
3 sky? Al - le - lu - ia, al - le - lu - ia.
4 bove,
5 cord.
Christ, by a road be -
And with the vir - gin -
A - gain shall you be -
Where soon our Sa - vior
You are, while end - less
1 fore un - trod, As - cend - ed to the throne of God.
2 moth - er see Their Lord as - cend in maj - es - ty.
3 hold him so As you to - day have seen him go.
4 we shall see And praise thru all e - ter - ni - ty.
5 a - ges run, With Fa - ther and with Spir - it one.
Al - le - lu - ia,
al - le - lu - ia! Al - le - lu - ia, al - le - lu - ia, al - le - lu - ia!

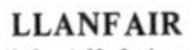
LLANFAIR

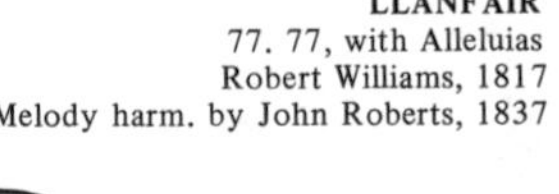
77. 77, with Alleluias
Robert Williams, 1817
Melody harm. by John Roberts, 1837

289

HAIL THE DAY THAT SEES HIM RISE
Charles Wesley, 1739, alt.

Higher Key at No. 277

1 Hail the day that sees him rise,
2 There the glo - rious tri - umph waits;
3 See! He lifts his hands a - bove;
4 Lord be - yond our mor - tal sight,
Al - le - lu - ia!

1 Glo - rious to his na - tive skies;
2 Lift your heads, e - ter - nal gates!
3 See! He shows the prints of love:
4 Raise our hearts to reach your height;
Al - le - lu - ia!

1 Christ, a - while to men sent down,
2 He has con - quered death and sin;
3 Hear! His gra - cious lips be - stow,
4 There shall we with you re - main,
Al - le - lu - ia!

1 Now as - cends to take his crown!
2 Take the King of glo - ry in!
3 Bless - ings on his church be - low.
4 Part - ners of your end - less reign!
Al - le - lu - ia!

290

HYMNUM CANAMUS GLORIAE
The Venerable Bede, 673-735
Tr., Ronald A. Knox, 1939

Higher Key at No. 431

ST. DENIO (JOANNA)
11. 11. 11 11
Welsh Melody
Adapted, 1839

1 New prais - es be giv - en to Christ new - ly crowned, Who
2 His glo - ry still prais - ing on thrice ho - ly ground, Th'a -
3 "No star can dis - close him." the bright an - gels said; "E -
4 Thus spoke they, and straight-way, where le - gions de - fend Heav'n's
1 back to his hea - ven a new way has found;
2 pos - tles stood gaz - ing, his moth - er a - round;
3 ter - ni - ty knows him, your con - quer - ing Head:
4 glit - ter - ing gate - way, their Lord they at - tend,
1 God's bles - sed - ness shar - ing, be - fore us he goes, What
2 With hearts that beat fast - er, with eyes full of love, They
3 Those high ha - bi - ta - tions he leaves not a - gain Till,
4 And cry, look - ing thi - ther, "Your por - tals let down For
1 man - sions pre - par - ing, what end - less re - pose!
2 watched while their Mas - ter as - cend - ed a - bove.
3 judg - ing all na - tions, on earth he shall reign."
4 him who rides hith - er in peace and re - nown."

5 They asked, who keep sentry in that blessed town,
"Who thus claims an entry, a king of renown?"
"The Lord of all valiance," the herald replied,
"Who Satan's battalions laid low in their pride."

SEE THE CONQUEROR MOUNTS
Christopher Wordsworth, 1862, alt.

291

IN BABILONE
87. 87. D.
Traditional Dutch Melody

1 See, the Con - qu'ror mounts in tri - umph;
2 He who on the cross did suf - fer,
3 He has raised our hu - man na - ture
4 See him who is gone be - fore us
1 See the King in roy - al state, Rid - ing on the
2 He who from the grave a - rose, He has van - quished
3 On the clouds to God's right hand: There we sit in
4 Heav'n - ly man - sions to pre - pare; See him who is
1 clouds, his char - iot, To his heav'n - ly pal - ace gate!
2 sin and Sa - tan And by death de - spoiled his foes.
3 heav'n - ly pla - ces, There with him in glo - ry stand.
4 ev - er plead - ing For us with pre - vail - ing prayer;
1 Hark! The choirs of an - gel voi - ces
2 While he lifts his hands in bless - ing,
3 Je - sus reigns, a - dored by an - gels;
4 See him who with sound of trum - pet

ASCENSION

1 Joy - ful al - le - lu - ias sing,
2 He is part - ed from his friends;
3 Man with God is on his throne;
4 And with his an - gel - ic train,
1 And the por - tals high are lift - ed
2 While their ea - ger eyes be - hold him,
3 Might - y Lord, in your as - cen - sion,
4 Sum - mon - ing the world to judge - ment,
1 To re - ceive their heav'n - ly King.
2 He up - on the clouds as - cends.
3 We by faith be - hold our own.
4 On the clouds will come a - gain.

5 Glory be to God the Father;
Glory be to God the Son,
Dying, ris'n, ascending for us,
Who the heav'nly realm has won
Glory to the Holy Spirit:
To one God in persons three
Glory both in earth and heaven,
Glory endless glory be.

KOMM, HEILIGER GEIST
Martin Luther, 1524
Tr., Edward Traill Horn III, b. 1909, alt.

292

Lower Key at No. 244

SAINT BONIFACE
L. M.
Mainz *Gesangbuch*, 1833

1 Come, Ho - ly Spir - it, God and Lord; May all your gifts on
2 O, by the bright - ness of your light, In ho - ly faith all
3 O strong De - fence, O ho - ly Light! That we may know our
4 O sa - cred Ar - dor, Com - fort sweet! Make will - ing hearts and

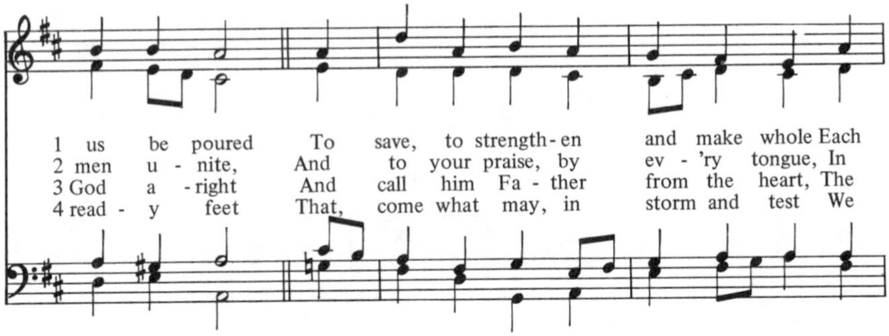

1 us be poured To save, to strength - en and make whole Each
2 men u - nite, And to your praise, by ev - 'ry tongue, In
3 God a - right And call him Fa - ther from the heart, The
4 read - y feet That, come what may, in storm and test We

1 read - y mind, each wait - ing soul.
2 ev - 'ry land, our hymn be sung.
3 word of life and truth im - part.
4 do but what we know is best.
A - men.

5 Enliven us with all your pow'rs,
Make strong our faith in weaker hours,
That, as good Christians in the strife,
We turn to you in death and life. Amen.

MENDON
L. M.

COME, GRACIOUS SPIRIT
Simon Browne, 1720, alt.

293

Traditional German Melody
arr. by Samuel Dyer, 1828

1 Come, gra - cious Spir - it, heav'n - ly Dove, With light and
2 The light of truth to us dis - play, And make us
3 Lead us to Christ, the liv - ing Way, Nor let us
4 Lead us to heav'n, that we may share The high - est

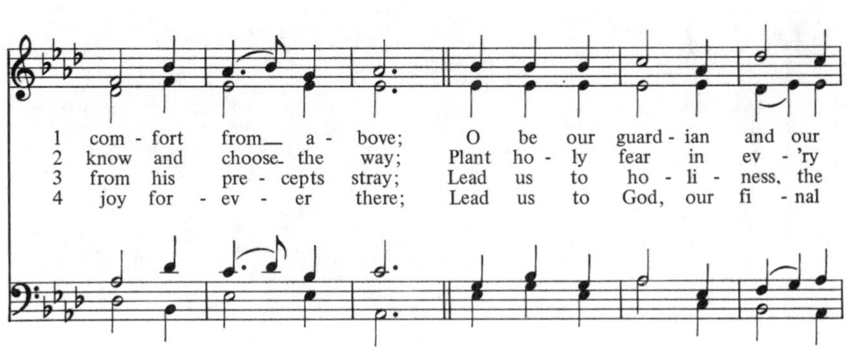
1 com - fort from a - bove; O be our guard - ian and our
2 know and choose the way; Plant ho - ly fear in ev - 'ry
3 from his pre - cepts stray; Lead us to ho - li - ness, the
4 joy for - ev - er there; Lead us to God, our fi - nal

1 guide; O'er ev - 'ry thought and step pre - side.
2 heart, That we from you may nev - er part.
3 road That we must take to dwell with God.
4 rest, To be with him for - ev - er blest.

Alternative Tune: ST. BONIFACE, No. 272

294

VENI SANCTE SPIRITUS
12th cent.
Tr., John Webster Grant, 1919-

VENI SANCTE SPIRITUS
777. 777
Samuel Webbe, 1782

1 Ho - ly Spir - it, font of light, Fo - cus of God's glo - ry bright,
2 Source of strength and sure re-lief, Com - fort - er in time of grief,
3 En - ter each as - pir - ing heart, Oc - cu - py its in - most part
4 With your soft, re - fresh - ing rains Break our drought, re - move our stains;

1 Shed on us a shin - ing ray. Fa - ther of the fa - ther-less,
2 En - ter in and be our guest. On our jour - ney grant us aid,
3 With your daz - zling pur - i - ty. All that gives to man his worth,
4 Bind up all our in - jur - ies. Shake with rush - ing wind our will;

1 Giv - er of gifts lim - it - less, Come and touch our hearts to - day.
2 Fresh-'ning breeze and cool - ing shade, In our la - bor in - ward rest.
3 All that ben - e - fits the earth, You bring to ma - tur - i - ty.
4 Melt with fire our i - cy chill; Bring to light our per - jur - ies.

5 As your promise we believe,
Make us ready to receive
Gifts from your unbounded store.
Grant enabling energy,
Courage in adversity,
Joys that last forevermore.

BEATA NOBIS GAUDIA
ascr. St. Hilary of Poitiers, d. 386
Tr., Robert Campbell, 1814-68, alt.
295
Lower Key at No. 268
VICTIMAE PASCHALI LAUDES
77. 77. D.
Traditional Melody
1 Hail this joy - ful day's re - turn, Hail the pen - te - cost - al morn,
2 Hear the speech be - fore un - known; Trem - bling crowds the won - der own;
3 Lord, to you your peo - ple bend; Un - to us your Spir - it send;
1 Morn when our as - cend - ed Head On his church his Spir - it shed!
2 What though hard - ened some a - bide And the ho - ly work de - ride?
3 Bless - ings of this sa - cred day Grant us, dear - est Lord, we pray.
1 Like to clo - ven tongues of flame On the twelve the Spir - it came
2 Mys - tic hour, when East - er's sun Sev'n times sev'n its course has run;
3 To our fa - thers you were guide; With their chil - dren still a - bide;
1 Tongues, that earth may hear their call, Fire, that love may burn in all.
2 Church of God, from debt made free, Hail your day of ju - bi - lee.
3 Grant us par - don, grant us peace, till our earth - ly wan - d'rings cease.

DISCENDI, AMOR SANTO
Bianco da Siena, c. 1367
Tr., R. F. Littledale, 1867, alt.

296

Higher Key

DOWN AMPNEY
66. 11. D.
Ralph Vaughn Williams, 1906

1 Come down, O love di - vine, Seek out this heart of mine, And vis - it it with your own ar - dor glow - ing;
2 O let it free - ly burn, Till earth - ly pas - sions turn To dust and ash - es, in its heat con - sum - ing;
3 Let ho - ly char - i - ty My sim - ple ves - ture be, And low - li - ness be - come my dai - ly cloth - ing:
4 And so the yearn - ing strong, With which the soul will long, Shall far out - pass the pow'r of hu - man tell - ing;
1 Great Com - fort - er, draw near, With - in my heart ap - pear, And kin - dle it, your ho - ly flame be - stow - ing.
2 And let your glo - rious light Shine ev - er on my sight, And clothe me round, the while my path il - lum - ing.
3 True low - li - ness of heart, Which takes the hum - bler part, And on its own short - com - ings weeps with loath - ing.
4 For none can guess its grace, Till he be - come the place In which the Ho - ly Spir - it makes his dwell - ing.

296[2]
Lower Key
297
LEW TRENCHARD
77. 77
HOLY SPIRIT, TRUTH DIVINE
Samuel Longfellow, 1864
Traditional English Melody
harmonized by W. D., 1918
1 Ho - ly Spir - it, Truth di - vine, Dawn up - on this soul of mine;
2 Ho - ly Spir - it, Love di - vine, Glow with - in this heart of mine;
1 Breath of God, and in - ward Light, Wake my spir - it, clear my sight.
2 Kind - le ev - 'ry high de - sire; Per - ish self in your pure fire!

VENI, CREATOR SPIRITUS
ascr. Rabanus Maurus, d. 856
Tr., John Webster Grant, b. 1919
Tr., St. 6, E. Caswall, 1814-78, alt.
298[1]
Higher Key
VENI, CREATOR SPIRITUS
L. M.
Plainsong Melody
1 Ve - ni cre - a - tor_ Spi - ri - tus, Men - tes tu - o - rum_ vi - si - ta; Im - ple_ su - per - na_ gra - ti - a, Quae_ to cre - a - sti_ pec - to - ra.
Come, Ho - ly_ Spir - it,_ by whose breath Life ris - es vi - brant_ out of death: Come to_ cre - ate,_ re - new, in - spire; Come,_ kin - dle_ in our_ hearts your fire.
2 Qui di - ce - ris Pa - ra - cli - tus, Al - tis - si - mi do - num De - i, Fons vi - vus_ i - gnis_ ca - ri - tas Et_ spi - ri - ta - lis_ un - cti - o.
You are the_ seek - er's sure re - source, Of burn - ing love the_ liv - ing source, Pro - tec - tor_ in_ the_ midst of strife, The_ giv - er_ and the_ Lord of life.
3 Tu sep - ti - for - mis_ mu - ne - re, Digi - tis pa - ter - nae_ dex - te - rae, Tu ri - te_ pro - mis - sum Pa - tris Ser - mo - ne_ di - tans_ gut - tu - ra. A - men.
In you God's en - er - gy is shown, To us your var - ied_ gifts made known. Teach us_ to_ speak;_ teach_ us to hear; Yours_ is the_ tongue and_ yours the ear. A - men.

4 Accende lumen sensibus,
Infunde amorem cordibus,
Infirma nostri corporis
Virtute firmans perpeti.

5 Hostem repellas longius
Pacemque dones protinus;
Ductore sic te prævio
Vitemus omne noxium.

6 Per te sciamus da Patrem
Noscamus atque Filium,
Teque utriusque Spiritum
Credamus omni tempore.

7 Deo Patri sit gloria,
Ejusque soli Filio,
Cum Spiritu Paraclito
Et nunc et in perpetuum Amen.

4 Flood our dull senses with your light;
In mutual love our hearts unite.
Your pow'r the whole creation fills;
Confirm our weak uncertain wills.

5 From inner strife grant us release;
Turn nations to the ways of peace;
To fuller life your people bring,
That as one body we may sing.

6 Thru you may we the Father learn
And know the Son and you discern
You come from both, And we'll adore
In perfect faith for evermore.

7 Praise to the Father, Christ his word,
And to the Spirit, God the Lord;
To them all honor, glory, be
Both now and for eternity. Amen.

298[2]

Lower Key

VENI, CREATOR SPIRITUS
ascr. Rabanus Maurus, d. 856
Tr., Edward Caswall, 1849, alt.
299
HOLY SPIRIT
L. M.
L. Lambillotte
1 Come, Ho - ly Ghost, Cre - a - tor blest, And in our hearts take up thy rest; Come with thy grace and heav'n - ly aid To fill the hearts which thou hast made, To fill the hearts which thou hast made.
2 O Com - fort - er, to thee we cry, Thou gift of God sent from on high, Thou fount of life and fire of love, The soul's a - noint - ing from a - bove, The soul's a - noint - ing from a - bove.
3 O Ho - ly Ghost, through thee a - lone Know we the Fa - ther and the Son; And may this be our change - less creed: That thou dost from them both pro - ceed, That thou dost from them both pro - ceed.
4 Praise be to thee, Fa - ther and Son, And Ho - ly Spir - it with them one; And may the Son on us be - stow The gifts that from the Spir - it flow, The gifts that from the Spir - it flow.

WER SIND DIE VOR GOTTES THRONE
Theobald Heinrich Schenck, 1719
Tr., Frances E. Cox, 1841, 1864, alt.

300

ALL SAINTS
87. 87. 77
Geistreiches Gesangbuch, Darmstadt, 1698

1 Who are these like stars ap - pear - ing, These, be - fore God's throne who stand? Each a gold - en crown is wear - ing; Who are all this glo - rious band? "Al - le - lu - ia!" now they sing, Prais - ing loud their heav'n - ly King.
2 Who are these of dazz - ling bright - ness, These in God's own truth ar - rayed. Clad in robes of pure - est white - ness, Robes whose lus - ter will not fade, Nor be touched by time's rude hand? Whence comes all this glo - rious band?
3 These are they who have con - tend - ed For their Sa - vior's hon - or long, Wrest - ling on till life was end - ed, Fol - l'wing not the sin - ful throng: These, who well the fight sus - tained, Tri - umph by the Lamb have gained.
4 These like priests, have watched and wait - ed, Of - f'ring up to Christ their will, Soul and bod - y con - se - crat - ed, Day and night they serve him still. Now in God's most ho - ly place, Blest they stand be - fore his face.

Alternative Tune: COBLENZ, No. 361

REST (BEATI) (MAGDALEN)
88. 88. 88
John Stainer, 1873
THE SAINTS OF GOD
William Dalrymple Maclagan, 1869
301[1]
Higher Key
1 The saints of God! their con - flict past, And
2 The saints of God! their wan - d'rings done, No
3 The saints of God! life's voy - age o'er, Safe
1 life's long bat - tle won at last,
2 more their wea - ry course they run,
3 land - ed on that bliss - ful shore,
1 No more they need the shield or sword, They
2 No more they faint, no more they fall, No
3 No storm - y tem - pests now they dread, No
1 cast them down be - fore the Lord:
2 foes op - press, no fears ap - pall:
3 roar - ing bil - lows lift their head:

ALL SAINTS

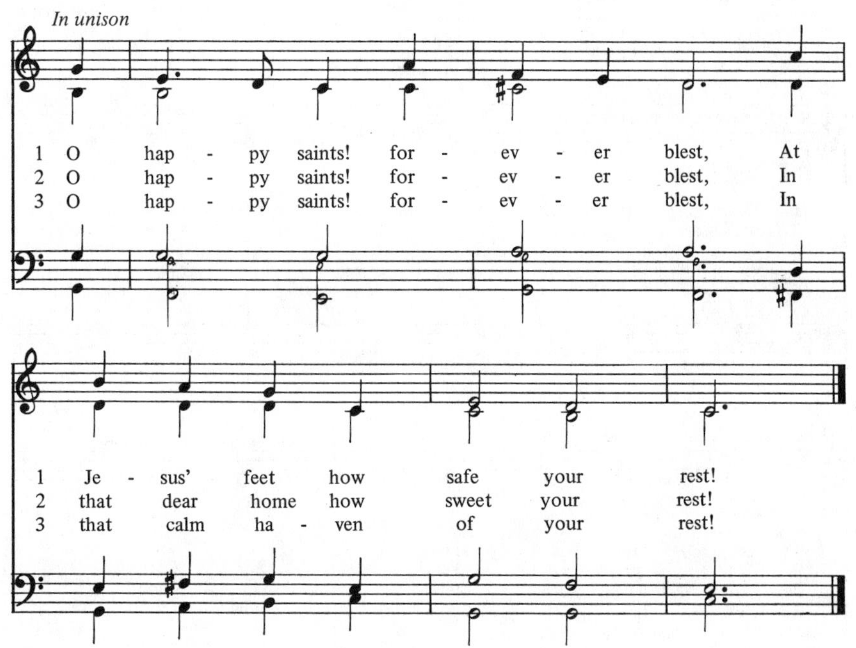
In unison
1 O hap - py saints! for - ev - er blest, At
2 O hap - py saints! for - ev - er blest, In
3 O hap - py saints! for - ev - er blest, In
1 Je - sus' feet how safe your rest!
2 that dear home how sweet your rest!
3 that calm ha - ven of your rest!

301[2]

Lower Key

MOULTRIE
87. 87. D.
HARK! THE SOUND OF HOLY VOICES
Christopher Wordsworth, 1862, alt.
302
Gerard F. Cobb, 1838-1904
Higher Key at No. 413
1 Hear the sound of ho - ly voi - ces,
2 Pa - tri - arch, and ho - ly pro - phet,
3 They have come from trib - u - la - tion,
4 March - ing with your cross, their ban - ner,
1 Sing - ing in the heav'n - ly blue,
2 Who pre - pared the way for Christ,
3 And have washed their robes in Blood,
4 They have tri - umphed, fol - low - ing
1 "Al - le - lu - ia, al - le - lu - ia, Al - le - lu - ia,"
2 King, a - pos - tle, saint, con - fes - sor, Mar - tyr and e -
3 Washed them in the blood of Je - sus; Tried they were, and
4 You, the Cap - tain of sal - va - tion, You, their Sa - vior
1 Lord to you! Mul - ti - tude which none can num - ber
2 van - gel - ist, Saint - ly maid - en, ho - ly ma - tron,
3 firm they stood; Mocked, im - pris - oned, stoned, tor - men - ted,
4 and their King. Glad - ly, Lord, with you they suf - fered,

ALL SAINTS

1 Like the stars in glo - ry stands,
2 Wid - ows who have watched in prayer,
3 Torn a - sun - der, slain with sword,
4 Glad - ly, Lord, with you they died;

1 Clothed in white ap - par - el, hold - ing
2 Joined in ho - ly con - cert, sing - ing
3 They have con - quered death and Sa - tan
4 And by death to life im - mor - tal

1 Palms of vic - t'ry in their hands.
2 To the Lord of all, are there.
3 By the might of Christ the Lord.
4 They were born and glo - ri - fied.

5 Now they reign in heav'nly glory.
Now they walk in golden light,
Now they drink, as from a river,
Holy bliss in God's own sight:
Love and peace they taste forever,
And all truth and knowledge see
In a beatific vision
Of the blessèd Trinity.

6 God of God, the One-begotten,
Light of Light, Emmanuel,
In whose Body joined together
All the saints forever dwell;
Pour upon us of your fulness,
That we may forevermore
God the Father, God the Son, and
God the Spirit, One, adore.

FOR ALL THE SAINTS
William Walsham How, 1864
Adapted by Anthony G. Petti, 1972
303
SINE NOMINE
10 10 10, with Alleluias
Ralph Vaughan Williams, 1906
1 For all the saints who from their la - bors rest, Who their great faith to all the world con - fessed, Your name, O Je - sus be for - ev - er blessed.
2 You were their rock, their for - tress and their might, Their val - iant cap - tain in the well - fought fight, And in the dark - ness their un - fail - ing light.
3 May all the faith - ful, joined with - in one fold, Strive as the saints who brave - ly fought of old, And win, like them, the vic - tor's crown of gold.
4 O blest com - mun - ion, fel - low - ship di - vine, We feeb - ly strug - gle, they in glo - ry shine, Yet all in Christ u - nite, in him com - bine.

ALL SAINTS

Al - - le - lu - ia, Al - le - lu - ia!

5 And, when the strife is fierce,
  the struggle long,
Then from the distance sounds
  the triumph song,
And hearts are bold again,
  and courage strong.

6 The golden evening
  brightens in the west,
Soon to the steadfast
  faithful comes their rest:
The soothing calm of
  Paradise so blest.

7 But still there breaks a
  far more glorious day,
The saints triumphant
  rise in bright array,
The King of Glory
  passes on his way.

8 From earth's wide bounds, from
  ocean's farthest coast,
Through gates of pearl streams
  in the countless host,
And sing to Father,
  Son, and Holy Ghost.

303

Optional Accompaniment

CHRIST IS THE KING
George Kennedy Allen Bell, 1933

304

GELOBT SEI GOTT
888, with Alleluias
M. Vulpius, 1609

1 Christ is the King! O friends, re - joice;
2 O mag - ni - fy the Lord, and raise
3 They, with a faith for - ev - er new,
4 O Chris - tian wom - en, Chris - tian men,
1 Broth - ers and sis - ters, with one voice
2 An - thems of joy and ho - ly praise
3 Fol - lowed the King, and round him drew
4 All the world o - ver, seek a - gain
1 Make all men know he is your choice.
2 For Christ's brave saints of an - cient days.
3 Thou - sands of faith - ful men and true.
4 The way dis - ci - ples fol - lowed then.
Al - le - lu - ia! Al - le - lu - ia! Al - le - lu - ia!

5 Christ through all ages is the same:
Place the same hope in his great name,
With the same faith his word proclaim.
Alleluia!

6 So shall God's will on earth be done,
New lamps be lit, new tasks begun,
And the whole Church at last be one.
Alleluia!

FRANCONIA

S. M.

305

BLEST ARE THE PURE IN HEART
Anthony G. Petti, 1972
After John Keble, 1792-1866

J. B. Koenig, 1691-1758
Adapted and harmonized by
W. H. Havergal, 1793-1870

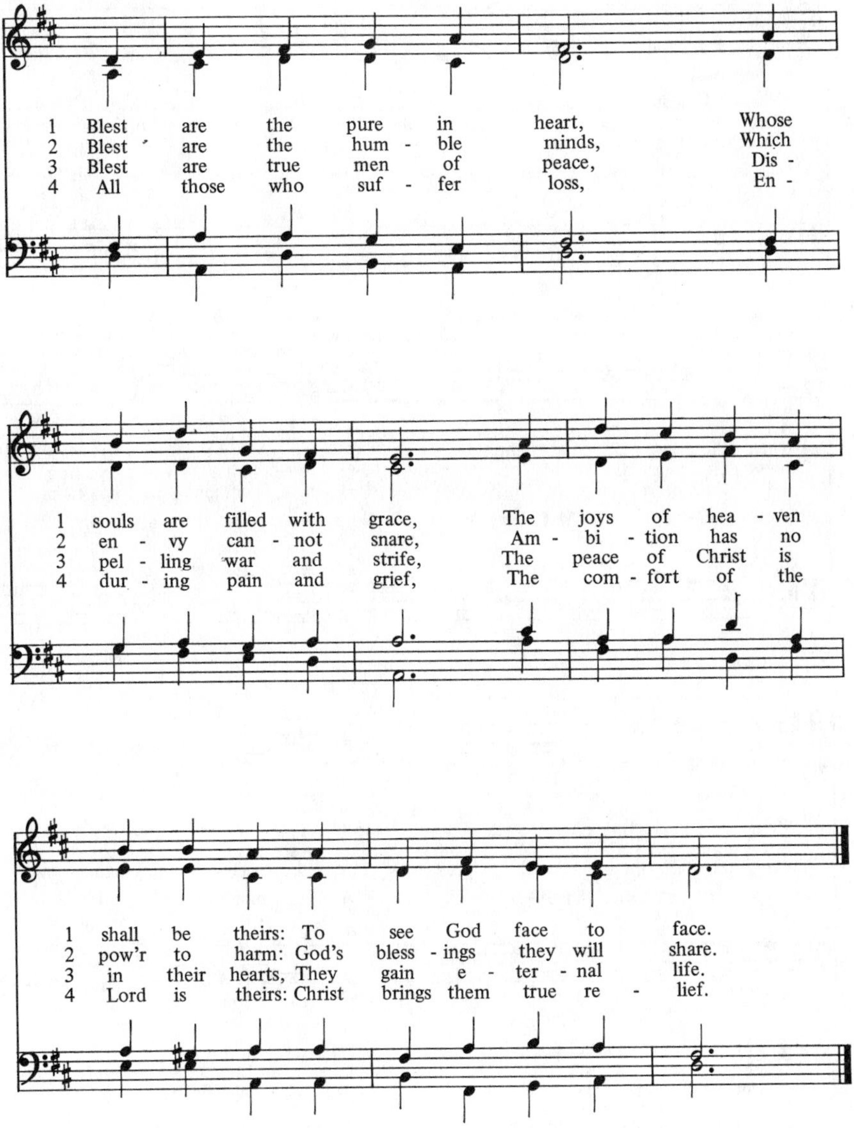

1 Blest are the pure in heart, Whose
2 Blest are the hum - ble minds, Which
3 Blest are true men of peace, Dis -
4 All those who suf - fer loss, En -

1 souls are filled with grace, The joys of hea - ven
2 en - vy can - not snare, Am - bi - tion has no
3 pel - ling war and strife, The peace of Christ is
4 dur - ing pain and grief, The com - fort of the

1 shall be theirs: To see God face to face.
2 pow'r to harm: God's bless - ings they will share.
3 in their hearts, They gain e - ter - nal life.
4 Lord is theirs: Christ brings them true re - lief.

5 Lord, keep us in your care,
Your mercy still impart,
And help us to preserve for you
A pure and perfect heart.

306

YE WHO OWN THE FAITH OF JESUS
Vincent Stucky Stratton Coles, 1845-1929, alt.

DISMISSAL
87. 87. 87
William Letton Viner, 1845

1 You who put your faith in Je - sus, Sing the won - ders that were done
2 Bless - ed were the cho - sen peo - ple Out of whom the Lord did come;
3 There - fore let all faith - ful peo - ple Sing the hon - or of her name;
7 Praise, O Mar - ry, praise the Fa - ther, Praise your Sav - ior and your Son;
1 When the love of God the Fa - ther O - ver sin the vic - t'ry won,
2 Bless - ed was the land of prom - ise Fash - ioned for his earth - ly home;
3 Let the Church, in her fore - shad - owed, Part in her thanks - giv - ing claim;
7 Praise the ev - er - last - ing Spir - it, Who has made you ark and throne,
1 When he made the Vir - gin Mar - y Moth - er of his on - ly Son.
2 But more bless - ed far the Moth - er, She who bore him in her womb.
3 What Christ's moth - er sang in glad - ness Let Christ's peo - ple sing the same.
7 O - ver all men high ex - alt - ed, Low - ly praise the Three - in - One.

4 Let us join our supplications,
She with us and we with her,
For the progress of the faithful,
For each faithful worshipper,
For the doubting, for the sinful,
For each heedless wanderer.

5 May the Mother's intercessions
On our homes a blessing win,
That the children be successful,
Strong, and fine, and pure within,
Following our Lord's own footsteps,
Firm in faith and free from sin.

6 For the sick and for the aged,
For our dear ones far away,
For the hearts that mourn in secret,
All who need our prayers today,
For the faithful gone before us,
May the Holy Virgin pray.

Alternative Tune: PICARDY, No. 360

SING OF MARY
Anonymous, 1914
Adapted by Roland F. Palmer, 1938
307
Lower Key at No. 507
PLEADING SAVIOR
87. 87. D.
Leavitt's *Christian Lyre*, 1830
1 Sing of_ Mar - ry,_ pure and low - ly, Vir - gin_moth - er_ un - de - filed,
2 Sing of_ Je - sus,_ Son of Mar - y, In the_home at_ Naz - a - reth.
3 Sing of_ Mar - ry,_ sing of Je - sus, Ho - ly_moth - er's_ ho - lier Son.
4 Joy - ful_Moth - er,_ full of glad - ness, In your arms your Lord was borne.
1 Sing of_God's own_Son most ho - ly, Who be - came her_ lit - tle child.
2 Toil and_ la - bor_ can - not wea - ry Love en - dur - ing_ un - to death.
3 From his_throne in_ heav'n he sees us, There he_ calls us_ ev - 'ry one.
4 Mourn - ful_Moth - er,_ full of sad - ness, All your heart with_pain was torn.
1 Fair - est_child of fair - est_moth - er, God the_Lord who came to_ earth,
2 Con - stant was the love he_gave her, Though he_went forth from her_ side,
3 Where he_wel - comes home his_moth - er To a_ place at his right hand,
4 Glo - rious Moth - er, now re - ward - ed With a_ crown at Je - sus'_ hand,
1 Word made flesh, our_ver - y broth - er, Takes our_na - ture_ by his birth.
2 Forth to_preach, and_heal, and suf - fer, Till on_Cal - va - ry he died.
3 There his faith - ful_ ser - vants gath - er, There the_bless - ed_ vic - tors stand.
4 Age to_ age your name re - cord - ed Shall be_blest in_ ev - 'ry land. A-men.

5 Glory be to God the Father,
Glory be to God the Son;
Glory be to God the Spirit;
Glory to the Three-in-One.

From the heart of blessed Mary,
From all saints the song ascends,
And the church the song re-echoes
Unto earth's remotest ends. Amen.

308
MARY THE DAWN
Paul Cross, 1949
MARY THE DAWN
Irregular
Paul Cross, 1949
1. Ch: Mar - y the Dawn, All: Christ the Per - fect Day;
2. Mar - y the Root, Christ the Mys — tic Vine;
3. Mar - y the Wheat-Sheaf, Christ the Liv - ing Bread;
4. Mar - y the Font, Christ the Cleans - ing Flood;
5. Mar - y the Tem - ple, Christ the Tem - ple's Lord;
6. Mar - y the Bea - con, Christ the Ha - ven's Rest;
1. Ch: Mar - y the Gate, All: Christ the Heav'n- ly Way!
2. Mar - y the Grape, Christ the Sa - cred Wine!
3. Mar - y the Rose - Tree, Christ the Rose, blood - red!
4. Mar - y the Chal - ice, Christ the Sav - ing Blood!
5. Mar - y the Shrine, Christ the God a - dored!
6. Mar - y the Mir - ror Christ the Vi - sion blest!
7. Ch: Mar - y the Moth - er All: Christ the Moth - er's Son,
8. Ch: Both ev - er blest while end - less ag - es run. All: A - men.

309

O MARY OF GRACES
After an anonymous Gaelic hymn
Douglas Hyde 1949, alt.

SIOBAN NI LAOGHAIRE
11 11. 11 11
Traditional Gaelic tune

1 O Mary of graces and Mother of God, O help me to tread where the righteous have trod. I pray you to save me from evil's control, And also to save me in body and soul.
2 I beg you to save me by land and by sea, And Mary, please save me from tortures to be. May my guardian angel above me abide; May God be before me and God at my side.

PRAISE WE THE LORD THIS DAY
Anonymous, 1847

310[1]

Higher Key

WELCOME VOICE
S. M. D.
Louis Hartsough, 1872

1 O __ praise the Lord this day, This day so long fore-
2 Ask __ not how this should be, But wor - ship and a -
3 And __ Blest shall be her name In all the Church on
1 told, Whose prom - ise shone with cheer - ing ray On
2 dore; Like her, whom heav - en's maj - es - ty Came
3 earth, Through whom that won-drous mer - cy came, The
1 wait - ing saints of old. The proph - et gave the
2 down to shad - ow o'er. She meek - ly bowed her
3 Sa - vior's hu - man birth. O Je - sus, Vir - gin's
1 sign For faith - ful men to read: A Vir - gin, born of
2 head To hear the gra-cious word, Dear Mar - y, pure and
3 Son, We praise you and a - dore, For you are with the

Da - vid's line, Shall bear the prom - ised Seed.
low - ly maid, The fa - vored of the Lord.
Fa - ther one And Spir - it ev - er - more.

310[2]

Lower Key

AVE, MARIA, GRATIA PLENA
Luke 1:28, 42; Council of Ephesus

311

AVE, MARIA, GRATIA PLENA
Irregular
Plainsong Melody

A - ve, Ma - ri - a, gra - ti - a ple - na, Do - mi - nus
Greet - ings, O Mar - ry, filled with God's bless - ings, Ya - weh is
te - cum; be - ne - dic - ta tu in mu - li - e - ri -
with you; la - dy, you are blessed a - bove ev - 'ry wom -
bus, et be - ne - dic - tus fruc - tus ven - tris tu - i, Je -
an, and al - so blessed is he, the fruit of your womb, Je -

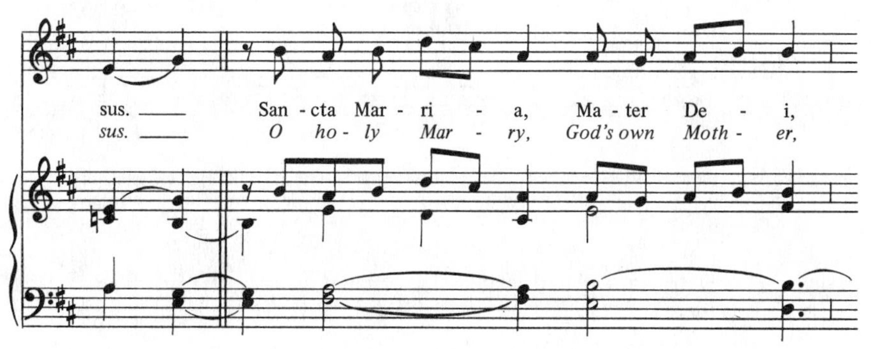
sus. Sancta Mari-a, Mater De-i,
sus. O holy Mary, God's own Mother,

Ora pro nobis peccatoribus nunc et
O holy Mary, for us sinners pray now and

in hora mortis nostræ. Amen.
at that time when our death comes. Amen.

AS MEN OF OLD
Frank von Christierson, 1960, 1972

312

BETHLEHEM (EVANGEL)
C. M. D.
Gottfried W. Fink, 1842

1 As men of old their first-fruits brought Of or-chard, flock, and field
2 A world in need now sum-mons us To la-bor, love, and give;
3 In grat-i-tude and hum-ble trust We bring our best to-day,
1 To God, the giv-er of all good, The source of boun-teous yield;
2 To make our life an of-fer-ing To God, that man may live;
3 To serve your cause and share your love With all a-long life's way.
1 So we to-day first-fruits would bring, The wealth of this good land,
2 The church of Christ is call-ing us To make the dream come true:
3 O God, who gave your-self for us In Christ, your on-ly Son,
1 Of farm and mar-ket, shop and home, Of mind and heart and hand.
2 A world re-deemed by Christ-like love, All life in Christ made new.
3 Teach us to give our-selves each day Un-til life's work is done.

THANKSGIVING DAY

MONKLAND
77. 77

PRAISE O PRAISE OUR GOD AND KING
Henry W. Baker, 1821-77

313

Higher Key at No. 433

Anonymous Melody, Manchester, 1824
arr. by John Bernard Wilkes, 1861

1 Praise O praise our God and King;
2 Praise him that he gave the rain
3 Praise him for our har - vest store,
4 Glo - ry to our boun - teous King!
1 Hymns of ad - o - ra - tion sing;
2 To ma - ture the swell - ing grain;
3 He has filled the gar - ner floor;
4 Glo - ry let cre - a - tion sing,
1 For his mer - cies still en - dure,
2 For his mer - cies still en - dure,
3 For his mer - cies still en - dure,
4 Glo - ry to the Fa - ther, Son,
1 Ev - er faith - ful, ev - er sure.
2 Ev - er faith - ful, ev - er sure.
3 Ev - er faith - ful, ev - er sure.
4 And blest Spir - it, Three in One!

314

COME, YE THANKFUL PEOPLE
Henry Alford, 1844
Adapted by Anthony G. Petti, 1972

ST. GEORGE'S WINDSOR (ELVEY)
77. 77. D.
George J. Elvey, 1858

1 Let us with thanks-giv - ing come, Now the har - vest's safe - ly done,
2 We our - selves are God's own field, Fruits un - to his praise to yield;
3 For the Lord our God shall come, And shall take his har - vest home.
4 E - ven so, Lord, quick - ly come To your fin - al har - vest home;
1 All the crops and all the grain Stored a - gainst the wind and rain.
2 Wheat and tares to - geth - er sown, Un - to joy and sor - row grown;
3 From his field he'll clear a - way All of - fend - ing weeds that day;
4 Gath - er all your peo - ple in, Free from sor - row, free from sin;
1 All our needs has God sup - plied, He shall con - stant - ly pro - vide.
2 First the blade and then the ear, Then the full corn shall ap - pear:
3 Give his an - gels charge at last In the fire the tares to cast,
4 There, for - ev - er pu - ri - fied, In your pres - ence to a - bide:
1 There - fore to his tem - ple come; Raise the song of har - vest home!
2 Lord of har - vests, grant that we Pure and whole - some grain may be.
3 But the fruit - ful ears to store In his gar - ner ev - er - more.
4 Come, with all your an - gels, come; Raise the glo - rious har - vest home!

THANKSGIVING DAY

PRAISE TO GOD, IMMORTAL PRAISE
Anna Laetitia Barbauld, 1772, alt.
315
Higher Key at No. 234
TREUER HEILAND (DIX)
77. 77. 77
Konrad Kocher, 1838
1 Praise to God, im - mor - tal praise, For the love that
2 All the plen - ty sum - mer pours; Au - tumn's rich o'er -
3 Peace, pros - per - i - ty, and health, Pri - vate bliss, and
4 As your pros - p'ring hand has blest, May we give you
1 crowns our days; Boun - teous source of ev - 'ry joy,
2 flow - ing stores; Flocks that whi - ten all the plain;
3 pub - lic wealth, Knowl - edge with its glad - d'ning streams,
4 of our best; And by deeds of kind - ly love
1 Let your praise our tongues em - ploy: All to you, our
2 Yel - low sheaves of rip - ened grain: Lord, for these our
3 Pure re - li - gion's ho - lier beams: Lord, for these our
4 For your mer - cies grate - ful prove; Sing - ing thus thru
1 God, we owe, Source from which all bless - ings flow.
2 souls shall raise Grate - ful vows and sol - emn praise.
3 souls shall raise Grate - ful vows and sol - emn praise.
4 all our days Praise to God, im - mor - tal praise!

THANKSGIVING DAY

ELLACOMBE (AVE MARIA KLARER)
76. 76. D.
Gesangbuch der Herzogl. Wirtembergischen Katolischen Hofkapelle, 1784

SING TO THE LORD OF HARVEST
John S. B. Monsell, 1866, alt.

316

Higher Key at No. 254

1 Sing to the Lord of har - vest, Sing songs of love and praise;
2 By him the clouds drop fat - ness, The des - erts bloom and spring,
3 Bring to his sa - cred al - tar The gifts his good - ness gave,
1 With joy - ful hearts and voi - ces Your al - le - lu - ias raise.
2 The hills leap up in glad - ness, The val - leys laugh and sing.
3 The gold - en sheaves of har - vest, The souls he died to save.
1 By him the rol - ling sea - sons In fruit - ful or - der move;
2 He bless - es from his ful - ness All things with large in - crease,
3 Your hearts lay down be - fore him When at his feet you fall,
1 Sing to the Lord of har - vest A joy - ous song of love.
2 He crowns the year with good - ness, With plen - ty and with peace.
3 And with your lives a - dore him Who gave his life for all.

317

WIR PFÜLGEN UND WIR STREUEN
Matthias Claudius, 1782
Tr., Jane M. Campbell, 1861, alt.

WIR PFLÜGEN (CLAUDIUS)
76. 76. D., with Refrain
Johann A. P. Schulz, 1800

1 We plow the fields and scat - ter The good seed on the land, But it is fed and
2 Oh, he a - lone is Ma - ker Of all things near and far; He paints the way-side
3 We thank you, then, O Fa - ther, For all things bright and good, The seed-time and the
1 wa - tered By God's al - might - y hand; He sends the snow in win - ter, The
2 flow - er, He lights the eve - ning star; The winds and waves o - bey him, By
3 har - vest, Our life, our health, our food: No gifts have we to of - fer For
1 warmth to swell the grain, The breez-es and the sun-shine, And soft re - fresh-ing rain.
2 him the birds are fed; Much more to us, his chil - dren, He gives our dai - ly bread.
3 all your love im - parts Ex - cept the gift most pleas - ing, Our hum - ble thank-ful hearts.
All good gifts a - round us Are sent from heav'n a - bove,
So thank the Lord, O thank the Lord For all his love.

NOT ALONE FOR MIGHTY EMPIRE
William Pierson Merrill, 1909, 1910, alt.
318
GENEVA
87. 87. D.
George Henry Day, 1940
1 Not a - lone for might- y — em - pire Stretch-ing - far be - yond our - view,
2 Not for - bat - tle - ship and for - tress, Not for - con - quests of the - sword,
3 For the - ar - mies of the - faith - ful, Souls that passed and left no - name;
4 God of - jus - tice, save the - peo - ple From the - clash of race and - creed,
1 Not a - lone for boun - teous har-vests, Do we - lift our - hearts to you.
2 But for - con - quests of the - spir - it We give thanks to - you, O Lord;
3 For the - glo - ry that il - lu - mines Pa - triot lives of - death-less fame;
4 From the - strife of class and - fac - tion: Make our - na - tion - free in - deed.
1 Stand-ing - in the liv - ing pres-ent, Mem - o - ry and hope be - tween,
2 For the - price-less gift - of - free-dom, For the - home, the church, the - school,
3 For our proph-ets and - a - pos - tles, Loy - al - to the liv - ing - Word,
4 Keep her - faith in sim - ple - man-hood Strong as - when her life be - gan,

1 Lord, we would with deep thanks-giv-ing Praise you most for things un - seen.
2 For the o - pen door to man-hood In a land the peo - ple rule.
3 For all he - roes of the spir - it, We give thanks to you, O Lord.
4 Till it find its full fru - i - tion In the broth-er - hood of man. A - men.
319
GOD OF OUR FATHERS
Higher Key at No. 475
NATIONAL HYMN
10 10. 10 10
Daniel Crane Roberts, 1876, alt.
George William Warren, 1892
1 God of our fa - thers, whose al - might - y hand Leads forth in
2 Your love di - vine has led us in the past; In this free
3 From war's a - larms, from dead - ly pes - ti - lence, May your strong
4 Strength-en your peo - ple on their toil - some way; Lead us from
1 beau - ty all the star - ry band Of shin - ing worlds in
2 land by you our lot is cast; O be our rul - er,
3 arm be ev - er our de - fence; Your true re - li - gion
4 night to nev - er - end - ing day; Fill all our lives with
1 splen - dor through the skies, Our grate - ful songs be - fore your throne a - rise.
2 guar - dian, guide and stay, Your word our law, your paths our cho - sen way.
3 in our hearts in - crease, Your gra - cious good - ness nour - ish us in peace.
4 love and grace a - new; Glo - ry and praise and bless - ing be to you.

O SAY, CAN YOU SEE
Francis Scott Key, 1814

320

Irregular
John Stafford Smith, c. 1771

1 O say can you see by the dawn's ear - ly
2 O thus be it ev-er, when free men shall
1 light, What so proud - ly we hailed at the twi - light's last
2 stand Be - tween their loved homes and the war's des - o -
1 gleam - ing, Whose broad stripes and bright stars, through the per - il - ous
2 la - tion! Blest with vic - t'ry and peace, may the heav'n-res - cued
1 fight, O'er the ram - parts we watched, were so gal - lant - ly
2 land Praise the Pow'r that hath made and pre - served us a

1 stream - ing? And the roc - ket's red glare, the bombs burst - ing in
2 na - tion! Then — con - quer we must, when our cause it is
1 air, Gave proof through the night that our flag was still there.
2 just, And this be our mot-to "In — God is our trust."
1 O — say does that — star - span - gled ban - ner — yet — wave —
2 And the star - span - gled — ban - ner in tri - umph — shall — wave —
1 O'er the land — of the free and the home of the brave?
2 O'er the land — of the free and the home of the brave!

O BEAUTIFUL FOR SPACIOUS SKIES
Katherine Lee Bates, 1893, 1904

321

Lower Key at No. 286

MATERNA
C. M. D.
Samuel A. Ward, 1882

1 O beau - ti - ful for spa - cious skies, For am - ber waves of grain,
2 O beau - ti - ful for pil - grim feet, Whose stern im - pas - sioned stress
3 O beau - ti - ful for her - oes proved In lib - er - ty and strife,
4 O beau - ti - ful for pat - triot dream That sees be - yond the years
1 For pur - ple moun - tain ma - jes - ties A - bove the fruit - ed plain!
2 A thor - ough - fare for free - dom beat A - cross the wild - er - ness!
3 Who more than self their coun - try loved, And mer - cy more than life!
4 Thine al - a - bas - ter cit - ies gleam, Un - dimmed by hu - man tears!
1 A - mer - i - ca! A - mer - i - ca! God shed his grace on thee
2 A - mer - i - ca! A - mer - i - ca! God mend thine ev - 'ry flaw,
3 A - mer - i - ca! A - mer - i - ca! May God thy gold re - fine
4 A - mer - i - ca! A - mer - i - ca! God shed his grace on thee
1 And crown thy good with broth - er - hood From sea to shin - ing sea!
2 Con - firm thy soul in self - con - trol, Thy lib - er - ty in law!
3 Till all suc - cess be no - ble - ness And ev - 'ry gain di - vine!
4 And crown thy good with broth - er - hood From sea to shin - ing sea!

OTHER NATIONAL DAYS

MY COUNTRY, 'TIS OF THEE
Sts. 1 & 2, Samuel Francis Smith, 1832
St. 3, Siegfried A. Mahlmann, 1815
Tr., St. 3, C. T. Brooks, c. 1832
St. 4, William E. Hickson, 1835

322

AMERICA
664. 6664
Thesaurus Musicus, 1740

1 My coun - try, 'tis of thee, Sweet land of
2 Our Fa - thers' God, to thee, Au - thor of
3 God bless our na - tive land; Firm may she
4 And not to us a - lone But be thy
1 li - ber - ty, Of thee I sing; Land where my
2 li - ber - ty, To thee we sing; Long may our
3 ev - er stand Through storm and night: When the wild
4 mer - cies known From shore to shore. Lord, make the
1 fa - thers died, Land of the pil - grims' pride,
2 land be bright With free - dom's ho - ly light;
3 tem - pests rave, Ru - ler of wind and wave,
4 na - tions see That men should bro - thers be
1 From ev - 'ry moun - tain - side Let free - dom ring.
2 Pro - tect us by thy might, Great God, our King.
3 Do thou our coun - try save By thy great might.
4 And form one fam - i - ly The wild world o'er.

323

MORNING HAS BROKEN
Eleanor Farjeon, 1881-1965

Lower Key at No. 494

BUNESSAN
55. 54. D.
Old Gaelic Melody

1 Morn - ing has bro - ken Like the first morn - ing; Black - bird has
2 Sweet the rain's new fall, Sun - lit from heav - en, Like the first
3 Mine is the sun - light! Mine is the morn - ing Born of the
1 spo - ken Like the first bird. Praise for the sing - ing! Praise for the
2 dew - fall On the first grass. Praise for the sweet - ness Of the wet
3 one light E - den saw play! Praise with e - la - tion, Praise ev - 'ry
1 morn - ing! Praise for them spring - ing Fresh from the word!
2 gar - en, Spring in com - plete - ness Where his feet pass.
3 morn - ing, God's re - cre - a - tion Of the new day!

MORNING

THIS DAY GOD GIVES ME
Based on a hymn of St. Patrick, 372-466
J. Quinn, 1969

324

Lower Key at No. 494

BUNESSAN
55. 54. D
Old Gaelic Melody

1 This day God gives me Strength of high heav - en, Sun and moon
2 This day God sends me Strength as my steers - man, Might to up -
3 God's way is my way, God's shield is 'round me, God's hosts de -
4 Ris - ing, I thank you, Might - y and strong One, King of cre -
1 shin - ing, Flame in my hearth,— Flash - ing of light - ning, Wind in its
2 hold me, Wis - dom as guide.— Your eyes are watch - ful, Your ears are
3 fend me, Sav - ing from ill.— An - gels of heav - en, Drive from me
4 a - tion, Giv - er of rest,— Firm - ly con - fess - ing Three-ness of
1 swift - ness, Deeps of the o - cean, Firm - ness of earth.—
2 lis - t'ning, Your lips are speak - ing, Friend at my side.—
3 al - ways All that would harm me; Stand by me still.—
4 per - sons, One - ness of God - head, Trin - i - ty blest.—

MORNING

JAM LUCIS ORTO SIDERE
6th cent.
Tr., Peter Scagnelli, 1972 and
John Mason Neale, 1851

325

JAM LUCIS ORTO SIDERE
L. M.
G. Guidetti, *Directorium Chori,* 1582

1 Now that the day - light fills the sky, We lift our hearts to
2 Our hearts and lips may he re - strain; Keep us from caus - ing
3 From e - vil may he guard our eyes, Our ears from emp - ty
4 That we, when this new day is gone, And night in turn is
5 Al - might - y Fa - ther, hear our cry Thru Je - sus Christ, our
1 God on high, That he, in all we do or say, May
2 oth - ers pain, That we, by lov - ing ev - 'ry - one, May
3 praise and lies, From self - ish - ness our hearts re - lease, That
4 draw - ing on, With con - science free from sin and blame, May
5 Lord most high, To - geth - er with the Par - a - clete, Whose
1 keep us free from harm this day.
2 learn to see and serve his Son.
3 we may serve and know his peace:
4 praise and bless his ho - ly name.
5 reign the end - less a - ges greet. A men.

326

NOCTE SURGENTES VIGILEMUS OMNES
10th cent.
Tr., Percy Dearmer, 1906, alt.

Higher Key at No. 415

HERR, DEINEN ZORN
11 11. 11 5
Johan Crüger, 1653

1 Father, we praise you, now that night is over;
Active and watchful, stand we all before you;
Singing, we offer prayer and meditation:
Thus we adore you;
2 Ruler of all things, fit us for your service;
Banish our weakness, health and wholeness sending.
Lead us to heaven, where your saints united
Joy without ending.
3 All holy Father, Son, and Holy Spirit,
Trinity blessed, send us your salvation.
Yours is the glory, gleaming and resounding
Through all creation.
Amen.

327

TE LUCIS ANTE TERMINUM
7th cent.
Tr., Peter Scagnelli, 1973

TE LUCIS ANTE TERMINUM
L.M.
Plainsong Melody
Harm. D.F., 1977

1. Be - fore the end - ing of the day, Cre - a - tor of the world, we pray: Pro - tect us by your love and might, And keep us safe through - out the night!
2. Let ev - 'ry heart rest free from fear, At peace, to feel your pres - ence near; Our souls, through night hours veiled in sleep, In your blest light, their vig - il keep.
3. Let peace - ful rest the strength re - new Of all who place their trust in you; Let e - vil nev - er have its way; Pre - serve us for an - oth - er day.
4. Al - might - y Fa - ther, hear our cry Through Je - sus Christ, our Lord most high, And with the Spir - it, Par - a - clete, Whose reign the end - less a - ges greet.
A - men.

328

DIE NACHT IST KOMEN
Petrus Herbert, 1566
Tr., George R. Woodward, 1904, et al., alt.

ROUEN
11 11. 11 5
Rouen Church Melody,
harm. by Healey Willan, 1918

1 Now it is eve - ning, time to rest from la - bor:
2 Far from our homes, Lord, drive a - way temp - ta - tion;
3 As your be - lov - ed, care for all who suf - fer;
4 O be your name re - vered by all, our Fa - ther;
1 Fa - ther, ac - cord - ing to your will and pleas - ure,
2 Lord, be our guard - ian through the hours of dark - ness;
3 Com - fort the pris - oned, those in lone - ly trou - ble,
4 Your king - dom come; your will be done a - mong us.
1 Through all the night hours have your whole cre - a - tion
2 Un - der the sha - dow of your wings de - fend us;
3 Wid - ows and orph - ans; from the pow'r of mal - ice
4 Feed us, for - give us, free us from all e - vil,
1 Safe in your keep - ing.
2 Send us your an - gel.
3 Keep them in safe - ty.
4 Save us, re - deem us.

DAY IS DONE
James Quinn, 1969

329

AR HYD Y NOS
84. 84. 88. 84
Welsh Traditional Melody

1 Day is done, but Love un-fail - ing Dwells ev - er here;
2 Dark de-scends, but Light un-end - ing Shines through our night;
3 Eyes will close, but you un-sleep - ing Watch by our side;
1 Shad - ows fall, but hope, pre - vail - ing, Calms ev - 'ry fear.
2 You are with us, ev - er lead - ing New strength to sight;
3 Death may come: in Love's safe keep - ing Still we a - bide.
1 Lov - ing Fa - ther, none for - sak - ing, Take our hearts, of Love's own mak - ing,
2 One in love, your truth con - fess - ing, One in hope of heav - en's bless - ing,
3 God of love, all e - vil quell - ing, Sin for - giv - ing, fear dis - pell - ing,
1 Watch our sleep - ing, guard our wak - ing, Be al - ways near!
2 May we see, in love's pos - sess - ing, Love's end - less light!
3 Stay with us, our hearts in - dwell - ing, This e - ven - tide!

NOW THE DAY IS OVER
Sabine Baring-Gould, 1865, alt.

330

MERRIAL
65. 65
Joseph Barnby, 1868

1 Now the day is o - ver,
2 Je - sus, give the wea - ry
3 Grant to lit - tle chil - dren
4 Com - fort ev - 'ry suf - f'rer

1 Night is draw - ing nigh, Shad - dows of the
2 Calm and sweet re - pose; With your ten - d'rest
3 Grace your love to see; Guard the sail - ors
4 Watch - ing late in pain; Those who plan some

1 eve - ning Steal a - cross the sky.
2 bless - ing May our eye - lids close.
3 toss - ing On the deep, blue sea.
4 e - vil From their sin re - strain.

5 Through the long night watches
May your angels spread
Their kind wings above me,
Watching 'round my bed.

6 When the morning wakens,
Then may I arise
Pure and fresh and sinless
In your holy eyes.

Based on Mark 10:13-16
LIEBSTER JESU,WIR SIND HIER
Benjamin Schmolck, 1704, cento
Tr., Catherine Winkworth, 1863, alt.

331

Lower Key at No. 482

LIEBSTER JESU, WIR SIND HEIR
78. 78. 88
Johann R. Ahle, 1664

1 Dear - est Je - sus, we are here, Glad - ly your com - mand o - bey - ing;
2 Yes, your word is clear and plain, And we would o - bey it du - ly:
3 There- fore now we come to you,, In our arms this in - fant bear - ing;
4 Gra - cious Head, your mem - ber own; Shep-herd, take your lamb and feed it;
1 With this child we now draw near In ac-cord with your own say - ing
2 "He who is not born a - gain, Heart and life re - new-ing tru - ly,
3 Let us here your love pur-sue; Let this child, your mer-cy shar - ing,
4 Prince of Peace, make here your throne; Way of Life, to heav-en lead it;
1 That to you it shall be giv - en As a child and heir of heav - en.
2 Born of wa - ter and the Spir - it, Can my king-dom not in - her - it."
3 In your arms be shield-ed ev - er, Yours on earth and yours for - ev - er.
4 Pre-cious Vine, let noth-ing sev - er From your side this branch for - ev - er.

5 Now to your dear heart we pour
Prayers that from our hearts proceeded.
Our petitions heav'nward soar;
May our deep desires be heeded!
Write the name we now have given;
Write it in the book of heaven.

332

THE SAVIOR KINDLY CALLS
Phillip Doddridge, 1755, cento
Adapted by Henry U. Onderdonk, 1826, alt.

VENICE
S. M.
William Amps, 1858

1 The Sav - ior kind - ly calls Our
2 "Let them ap - proach," he cries, "Nor
3 With joy we bring them, Lord, Your

1 chil - dren to his breast; He folds them in his
2 scorn their hum - ble claim; The heirs of heav'n are
3 lov - ing care to see, Im - plor - ing that, as

1 gra - cious arms, Him - self de - clares them best.
2 such as these; For such as these I came."
3 we are yours, Yours may our off - spring be.

O COME, GOOD SPIRIT
Gabriel Huck, 1965

333

Higher Key at No. 359

UNDE ET MEMORES
10 10. 10 10. 10 10
William H. Monk, 1875, alt.

1 O come, good Spir - it, come, fill all the earth, And in these wa - ters
2 Once wa - ter part - ed, saved God's cho - sen flock, And faith brought wa - ter
3 To Nic - o - de - mus Je - sus spoke of breath, Of birth in Spir - it
4 This wa - ter brings the death that Je - sus died; This wa - ter is the
1 give your child new birth. So when the sav - ing heal - ing wa - ter's
2 flow - ing from a rock. All signs of Spir - it's liv - ing wa - ter
3 thru a wa - ter's death. For men in liv - ing wa - ters are to
4 death he cru - ci - fied. This tomb keeps all that we re - fuse to
1 poured She He shall be born our sis - ter broth - er in the Lord.
2 here, That saves, re - fresh - es all who would come near.
3 die, And rise a - gain to live and tes - ti - fy.
4 give To Christ our ris - en Lord in whom we live.
Be glad! Sing out! Go
show to all the earth The life in Christ that comes in this new birth!

5 O creature water, source of life restored,
The Church's womb made fruitful by her Lord,
The mother of all things on earth that live,
The spring that now has Christ's own life to give.

6 In signs that we can hear and feel and see
The Spirit comes to set his people free.
No longer turned to self in pride and fear,
As God's own children live in love sincere.

334

BREAK THE GOOD NEWS
C. Marivoet

BREAK THE GOOD NEWS
78. 78
F. Mehrtens
Harm. by Jerry R. Brubaker

1. Break the good news far and wide, Shout to all men the glad
2. See the great deeds of the Lord: Is - ra - el passed thru the
3. Sing with a ju - bi - lant voice: Christ has de - liv - ered his
4. And, when bap - tized in - to Christ, Dy - ing with him, we were

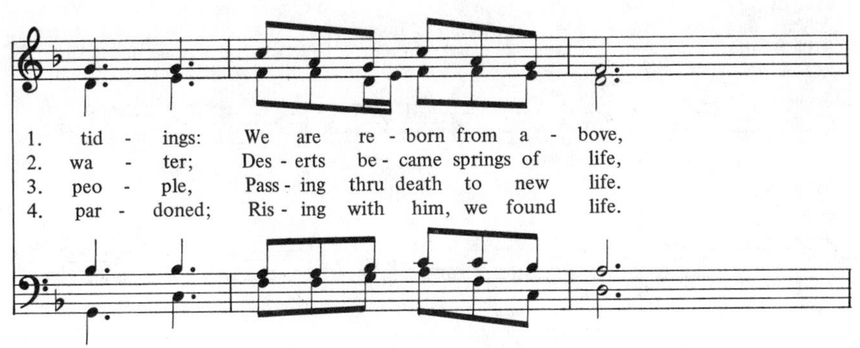
1. tid - ings: We are re - born from a - bove,
2. wa - ter; Des - erts be - came springs of life,
3. peo - ple, Pass - ing thru death to new life.
4. par - doned; Ris - ing with him, we found life.

1. Born of the Spir - it and wa - ter.
2. Roads to a land that was prom - ised.
3. Glo - ry to God in the high - est.
4. Let us give thanks to the Fa - ther.

HOLY SPIRIT, LORD OF LOVE
W. D. Maclagan, 1873, alt.
335
Higher Key at No. 275
SALZBURG
77. 77. D.
Jakob Hintze, 1678, alt.
1 Ho - ly Spir - it, Lord of love, You who came down from a - bove
2 You have been their con - stant guide, Watch - ing ev - er at their side;
3 Shield them from temp - ta - tion's breath, Keep them faith-ful un - to death.
1 Gifts of bless - ing to be - stow On your wait-ing Church be - low,
2 May they now till life shall end Choose and know you as their friend.
3 When the sa - cred vow is made, When the hands are on them laid,
1 Once a - gain in love draw near To your ser - vants gath - ered here:
2 Give them light your truth to see; Give them life, your own to be;
3 Come in this most sol - emn hour With your sev'n - fold gifts of pow'r.
1 From their bright bap - tis - mal day You have led them on their way.
2 Dai - ly pow'r to con - quer sin; Pa - tient faith, the crown to win.
3 Come, O bless - ed Spir - it, come, Make each heart your hap - py home.

336

ENHVER SOM TROR OG BLIVER DÖBT
Thomas Hansen Kingo, 1689
Tr., George A. T. Rygh, 1909

Higher Key at No. 514

MIT FREUDEN ZART
(BOHEMIAN BRETHREN)
87. 87. 887
Genevan Psalter, 1551
Adapted by Unitas Fratrum, 1566

1 He who be- lieves and is bap - tized Shall_ see the Lord's sal -
2 With one ac - cord, O God, we pray: Grant_ us your Ho - ly
1 va - tion; Bap - tized in - to the death of Christ, He_ is a new cre -
2 Spir - it; O look on our in - firm - i - ty Through Je - sus' blood and
1 a - tion. Thru Christ's re - demp - tion he shall stand A -
2 mer - it. Grant us to grow in grace each day That
1 mong the glo - rious heav'n - ly band Of_ ev - 'ry tribe and_ na - tion.
2 by this sac - ra - ment we may E - ter - nal life in - her - it.

LORD, HERE IS ONE
David Head, b. 1922

337

FONT
88. 87
Stanley Mountford, b. 1902

1 Lord, here is one to be bap - tized, Not
2 You, Lord, in Jor - dan were im - mersed, One
3 So at the font trans - cend our songs, Give
4 Yours the new Church by wa - ter born, Strong
1 know -ing how or when or where, Too fresh on earth to
2 flesh with ev - 'ry child of Cain. Earth's ang - ry chil - dren
3 us the sign of things made new: "New earth" is where this
4 for all fam - i - lies on earth. Our dead - ness, not your
1 be sur - prised By a hid - den cos - mic care.
2 fret and thirst, Un - til jus - tice falls like rain.
3 child be - longs, Who be - longs, earth's Goal, to you.
4 death, we mourn, As you bring fresh hope to birth.

5 High our surprise at what you do,
Calling our race from tomb of death.
Lord, here is faith and water, too;
Here is one to take deep Breath.

338

O GOD, THIS CHILD
Frank A. Brooks, Jr., 1972

NOEL
C. M. D.
English Melody, adapted by
Arthur Seymour Sullivan, 1874

1 O — God, this child from you did come, To you it shall — re - turn;
2 Real — acts of love and — words of truth We hope to teach this child,
3 Of — flesh and blood this — child is made, In im - age of — your - self.
1 But — to our trust and love you chose To — send it for some years.
2 And — con - stant may our guid - ance be In — like-ness of your Son.
3 To — men we come; on earth we live — Our — pur-pose clear to serve.
1 Be - cause we thank you for our life That to our lives has come,
2 Be - cause we thank you for our life That to our lives has come,
3 Be - cause we thank you for our life That to our lives has come,
1 To - geth - er we now — pledge our-selves To — help this child serve you.
2 To - geth - er we now — pledge our-selves To — help this child serve you.
3 To - geth - er we now — pledge our-selves To — help this child serve you.

ISTI SUNT AGNI NOVELLI
Dom J. Pothier, d. 1923
Tr., Roger Nachtwey, 1974
Vv. of Ps. 42 after Tate & Brady, 1696
339
ISTI SUNT AGNI NOVELLI
87. 87, with Refrain
Dom J. Pothier, d. 1923
Harm. by Roger Nachtwey, 1975
These are the lit - tle lambs of Christ, New - ly born, and ex - claim - ing:
I - sti sunt a - gni no - vel - li, Qui an - nun - ti - a ve - runt:
Al - le - lu - ia! Washed in the wa - ters of this font, They're
Al - le - lu - ia! Mo - do ve - ne - runt ad fon - tes, Re -
filled with all bright - ness and grace, Al - le - lu - ia, al - le - lu - ia!
ple - ti sunt cla - ri - ta - te, Al - le - lu - ia, al - le - lu - ia!
Fine
Fine

1 As the deer longs for the cool streams, When he's
2 Oh, for God, my liv - ing Sav - ior, Does my
3 Don't be rest - less, don't be down - cast; O my
Ut ju - cun - das cer - vus un - das Ae - stu -
1 heat - ed in the chase, So my soul longs for my
2 thirst - y soul now pine; When shall I be - hold his
3 soul, have hope and sing All the prais - es of your
ans de - si - de - rat, Sic ad De - um for - tem
1 Sav - ior And for his re - fresh - ing grace.
2 fa - vor And his maj - es - ty di - vine?
3 Sav - ior; He's your hope— E - ter - nal Spring!
vi - vum Mens fi - de - lis pro - pe - rat.

340

O HEAVENLY GRACE
Robert Nelson Spencer, 1939

CHARTERHOUSE
11 10. 11 10
David Evans, 1927

1 O heav'n - ly grace in
2 Here as they pledge to
3 May they con - tin - ue
1 ho - ly rite de - scend - ing To those who
2 fol - low you as Sa - vior, Je - sus their
3 yours, O God, for - ev - er, Dai - ly in -
1 kneel for lay - ing on of
2 Lord who for the Church have
3 creas - ing in the Spir - it's

1 hands; Yours be the strength, O
2 died; So may they live with -
3 gift, Un - til they bring the
1 Lord, for their de - fend - ing; Theirs be the
2 in that blest be - ha - vior You have en -
3 gift un - to the giv - er, Where time is
1 vows re - newed at your de - mands.
2 joined, and they have rat - i - fied.
3 end - ed, and earth's shad - ows lift.

341

BEHOLD US, LORD
W. Bright, 1824-1901, alt.

ST. CATHERINE
88. 88. 88
Henry F. Hemy, 1864
and James G. Walton, 1870

Higher Key at No. 474

1 Be - hold us, Lord, be - fore you met, Whom each bright an - gel
2 To you we look, in you con - fide, Our help is in your
3 The seed of our bap - tis - mal life, O liv - ing Word, by
4 We need you more than tongue can speak 'Mid foes that well might
1 serves and fears, Who on your throne can - not for - get
2 own dear name; For who on Je - sus e'er re - lied
3 you was sown; So where your sol - diers wage their strife
4 cast us down; But thou - sands, once as young and weak
1 Your spot - less boy - hood's qui - et years; Whose feet the hills of
2 And found not Je - sus still the same? Thus far your love our
3 Our post we take, our vows we own, And ask, in your ap -
4 Have fought the fight and won the crown; We ask the help that
1 Naz - 'reth trod, Who are true man and per - fect God.
2 souls has brought; O strength-en well what you have wrought.
3 point - ed way, Con - firm us in your grace to - day.
4 bore them through; We trust the Faith - ful and the True.

5 So bless us with the gift complete
By hands of your chief pastors giv'n,
That wondrous Presence kind and sweet
Which comes in sev'nfold might from heav'n;
Eternal Christ, to you we bow;
Give us your Spirit here and now.

Alternative Tune: REST (BEATI) No. 301

CONFIRMATION

LORD, IN THY PRESENCE
Anonymous, c. 1850
342
Lower Key at No. 403
MANNA
886. 886
J. G. Schlicht, 1753-1823
1 Lord, in your pres - ence dread and sweet, Your own dear Spir - it we en - treat His sev'n - fold gifts to shed On us, who come be - fore you now And bear the Cross up - on our brow On which our Mas - ter bled.
2 Spir - it of wis - dom, turn our eyes From earth and earth - ly van - i - ties To heav'n - ly truth and love. Spir - it of Un - der - stand - ing right, Come, fill our souls with ho - ly light To seek the things a - bove.
3 Spir - it of Coun - sel, be our guide; Teach us, by earth - ly strug - gles tried, Our heav'n - ly crown to win. Spir - it of For - ti - tude, your pow'r Be with us in temp - ta - tion's hour To keep us free from sin.
4 Spir - it of Knowl - edge, lead our feet In your own paths se - cure and sweet, By an - gel foot - steps trod; Where you, our Guard - ian true shall be, Spir - it of gen - tle Pi - e - ty, To keep us close to God.

5 But most of all, be ever near,
Spirit of God's most holy Fear,
In our heart's inmost shrine;
Our souls with loving rev'rence fill,
To worship his most holy will
All righteous and divine.

6 So, dearest Lord, thru peace or strife,
Lead us to everlasting life,
When our life here is through.
What matter where our lot is cast,
If only it may end at last
In Paradise with you.

MY GOD, ACCEPT MY HEART
Matthew Bridges, 1848, alt.

343

ST. AGNES
C. M.
John B. Dykes, 1866

1 My God, ac - cept my heart this day And keep it
2 Be - fore the cross of him who died, Be - hold, I
3 A - noint me with your heav - 'nly grace, And seal me
4 Let ev - 'ry thought and work and word To you be

1 whol - ly true, That I by sin no
2 hum - bly fall; Let ev - 'ry sin be
3 as your own; That I may see your
4 ev - er giv'n; Then life shall be your

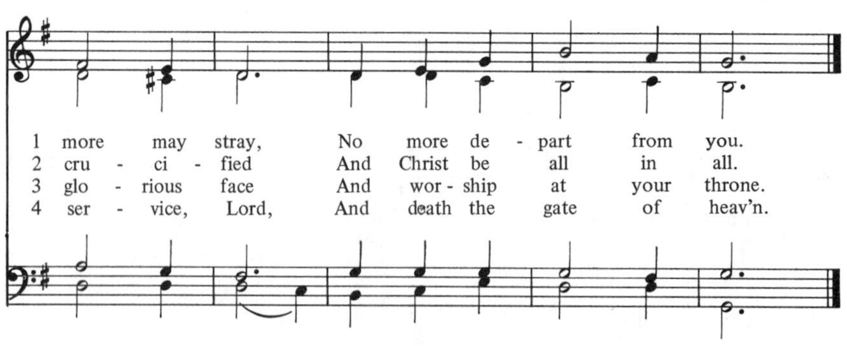
1 more may stray, No more de - part from you.
2 cru - ci - fied And Christ be all in all.
3 glo - rious face And wor - ship at your throne.
4 ser - vice, Lord, And death the gate of heav'n.

COME WITH YOUR MUSIC
J. Smith, 1970
344[1]
Higher Key
WIMBLEDON
10 7. 10 7
Kevin Mayhew
1 Come with your mu - sic and sing to the Lord,
2 He is your ref - uge, you peo - ple of God,
3 Of - fer him glo - ry and pow-er and praise,
Praise to the name of the Lord!
Gath - er and lift up your
Mas - ter of space and the
Lord and Cre - a - tor, our
1 voice in his praise,
2 mak - er of earth,
3 Fa - ther and God,
Lord of our glad - ness and joy!
344[2]
Lower Key

TUT MIR AUF DIE SCHÖNE PFORTE
Benjamin Schmolck, 1732, cento
Tr., Catherine Winkworth, 1863, alt.

345[1]

NEANDER
87. 87. 77
Joachim Neander, 1680

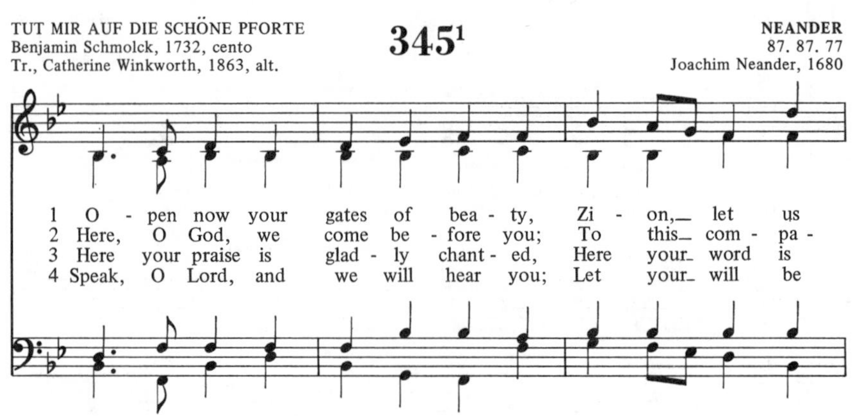

1 O - pen now your gates of bea - ty, Zi - on,— let us
2 Here, O God, we come be - fore you; To this— com - pa -
3 Here your praise is glad - ly chant - ed, Here your— word is
4 Speak, O Lord, and we will hear you; Let your— will be

1 en - ter there, Where we may in joy - ful du - ty
2 ny come down; Where we find you and a - dore you,
3 du - ly sown; Let our hearts, where it is plant - ed,
4 done in - deed. May we with our songs draw near you

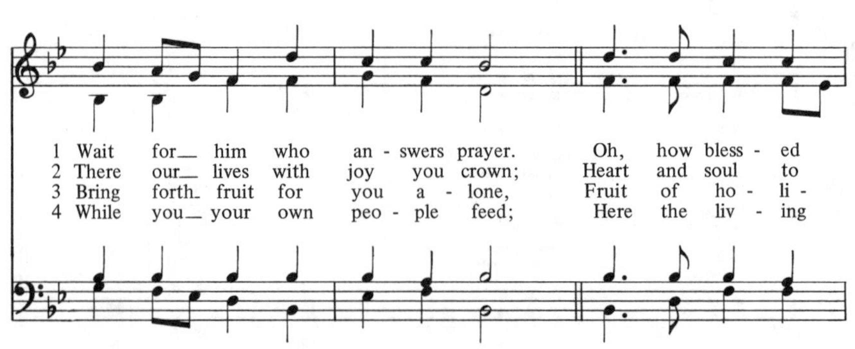

1 Wait for— him who an - swers prayer. Oh, how bless - ed
2 There our— lives with joy you crown; Heart and soul to
3 Bring forth— fruit for you a - lone, Fruit of ho - li -
4 While you— your own peo - ple feed; Here the liv - ing

1 is this place, Filled with light and truth and grace.
2 you we bow, Let them be your tem - ple now.
3 ness and love, Draw - ing all to you a - bove.
4 foun - tain flows, Here is sol - ace for our woes.

345²

Lower Key

O HOLY LORD
Traditional

346

ELBING
87. 87. 88. 7
Peter Sohren, 1668

1 O ho - ly Lord, by all a - dored, Our weak - ness - es con -
2 To God on high be thanks and praise, Who brings us all to -
1 fess - ing, To you this day your chil - dren pray, Our
2 geth - er; His care shall guide us all our days, And
1 ho - ly faith pro - fess - ing! Ac - cept, O King, the gifts we bring, Our
2 harm shall reach us nev - er. In him we trust with faith as - sured; Of
1 words of praise, the songs we raise; And grant us, Lord, your bless - ing.
2 all that live he is the Lord, For - ev - er and for - ev - er.

Alternative Tune: MIT FREUDEN ZART, No. 336.

VAYAMOS JUBILOSOS
E.G. Arrondo, 1960
Tr., in Prayer and Song, 1971
347
VAYAMOS JUBILOSOS
88. 88, with Refrain
E. G. Arrondo, 1960
rit.
With joy - ful hearts we en - ter God's all ho - ly place!
1 May your
2 Let us
3 Let us
4 Glo - ry
1 faith - ful - ness and jus - tice Draw us to your ho - ly al - tar, There the
2 praise our God and Sav - ior Who re - news our joy in liv - ing As we
3 of - fer there to - geth - er God's own Son, the sav - ing Vic - tim, Who by
4 be to God the Fa - ther, Glo - ry be to Christ, our lead - er; And to
dal segno
1 sac - ri - fice to of - fer Which to God gives end - less glo - ry. With
2 near the ho - ly moun - tain Where God gives his life to save us. With
3 dy - ing makes us shar - ers In his light and life e - ter - nal. With
4 God the Ho - ly Spir - it Praise be giv - en with - out end - ing. With

Based on Psalms 103 & 150
LOBE DEN HERREN
Joachim Neander, 1679
St. 2, Irvin Udulutsch, 1957

348

Lower Key at No. 419

PRAISE TO THE LORD
14 14. 478
Stralsund Gesangbuch, 1665
The Chorale Book for England, 1863

1 Praise to the Lord, the Al - might - y, the King of cre -
2 Praise to the Lord! Let us of - fer our gifts at the
3 Praise to the Lord! O let all that is in me a -
1 a - tion! O my soul, praise him, for he is your
2 al - tar. Let not our sins and of - fen - ses now
3 dore him! All that have life and breath, come now with
1 health and sal - va - tion! All you who hear, now to the
2 cause us to fal - ter. Christ the High Priest, bids us all
3 prais - es be - fore him! Let the A - men sum all our
1 al - tar draw near; Join in pro - found a - dor - a - tion!
2 join in his feast, Vic - tims with him on the al - tar.
3 prais - es a - gain, Now as we wor - ship be - fore him.

349

LET US NOW ENTER IN GOD'S HOUSE
Sr. G. S., alt.

ALBANO
C. M.
Vincent Novello, 1800

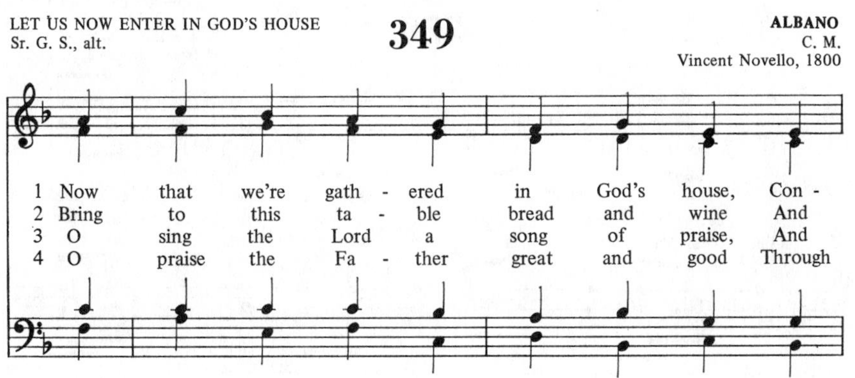
1 Now that we're gath - ered in God's house, Con -
2 Bring to this ta - ble bread and wine And
3 O sing the Lord a song of praise, And
4 O praise the Fa - ther great and good Through

1 fes - sing our mis - deeds, May Je - sus Christ for -
2 give it to the Lord. He will re - turn it
3 bless his ho - ly name. Lift up your hearts and
4 Je - sus Christ, our Lord, Who with the Spir - it

1 give them all And take us in his love.
2 in good time And give him - self in love
3 give him thanks For all his love and grace.
4 live and reign Through all e - ter - ni - ty. A - men.

350

REAP ME THE EARTH
Peter Icarus, 1970

JUCUNDA LAUDATIO
10 7. 10 7, with Chorus
A. Gregory Murray, 1970
Harm. by Jerry R. Brubaker

1 Reap me the earth as a har - vest to God, Gath - er and
2 Go with your song and your mu - sic, with joy, Go to the
3 Glad - ness and pit - y and pas - sion and pain, All that is
1 bring it a - gain; All that is his, to the
2 al - tar of God. Car - ry your of - fer - ings,
3 mor - tal in man, Lay all be - fore him, re -
1 Mak - er of all, Lift it and of - fer it high.
2 fruits of the earth, Work of your la - bor - ing hands.
3 turn him his gift, God, to whom all shall go home.
Bring bread and wine, Give glo - ry to the Lord; Whose is the earth but
God's, Whose is the praise but his?

WE PRAY THEE, HEAVENLY FATHER
Vincent Stucky Stratton Coles, 1845-1929
351
GEDULD, DIE SOLL'N WIR HABEN
76. 76. D.
Geistliche Lieder, Frankfurt, 1607
1 We pray you heav'n-ly Fa-ther, To hear us in your love,
2 Lord, all we have we of-fer, For it is all your own;
3 With-in the pure ob-la-tion, Be-neath the out-ward sign,
4 Where-fore, though all un-worth-y To of-fer sac-ri-fice,
1 And pour up-on your chil-dren Your bless-ings from a-bove,
2 All gifts, by your ap-point-ment, In bread and wine are shown.
3 By his blest op-er-a-tion (The Spir-it all-di-vine)
4 We pray that this our du-ty Be pleas-ing in your eyes;
1 That so, in love a-bid-ing, With minds on things_a-bove,
2 One thing, a-lone we_bring not, The will-ful-ness_of sin;
3 Lies hid the sa-cred_Bod-y, Lies hid_the pre-cious Blood
4 For praise and thanks and_wor-ship, For mer-cy and_for aid,
1 We may in pure-ness of-fer Our Eu-cha-rist of love.
2 And all we bring is noth-ing Ex-cept what is with-in.
3 Of Christ, now ev-er glo-rious, Once slain, but still our God.
4 The u-ni-ver-sal of-f'ring Of Je-sus Christ is made.

REX SUMMAE MAJESTATIS
Manuale Cantus Sancti, Ratisbon, 19th cent.
Tr., A. Gregory Murray, 1950, alt.
352
Lower Key at No. 400
ALL HALLOWS
76. 76. D.
George C. Martin, 1892
1 O King of might and splen - dor, Cre - a - tor_most a - dored,
2 Your Bod - y you have giv - en, Your Blood you have out - poured
1 Our gifts and praise we ren - der To you as sov - 'reign Lord.
2 That sin might be for - giv - en, O Je - sus, lov - ing_Lord.
1 May these our gifts be_ pleas - ing: Our_faith and love re - new,
2 As now with love most_ten - der Your death we cel - e - brate,
1 Man - kind from sin re - leas - ing, Who have of - fend - ed you.
2 Our lives in self - sur - rend - er To you we con - se - crate.

WAREHAM
RECEIVE, DEAR FATHER
353
L. M.
D. M. Coffey
Later version of melody by
New Catholic Hymnal, 1971
Lower Key at No. 455
W. Knapp, 1698 (?)-1768
1 Re - ceive, dear Fa - ther, God of might, This
2 This sav - ing cup we al - so bring; Re -
3 For all the liv - ing and the dead, For
4 And, be - ing pleased, your gift be - stow: The
1 host un - blem - ished in your sight.
2 ceive it gra - cious Lord and King.
3 our poor lives so bad - ly led,
4 life of grace in us be - low.
1 Un - worth - y ser - vants though we be, We
2 With fra - grant o - dor may it rise To
3 We raise these gifts to you a - bove, And
4 Not just to us this bless - ing send; To
1 come be - fore you trust - ing - ly.
2 your high throne be - yond the skies.
3 join to them our - selves in love.
4 all the world your grace ex - tend.

LORD, ACCEPT THE GIFTS
Sister M. Teresine, 1958

354

Lower Key at No. 404

ST. THOMAS
87. 87. 87
J. F. Wade's *Cantus Diversi,* 1751

1 Lord, ac - cept the gifts we of - fer At this eu - char -
2 May our souls be pure and spot - less As the host of
3 Take our gifts, al - might - y Fa - ther, Liv - ing God, e -
1 is - tic feast, Bread and wine to be trans - formed now
2 wheat so fine; May all stain of sin be crushed out
3 ter - nal, true, Which we give through Christ, our Sav - ior,
1 Through the ac - tion of your priest. Take us, too, O
2 Like the grape that forms the wine, As we, too, be -
3 Plead - ing here for us a - new. Grant sal - va - tion
1 Lord; trans - form us. Be your grace in_ us in - creased.
2 come par - tak - ers In this sac - ri - fice di - vine.
3 to all pres - ent, And our faith and_ love re - new.

SANCTI, VENITE, CHRISTI CORPUS SUMITE
Antiphonary of Bennchar, 7th cent.
Tr., John Mason Neale, 1851, alt.

355

SONG 24
10 10. 10 10
Orlando Gibbons, 1623

1 Draw near and take the bod - y of the Lord,
2 Our lov - ing Sav - ior, Christ, the on - ly Son,
3 Let us ap - proach with thank - ful hearts sin - cere,
4 With heav'n - ly bread he makes the hun - gry whole,
1 Re - ceive the ho - ly blood for you out - poured,
2 Who by his cross and blood the vic - t'ry won,
3 And gain the safe - guard of sal - va - tion here.
4 Gives liv - ing wa - ters to the thirst - y soul.
1 Saved by that pre - cious bod - y and that blood,
2 Gave his own life for great - est and for least:
3 God, who all faith - ful serv - ants rules and shields,
4 The one e - ter - nal God, to whom shall bow
1 Where - by re - freshed, we of - fer thanks to God.
2 Him - self the Vic - tim and him - self the priest.
3 To all be - liev - ers life e - ter - nal yields.
4 All on the last day— he is with us now.

SANCTI, VENITE, CHRISTI CORPUS SUMITE
Antiphonary of Bennchar, 7th cent.
Tr., John Mason Neale, 1851, alt.

356

Higher Key at No. 357

ANIMA CHRISTI
10 10. 10 10
W. J. Maher, 1823-77

1 Draw near and take the bod - y of the Lord,
2 Our lov - ing Sav - ior, Christ, the on - ly Son,
3 Let us ap - proach with thank - ful hearts sin - cere,
4 With heav'n-ly bread he makes the hun - gry whole,
1 Re - ceive the ho - ly blood for you out - poured,
2 Who by his cross and blood the vic - t'ry won,
3 And gain the safe - guard of sal - va - tion here.
4 Gives liv - ing wa - ters to the thirst - y soul.
1 Saved by that pre - cious bod - y and that blood,
2 Gave his own life for great - est and for least:
3 God, who all faith - ful ser - vants rules and shields,
4 The one e - ter - nal God, to whom shall bow
1 Where - by re - freshed, we of - fer thanks to God.
2 Him - self the Vic - tim and him - self the Priest.
3 To all be - liev - ers life e - ter - nal yields.
4 All on the last day he is with us now.

357

ANIMA CHRISTI, SANTIFICA ME
ascr. Pope John XXII, 1249-1334
TR., anonymous

Lower Key at No. 356

ANIMA CHRISTI
10 10 10 10
William Maher, 1823-77

1 Soul of my Sav - ior, sanc - ti - fy my breast;
2 Strength and pro - tec - tion may thy pas - sion be;
3 Guard and de - fend me from the foe ma - lign;
1 Bod - y of Je - sus, be my sav - ing guest;
2 O bless - èd Je - sus, hear and an - swer me;
3 In death's dread mo - ments make me on - ly thine;
1 Blood of my Sav - ior, bathe me in thy tide;
2 Deep in thy wounds, Lord, hide and shel-ter me;
3 Call me, and bid me come to thee on high,
1 Wash_ me, ye wa - ters, flow - ing from his side.
2 So_ shall I nev - er, nev - er part from thee.
3 Where_ I may praise thee with thy saints for aye.

PRAISE NOW YOUR GOD
Based on the Dutch of L. de Vocht
C.J. Marivoet
358
PRAISE NOW YOUR GOD
11 11. 10 10, with Chorus
J. de Vocht
Harm. by Jerry R. Brubaker
1 Praise now your God, ev - 'ry tongue, ev - 'ry na - tion, Tell the good
2 Christ gave his word at the mul - ti - pli - ca - tion. Bread and sweet
3 Here is your Sav - ior; give deep ad - o - ra - tion, Sing of his
1 news to the next gen - er - a - tion: Christ, the Re - deem - er, who
2 wine are now Christ, our ob - la - tion. Cross and Last Sup - per are
3 glo - ry in glad cel - e - bra - tion. Come, for his man - na is
1 rose from the dead, Stays with his peo - ple as life giv - ing
2 with us to - day. Life now a - bounds, and God's will we o -
3 food for the road, Strength for the jour - ney, our glo - ry fore -
1 Bread.
2 bey Al - le - lu - ia, God is great!
3 showed.
Al - le - lu - ia, God is good!

O THOU, WHO AT THY FIRST EUCHARIST
William H. Turton, 1881
Adapted by Irvin Udulutsch, 1956
359
Lower Key at No. 333
UNDE ET MEMORES
10 10. 10 10. 10 10
William H. Monk, 1875, alt.
1 At that first Eu - char - ist be - fore you died, O Lord, you prayed that
2 For all your Church, O Lord, we in - ter - cede; O make our lack of
3 We pray for those who wan - der from the fold; O bring them back, Good
4 So, Lord, at length, when sac - ra - ments shall cease, May we be one with
1 all be one in you; At this our Eu - char - ist a - gain pre - side,
2 char - i - ty to cease; Draw us the near - er each to each we plead,
3 Shep-herd of the sheep, Back to the faith which saints be - lieved of old,
4 all your Church a - bove; One with your saints in one un - end - ing peace,
1 And in our hearts your law of love re - new.
2 By draw - ing all to you, O Prince of Peace.
3 Back to the Church which still that faith does keep.
4 One with your saints in one un - bound - ed love.
O may we all one
bread, one bod - y be Through this blest sac - ra - ment of u - ni - ty.

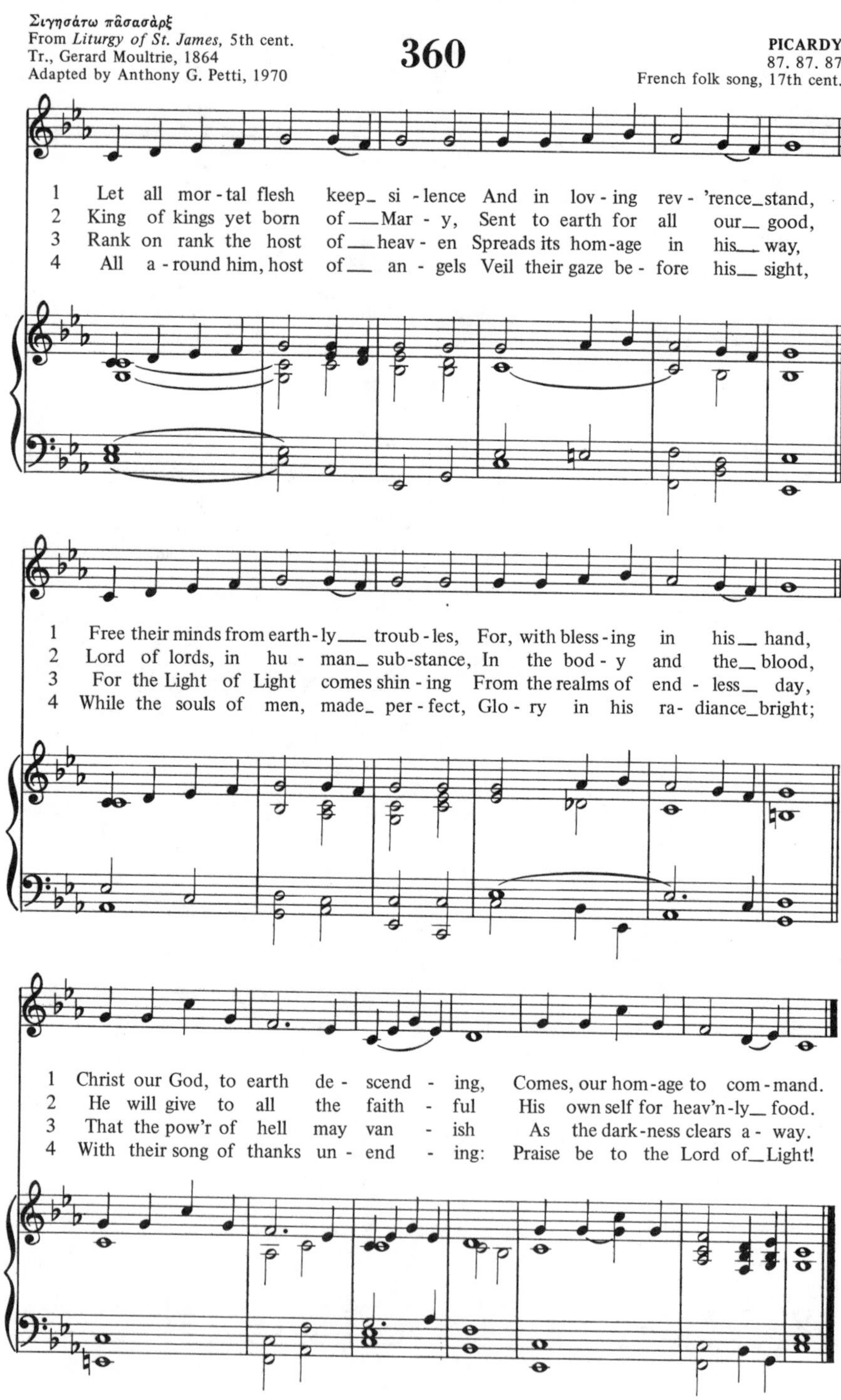
Σιγησάτω πᾶσασάρξ
From *Liturgy of St. James,* 5th cent.
Tr., Gerard Moultrie, 1864
Adapted by Anthony G. Petti, 1970
360
PICARDY
87. 87. 87
French folk song, 17th cent.
1 Let all mor - tal flesh keep_ si - lence And in lov - ing rev - 'rence_stand,
2 King of kings yet born of_Mar - y, Sent to earth for all our_ good,
3 Rank on rank the host of_heav - en Spreads its hom-age in his_ way,
4 All a - round him, host of_ an - gels Veil their gaze be - fore his_ sight,
1 Free their minds from earth - ly_ troub - les, For, with bless - ing in his_ hand,
2 Lord of lords, in hu - man_ sub - stance, In the bod - y and the_ blood,
3 For the Light of Light comes shin - ing From the realms of end - less_ day,
4 While the souls of men, made_ per - fect, Glo - ry in his ra - diance_bright;
1 Christ our God, to earth de - scend - ing, Comes, our hom - age to com - mand.
2 He will give to all the faith - ful His own self for heav'n - ly_ food.
3 That the pow'r of hell may van - ish As the dark - ness clears a - way.
4 With their song of thanks un - end - ing: Praise be to the Lord of_Light!

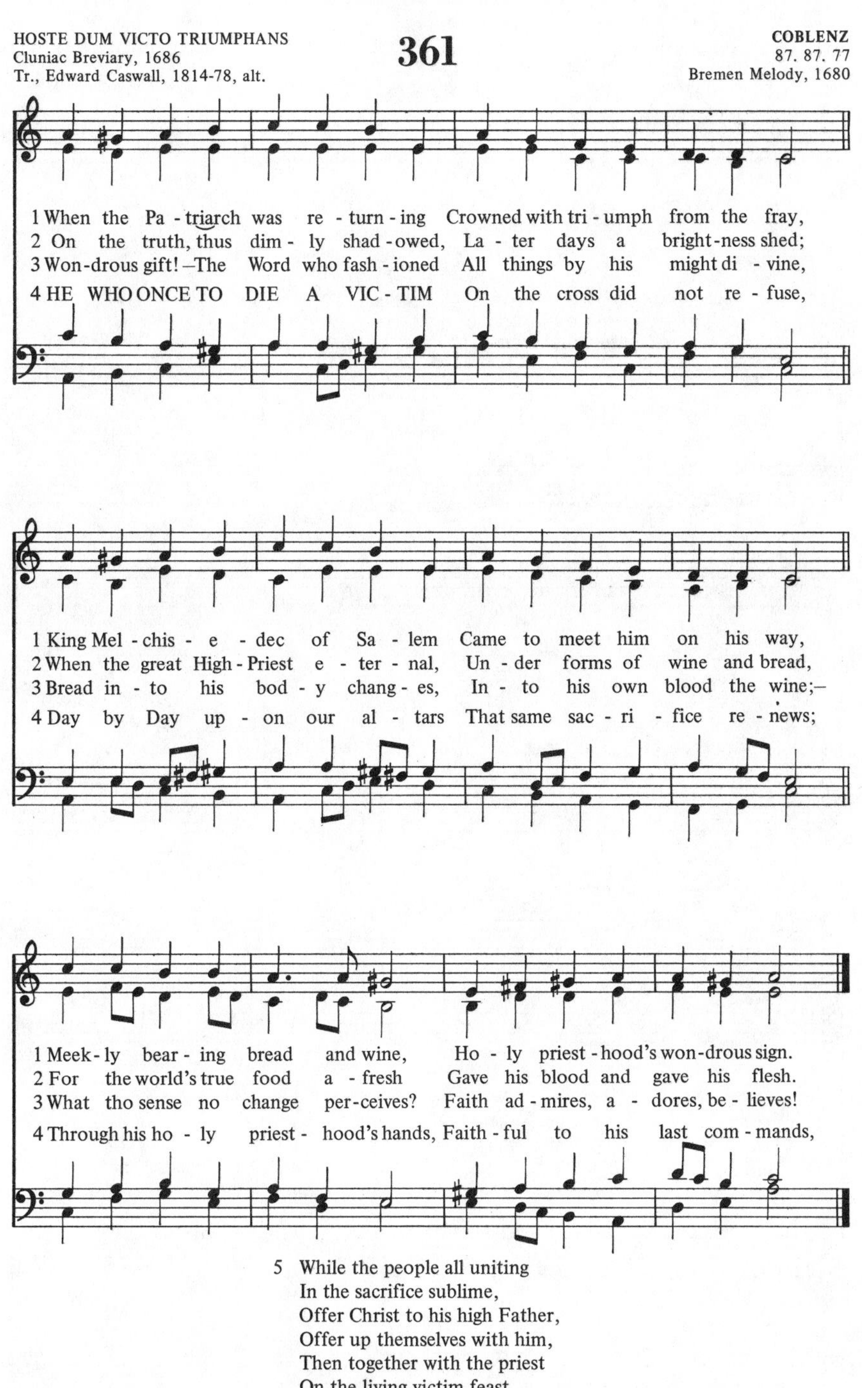
HOSTE DUM VICTO TRIUMPHANS
Cluniac Breviary, 1686
Tr., Edward Caswall, 1814-78, alt.
361
COBLENZ
87. 87. 77
Bremen Melody, 1680
1 When the Pa - triarch was re - turn - ing Crowned with tri - umph from the fray,
2 On the truth, thus dim - ly shad - owed, La - ter days a bright - ness shed;
3 Won - drous gift! —The Word who fash - ioned All things by his might di - vine,
4 HE WHO ONCE TO DIE A VIC - TIM On the cross did not re - fuse,
1 King Mel - chis - e - dec of Sa - lem Came to meet him on his way,
2 When the great High - Priest e - ter - nal, Un - der forms of wine and bread,
3 Bread in - to his bod - y chang - es, In - to his own blood the wine;—
4 Day by Day up - on our al - tars That same sac - ri - fice re - news;
1 Meek - ly bear - ing bread and wine, Ho - ly priest - hood's won - drous sign.
2 For the world's true food a - fresh Gave his blood and gave his flesh.
3 What tho sense no change per - ceives? Faith ad - mires, a - dores, be - lieves!
4 Through his ho - ly priest - hood's hands, Faith - ful to his last com - mands,

5 While the people all uniting
In the sacrifice sublime,
Offer Christ to his high Father,
Offer up themselves with him,
Then together with the priest
On the living victim feast.

JESU DULCEDO CORDIUM
Cento from "Jesu Dulcis Memoria" 12th cent.
Tr., Ray Palmer, 1858, alt.
362
Lower Key at No. 366
JESU, DULCIS MEMORIA
L. M.
Plainsong Melody
1 O Je - sus, joy of lov - ing hearts, O fount of
2 Your truth un - changed has ev - er stood; You save those
3 We taste you, Lord, our liv - ing bread, And long to
4 For you our rest - less spir - its yearn, Wher - e'er our
5 O Je - sus, ev - er with us stay, Make all our
1 life, O light of men, From all the pleas - ures earth im -
2 who up - on you call; To those who seek you, you are
3 feast up - on you still; We drink of you, the foun - tain -
4 change-ful lot is cast, Glad when to you our gaze we
5 mo - ments calm and bright; Chase the dark night of sin a -
1 parts We turn un - filled to you a - gain.
2 good, To them who find you, all in all.
3 head, And thirst our souls from you to fill.
4 turn, Blest when our faith can hold you fast.
5 way, Shed o'er the world your ho - ly light.

Alternative Tune: JESU, DULCIS MEMORIA (Modern Tune) No. 366

BEFORE CHRIST DIED
Peter de Rosa, 1970

363

LINDISFARNE
C. M.
Eric Welch

1 Be - fore Christ died he took some bread, And
2 "Now eat and drink; I am your food. I
3 We drink this wine, we eat this bread, As
4 By faith, in bro - ken bread we see The

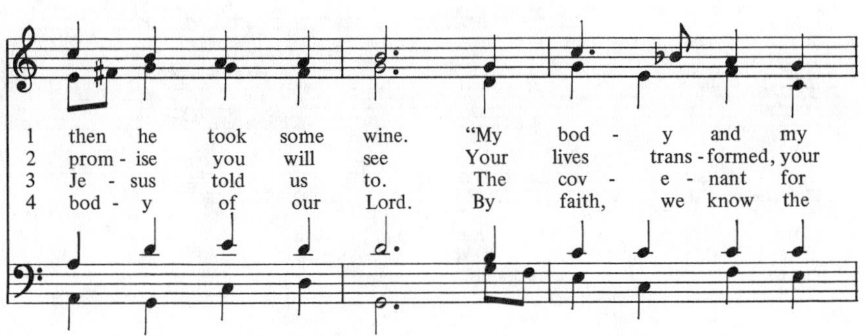
1 then he took some wine. "My bod - y and my
2 prom - ise you will see Your lives trans - formed, your
3 Je - sus told us to. The cov - e - nant for
4 bod - y of our Lord. By faith, we know the

1 blood," he said, "A sac - ri - fic - ial sign."
2 hearts re - newed; You'll die and live with me."
3 which he bled To - day we must re - new.
4 wine to be His ho - ly blood out - poured.

5 Each time the priest, for mem'ry's sake,
Repeats Christ's holy act,
Each time we of this meal partake,
Christ's death we re-enact.

6 From sunrise to the setting sun
This death will we proclaim.
Each day Christ promises to come
Until he comes again.

364
VOICE IN MY NAME
W. Bernard & C.J. Marivoet
SONG OF OUR NEEDS
Irregular
F. Meartens
Harm. by Jerry R. Brubaker
Voice in my name to the Fa - ther your needs;
Em C Am Em
What you ex - pect he ex - ceeds.
C Am Em sus4 Em
1 Wine for re - joic - ing and bread for food,
2 Seed that must die first to grow and live
3 Je - sus our nour - ish - ment on the way,
4 Of - fer our plead - ing, God's liv - ing Son;
5 Fa - ther, we pray you in Je - sus' name.
Am Em C Em
1 Words to en - light - en hearts all re - newed.
2 Ere it is read - y har - vest to give.
3 Dy - ing and ris - ing with us each day.
4 Bind us to - geth - er, make us all one.
5 Christ is our Sav - ior, free - dom and claim.
Am G Am Em

365

SEE US, LORD, ABOUT YOUR ALTAR
J. Greally, alt.

ALL FOR THEE
87. 87 (87. 87. 87)
The Hacker Hymnal
Harm. by Roger Nachtwey

1 See us, Lord, a - bout your al - tar; Though so man - y__ we are one;
2 Hear our prayers, O__ lov - ing Fa - ther, Hear in them your_ Son, our Lord;
3 Once were seen the_ blood and wa - ter; Now are seen but_ bread and wine;
4 Wheat and grape con - tain the mean - ing: Food and drink he__ is to all;
1 Man - y souls_ by love u - nit- ed In the heart_ of__ Christ, your Son,
2 Hear him speak our love and wor-ship, As we sing_ with_ one ac - cord,
3 Once in hu - man form he suf-fered, Now his form_ is__ but a sign.,
4 One in him__ we are God's fam - 'ly, Gath - ered by_ his__ lov - ing call,
1 Man - y__ souls by love u - nit - ed In the heart_ of__ Christ, your Son.
2 Hear him speak our love and_ wor - ship As we sing_ with_ one ac - cord.
3 Onee in_ hu - man form he__ suf - fered; Now his form_ is__ but a sign.
4 One in_ him we are God's fam - 'ly, Gath-ered by_ his__ lov - ing call.

5 Hear us yet; so much is needful
In our frail, disordered life;
Stay with us and tend our weakness
Till that day of no more strife,
Stay with us and tend our weakness
Till that day of no more strife.

6 Members of the Mystic Body,
Now we know our prayer is heard,
Heard by you, because your children
Have received th'eternal Word,
Heard by you, because your children
Have received th'eternal Word.

HOW BLEST ARE WE
James McMullen, 1965

366

Higher Key at No. 362

JESU, DULCIS MEMORIA
L. M.
Andernach, 1608

1 How blest are we who share this_ Bread, The Flesh and Blood of
2 O Lord, we eat this Bread of__ life, The Bread you give to
3 Our fa - thers ate the heav - 'nly_ food, The man - na gath - ered
4 This ban - quet brings e - ter - nal_ life, A life of love and
1 Christ our__ Lord. May love u - nite us grate - ful - ly
2 faith - ful__ sons. The peace of Christ, your Son, is__ ours
3 in the__ wild; Your God-sent Bread we now re - ceive,
4 u - ni - ty, For now we live in Je - sus__ Christ
1 As sons of God who live in peace.
2 U - nit - ing us who do your will.
3 Our dai - ly food and last - ing strength.
4 And share with him his ris - en might.

5 Give thanks to Jesus, saving Lord,
Our paschal Victim, newly slain;
He shares his Father's love with us,
He makes us worthy sons of God.

6 Lord Jesus Christ, we beg your grace;
We turn to you, our hope and guide.
This bread unite us, faithful sons,
Awaiting perfect unity.

7 Give praise to God, for he is good,
To him who made us like himself;
To Christ, his Son, who set us free,
To God's great Gift, our Source of life.

Alternative Tune: JESU, DULCIS MEMORIA (Plainsong) No. 362.

PANGE, LINGUA, GLORIOSI
Thomas Aquinas, 1263
Tr., E. Caswall, J.M. Neale, Sr. Teresine
Adapted by Sr. Teresine, 1958

367

WEISSE FLAGGEN
87. 87. D.
Tochter Sion, Cologne, 1741, alt.
Harm. by Roger Nachtwey

1 Sing with joy the Sav - ior's glo - ry, Of his flesh the mys - t'ry sing;
2 On the night of his last sup - per, Seat - ed with his cho - sen band,
3 While we bow in ad - dor - ra - tion, Let our hearts his gift re - vere;
1 Of his blood all price ex - ceed - ing, Shed by our im - mor - tal King.
2 He as food to all his breth - ren Gave him - self with his own hand.
3 Faith, its aid to vi - sion lend - ing, Tells that he, un - seen is here.
Men and an - gels, sing in cho - rus, And, a - dor - ing, bend the knee!
Praise our God whom here be - fore us In the sa - cred host we see.

LET US BREAK BREAD
Black Spiritual
Adapted by Paul Ashton
368
LET US BREAK BREAD
Black Spiritual
Adapted by Paul Ashton
Eb Ab Eb Db Eb Ab Eb
Let us break bread to - geth - er with the Lord,
Eb Bbm7 Eb7 F F7 Bb Eb Bb
Let us break bread to - geth - er with the Lord!
Eb Eb7 Ab
As we trav - el through this land with our broth - ers hand in
Abm Eb6 Cm7 F7 Bb7 Eb
hand, O Lord fill our liv - in' with your life!

2 Let us drink wine together with the Lord . . .
3 Let us sing songs together with the Lord . . .
4 Let us all work together with the Lord . . .
5 Let us make this a new world with the Lord . . .
6 Let us break down the old walls with the Lord . . .
7 O Lord, fill all our livin' with your life . . .

369

SING TO THE LORD OF FAITH
Based on the Dutch of M. Van der Plas
C. J. Marivoet

SING TO THE LORD OF FAITH
Irregular
J. Mul, alt.
Harm. by Jerry R. Brubaker

1 Sing to the Lord of faith and of love. People of God, he lives in our midst. This is the Lord; be glad and re - joice.
2 Sing to the liv - ing heav - en - ly bread, Par - don for sin - ners, food on the road, Rest for the wear - y, life af - ter death.
3 Sing to the Way that leads to our home, Sing to the Truth that frees us from doubt, Sing to the Life that wants to be lived.
4 Sing to the Love that o - pens our hearts, Sing to the Love that is to be shared, Sing to the Love that gath - ers us all.
Keep voic - ing your song; sing and bless him!
Al - le - lu - ia, al - le - lu - ia!

5 Sing to the Lord who is to return,
Sing to the Door that opens to us,
Sing to the Lord, the source of our joy.
Keep voicing your song; sing and bless him!
Alleluia, alleluia!

370

AVE, VIVENS HOSTIA
John Peckham, 1240-92
Tr., Ronald A. Knox, 1939

AVE, VIVENS HOSTIA
76. 76. D.
Traditional Melody
Harm. by Jerry R. Brubaker

1 Hail, true Vic - tim, life and light Un - to sin - ners_ lend - ing–
A - ve vi - vens ho - sti - a, Ve - ri - tas et__ Vi - ta,
2 Hail, true Man - na from the sky; Is - rael nev - er__ knew you;
A - ve, Man - na coe - li - cum, Ve - ri - us le - ga - li,
1 Ev - 'ry old - er form and rite Has in you its__ end - ing–
Per te sa - cri - fi - ci - a Cun - cta sunt fi - ni - ta;
2 Pil - grims, for the day's sup - ply, Dai - ly hom - age__ do you;
Da - tum in vi - a - ti - cum Mis - se - ro mor - ta - li;
1 Spot - less__ in the Fa - ther's sight Ev - er - more as - cend - ing,
Per__ te__ Pa - tri glo - ri - a Da - tur in - fi - ni - ta,
2 When__ our__ souls in sick - ness lie, Yields that sick - ness__ to__ you;
Me - di - ca - men my - sti - cum Mor - bo spi - ri - ta - li,
1 Ho - ly church in bit - ter fight Ev - er - more be - friend - ing.
Per te stat ec - cle - si - a Ju - gi - ter mu__ ni - ta.
2 Chris - tians, when they come to die, Live im - mor - tal__ through you.
Ro - rem dans ca - tho - li - cum Vi - tae im - mor - ta - li.

3 Hail, Christ's Body– gift he made,
His own death foreshowing,
(Godhead under earthly shade
Like a jewel glowing),
Sacred mem'ries, ne'er to fade,
On his Church bestowing,
When to earth farewell he bade,
To his passion going.

4 Plead, true Victim, in our stead
To the Father crying,
You, your children's daily bread,
Daily health supplying;
Banquet for the exile spread,
Grant us life undying;
May our love from yours be fed,
Self and sense denying!

371[1]

Higher Key

O ESCA VIATORUM
Maintzisch Gesangbuch, 1661
Tr., J. Athelstan L. Riley, 1906

O ESCA VIATORUM
776. 776 (6)
Johann M. Haydn, d. 1806
Harm. by Roger Nachtwey

1 O___ food of men way - far - ing, The bread of an - gels
O___ e - sca vi - a - to - rum, O pa - nis an - ge -
2 O___ stream of love past tell - ing, O pur - est foun - tain,
O___ lym - pha fons a - mo - ris, Qui pu - ro Sal - va -
1 shar - ing, O man - na from on high! We___ hun - ger; Lord, sup -
lo - rum, O man - na coe - li - tum! E - su - ri - en - tes___
2 well - ing From out the Sav - ior's side! We___ faint with thirst; re -
to - ris E cor - de pro - flu - is! Te___ si - ti - en - tes___
1 ply us, Nor your de - lights de - ny us, Whose
ci - ba, Dul - ce - di - ne non___ pri - va, Cor -
2 vive us, Of your a - bun - dance_ give us, And
po - ta, Hæc so - la no - stra___ vo - ta, His
1 hearts to you_ draw_ nigh, Whose hearts to you draw nigh.
da quae - ren - ti - um, Cor - da quae - ren - ti - um.
2 all we need_ pro - vide, And all we need pro - vide.
u - na suf - fi - cis, His u - na - suf - fi - cis.

3 O Jesus, by you bidden,
We here adore you hidden
'Neath forms of bread and wine.
Grant, when the veil is riven,
We may behold in heaven
Your countenance divine,
Your countenance divine.

O Jesu, tuum vultum
Quem colimus occultum
Sub panis specie.
Fac ut, remoto velo,
Aperta nos in coelo
Cernamus acie,,
Cernamus acie..

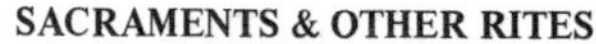

371²

LOWER KEY

372

VERBUM SUPERNUM PRODIENS
Thomas Aquinas, 1263

VERBUM SUPERNUM PRODIENS
L.M.
Plainsong Melody

1. Ver - bum su - per - num
2. In mor - tem a di -
3. Qui - bus sub bi - na
4. Se na - scens de - dit
5. O SA - LU - TA - RIS
6. U - ni tri - no - que

1. pro - di - ens, Nec Pa - tris lin - quens dex - te - ram.
2. sci - pu - lo Su - is tra - den - dus ae - mu - lis,
3. spe - ci - e Car - nem de - dit et san - gui - nem:
4. so - ci - um, Con - ve - scens in e - du - li - um,
5. ho - sti - a Quae cae - li pan - dis o - sti - um,
6. Do - mi - no Sit sem - pi - ter - na glo - ri - a,
1. Ad o - pus su - um ex - i - ens, Ve - nit
2. Pri - us in vi - tae fer - cu - lo Se tra -
3. Ut du - pli - cis sub - stan - ti - ae To - tum
4. Se mo - ri - ens in pre - ti - um, Se re -
5. Bel - la pre - munt ho - sti - li - a, Da ro -
6. Qui vi - tam si - ne ter - mi - no No - bis
1. ad vi - tae ve - spe - ram.
2. di - dit di - sci - pu - lis.
3. ci - ba - ret ho - mi - nem.
4. gnans dat in prae - mi - um.
5. bur fer au - xi - li - um.
6. do - net in pa - tri - a.
A - men.

VERBUM SUPERNUM PRODIENS
Thomas Aquinas, 1263
Tr., J.M. Neale, E. Caswall, et al.

373

VERBUM SUPERNUM PRODIENS
L.M.
Plainsong Melody

1. The Word of God, proceeding forth Yet leaving not his Father's side, And going to
2. By false disciple to be giv'n To foemen for his blood athirst, Himself, the liv-
3. In twofold form of sacrament He gave his Flesh, he gave his Blood, That man, of two-
4. In birth man's fellow man was he, His food while sitting at the board; He died, his ran-
5. O SAVING VICTIM, op'ning wide The gate of heav'n to man below, Our foes press on
6. To your great name be endless praise, Immortal Godhead, One in Three; Grant us at last,

1. his work on earth,
2. ing Bread from heav'n,
3. fold sub - stance blent,
4. som - er to be,
5. from ev - 'ry side;
6. for end - less days,
1. Had reached at length life's
2. He gave to his dis -
3. Might whol - ly feed on
4. He reigns to be his
5. Your aid sup - ply, your
6. In our true na - tive
1. e - ven - tide.
2. ci - ples first.
3. mys - tic food.
4. great re - ward.
5. strength be - stow.
6. land to be.
A - men.

PANGE, LINGUA, GLORIOSI
Thomas Aquinas, 1263

374

PANGE, LINGUA, GLORIOSI
87. 87. 87
Plainsong Melody, 13th cent.

1 Pan - ge lin - gua glo - ri - o - si
2 No - bis da - tus, no - bis na - tus
3 In su - pre - mæ noc - te cœ - næ
4 Ver - bum ca - ro pa - nem ve - rum
5 TAN - TUM ER - GO SA - CRA - MEN - TUM
6 Ge - ni - to - ri Ge - ni - to - que
1 Cor - po - ris my - ste - ri - um,
2 Ex in - tac - ta Vir - gi - ne,
3 Re - cum - bens cum fra - tri - bus,
4 Ver - bo car - nem ef - fi - cit:
5 Ve - ne - re - mur cer - nu - i:
6 Laus et ju - bi - la - ti - o,
1 San - gui - nis - que pre - ti - o - si,
2 Et in mun - do con - ver - sa - tus,
3 Ob - ser - va - ta le - ge ple - ne
4 Fit - que san - guis Chri - sti me - rum,
5 Et an - ti - quum do - cu - men - tum
6 Sa - lus, hon - or, vir - tus quo - que

1 Quem in mun - di pre - ti - um
2 Spar - so ver - bi se - mi - ne,
3 Ci - bus in - le - ga - li bus,
4 Et si sen - sus de - fi - cit,
5 No - vo ce - dat ri - tu - i:
6 Sit et be - ne - di - cti - o:
1 Fru - ctus ven - tris ge - ne - ro - si
2 Su - i mo - ras in - co - la - tus
3 Ci - bum tur - bæ du - o - de - næ
4 Ad fir - man - dum cor sin - ce - rum
5 Præ - stet fi - des sup - ple - men - tum
6 Pro - ce - den - ti ab u - tro - que
1 Rex ef - fu - dit gen - ti - um.
2 Mi - ro clau - sit or - di - ne.
3 Se dat su - is ma - ni - bus.
4 So - la fi - des suf - fi - cit.
5 Sen - su - um de - fe - ctu - i.
6 Com - par sit lau - da - ti - o.
A - men.

PANGE, LINGUA, GLORIOSI
Thomas Aquinas, 1263
Tr., Benedict Avery, 1955

375

PANGE, LINGUA, GLORIOSI
87. 87. 87
Plainsong Melody, 13th cent.

1 Sing, my tongue! Ac - claim Christ pres - ent,
2 Heav - en's prom - ised gift to man - kind,
3 Din - ing with his twelve a - pos - tles
4 Word - made - flesh makes bread his bod - y,
5 BOW - ING LOW, THEN, OF - FER HOM - AGE
6 Praise and glo - ri - fy the Fa - ther;
1 Veiled with - in this sa - cred sign:
2 Born to us of one most pure,
3 On the night be - fore he died,
4 Con - se - crates it by his word.
5 To a sac - ra - ment so great!
6 Bless his Son's life - giv - ing name,
1 Pre - cious blood and ris - en bod - y,
2 Spends his earth - ly days a - mong us,
3 Tak - ing for the pas - chal sup - per
4 Wine be - comes the blood of Je - sus;
5 Here is new and per - fect wor - ship;
6 Sing - ing their e - ter - nal God - head,

1 Un - der forms of bread and wine:
2 Plants the seed of faith se - cure,
3 Foods the law had spec - i - fied,
4 He it is whose voice is heard.
5 All the old must term - i - nate.
6 Pow - er, maj - es - ty, and fame,
1 Blood once shed for man's re - demp - tion
2 Ends his mis - sion, leaves a sym - bol
3 See, he sets new bread be - fore them,
4 Minds in doubt need faith's as - sur - rance:
5 Sens - es can - not grasp this mar - vel;
6 Of - fer - ing their Ho - ly Spir - it
1 By his king, of Da - vid's line.
2 Of the death he will en - dure.
3 Hand - ing each Christ cru - ci - fied!
4 God who spoke can - not have erred.
5 Faith must serve to com - pen - sate.
6 E - qual wor - ship and ac - claim. A - men.

376

FATHER, WE THANK THEE
Paraphrased from the *Didache*
F. Bland Tucker, 1941, alt.

RENDEZ A DIEU
98. 98. D.
Louis Bourgeois, 1543

1 Fa - ther, all thanks for hav - ing plant - ed Your ho - ly
2 Care for your church, O Lord, in mer - cy; Save it from
1 name with - in our hearts. Knowl - edge and faith and life im - mor - tal
2 e - vil, guard it still; Strength - en it in your love, u - nite it,
1 Je - sus your Son to us im - parts. O Lord, you made all for your
2 Cleansed and con - formed to your own will. As grain, once scat - tered on the
1 plea - sure And gave man food for all his days, Giv - ing in
2 hill - sides, Was in this bro - ken bread made one, So from all

1 Christ the Bread e - ter - nal; Yours is the pow'r, be yours the praise.
2 lands your Church be gath - ered In - to your king - dom by your Son.
PRAISE THE LORD, RISE UP
H. C. A. Gaunt, b. 1902
377
ALLES IST AN GOTTES
SEGEN (EVANGELISTS)
887. D.
From a chorale by J. Löhner, 1691
1 Praise the Lord, rise up re - joic - ing, Wor - ship, thanks, de - vo - tion voic - ing:
2 Scat - tered flock, one Shep-herd shar - ing, Lost and lone - ly, one voice hear - ing,
3 Send us forth a - lert and liv - ing, Sins for - giv - en, wrongs for - giv - ing,
1 Glo - ry be_ to_ God on high! Christ, your cross and pas - sion shar - ing,
2 Ears are o - pen_ to your word; By your Blood new life re - ceiv - ing,
3 In your Spir - it_ strong and free. Find - ing love in all cre - a - tion,
1 By this Eu - char - ist de - clar - ing Yours th'e - ter - nal_ vic - to - ry.
2 In your Bod - y firm, be - liev - ing, We are yours, and you the Lord.
3 Bring - ing peace in ev - 'ry na - tion, May we faith - ful_ fol - l'wers be.

378

ascr. Ephraim of Syria, c. 306-73
Tr., C. W. Humphreys & P. Dearmer, 1906, alt.

ACH GOTT UND HERR
87. 87
Neu-Leipziger-Gesangbuch, 1682

1 Make strong for serv - ice, Lord, the hands That ho - ly things have_ ta - ken;
2 Lord, may the tongues which "Ho - ly" sang Keep free from all de - ceiv - ing;
3 The feet that tread your ho - ly place From light don't ev - er__ ban - ish;
1 Let ears that now have heard your songs To clam - or nev - er__ wa - ken.
2 May eyes which saw your love be_bright, Your bless - ed hope_per - ceiv - ing.
3 The bod - ies by your Bod - y_ fed With your new life__re - plen - ish.

379[1]

I RECEIVED THE LIVING GOD
Anonymous

Higher Key

I RECEIVED THE LIVING GOD
77. 77, with Refrain
Anonymous
Harm. by Jerry R. Brubaker

I re - ceived the liv - ing God, and my heart is full of joy.
I re - ceived the liv - ing God, and my heart is full of joy.

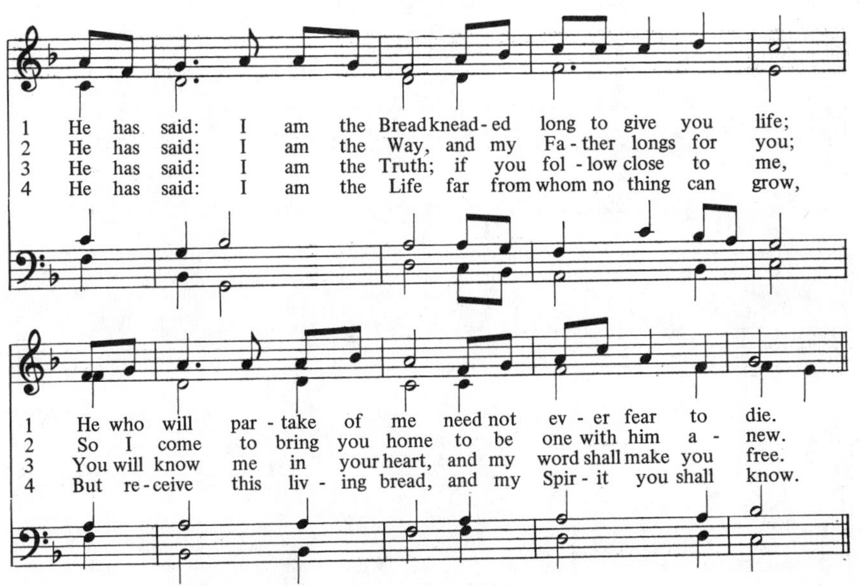
1 He has said: I am the Bread knead-ed long to give you life;
2 He has said: I am the Way, and my Fa-ther longs for you;
3 He has said: I am the Truth; if you fol-low close to me,
4 He has said: I am the Life far from whom no thing can grow,
1 He who will par-take of me need not ev-er fear to die.
2 So I come to bring you home to be one with him a-new.
3 You will know me in your heart, and my word shall make you free.
4 But re-ceive this liv-ing bread, and my Spir-it you shall know.

379[2]

Lower Key

WIE WOHL HAST DU GELABET
Johann Rist, 1651, cento
Tr., Catherine Winkworth, 1858, alt.
380
LLANFYLLIN
76. 76. D.
Traditional Welsh Melody
1 O liv - ing Bread from heav - en, How you have fed your guest!
2 My Lord, here have you led ___ me With - in your ho - ly place,
3 You gave me all I want - ed, Food that can death de - stroy;
4 Lord, grant me that, thus strength-ened With heav - 'nly food while here
1 The gifts you have just giv - en Have filled my heart with rest.
2 And you your - self have fed ___ me With treas - ures of your grace;
3 And you have free - ly grant - ed The cup of end - less joy.
4 My course on earth is length - ened I serve you free from fear;
1 O won - drous food of bless - ing, O cup that heals our woes,
2 And you have free - ly giv - en What earth could nev - er buy,
3 O Lord, I do not mer - it The fa - vor you have shown,
4 And, when you call my spir - it To leave this world be - low,
1 My heart, this gift pos - sess - ing, In thank-ful song o'er - flows!
2 The Bread of life from heav - en, That I may nev - er die.
3 And all my soul and spir - it Bow down be - fore your throne.
4 I en - ter, through your mer - it, Where end - less joys shall flow.

381

'Από δόξης εἰς δόξαν πορευόμενοι
Liturgy of St. James
Tr., C. W. Humphreys, 1906, alt.

SHEEN
14 14. 14 15
Gustave Holst, 1874-1934

1 From glo - ry to glo - ry ad - vanc - ing, we praise you, O Lord;
2 Thanks-giv - ing, and glo - ry, and wor - ship, and bless - ing, and love,
1 Your name with the Fa - ther and Spir - it be ev - er a - dored.
2 One heart and one song have the saints up - on earth and a - bove.
1 From strength un - to strength we go for - ward on Zi - on's high - way,
2 O Lord, ev - er - more to your ser - vants your pres - ence be nigh;
1 To ap - pear be - fore God in the cit - y of in - fi - nite day.
2 Ev - er fit us by serv - ice on earth for your serv - ice on high.

LORD, AS WE RISE
Fred Kaan, b. 1929
382
CLOISTERS
11 11. 11 5
Joseph Barnby, 1868
1 Lord, as we rise to leave the shell of wor - ship,
2 For all the strain with liv - ing in - ter - wov - en,
3 Give us an eye for o - pen - ings to serve you,
4 Lift from our life the blan - ket of con - ven - tion,
1 Called to the risk of un - pro - tect - ed liv - ing,
2 For the de - mands each day will make up - on us,
3 Make us a - lert when calm is in - ter - rup - ted,
4 Give us the nerve to lose our lives for oth - ers;
1 Will - ing to be at one with all your
2 And all the love we owe the world a -
3 Read - y and wise to use the un - ex -
4 Lead on your Church through death to res - ur -
1 peo - ple, We ask for cour - age.
2 round us, Lord, make us cheer - ful.
3 pect - ed; Sharp - en our in - sight.
4 rec - tion, Lord of all a - ges.

383

PARDONED THROUGH REDEEMING GRACE
Edward Osler, 1836, alt.

HARTS
77. 77
B. Milgrove, 1731-1810

1 Par - doned thru re - deem - ing grace,
2 This our sac - ri - fice re - ceive,
3 By the ho - ly out - ward sign,
4 Called to bear the Chris - tian name,
1 In your bless - ed Son re - vealed,
2 Hum - bly of - fered thru your Son;
3 By the cleans - ing grace with - in,
4 May our vows and life ac - cord,
1 Wor - ship - ing be - fore your face,
2 Quick - en us in him to live;
3 Seal us with your own de - sign;
4 And our ev - 'ry deed pro - claim:
1 Lord, to you our - selves we yield.
2 Lord, in us your will be done.
3 Wash and keep us pure from sin.
4 "Ho - li - ness un - to the Lord!"

NOW LET US FROM THIS TABLE
Fred Kaan, b. 1929

384

GRACE CHURCH
L. M.
Ignaz J. Pleyel, 1815

1 Now let us from this ta - ble rise, Re - newed in
2 With minds a - lert, up - held by grace, To spread the
3 To fill each hu - man house with love, It is the
4 Then give us cour - age, Fa - ther God, To choose a -

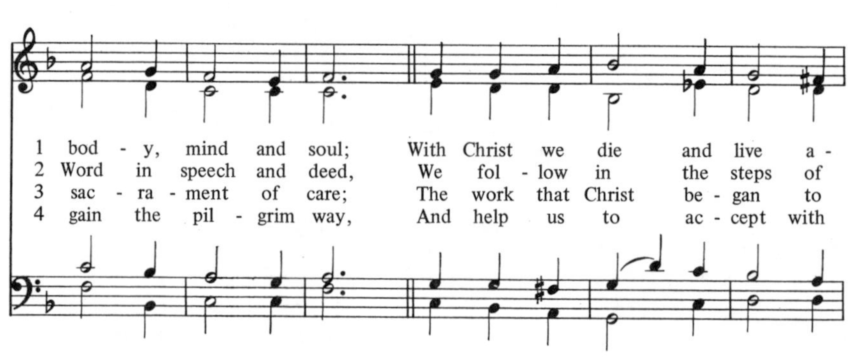
1 bod - y, mind and soul; With Christ we die and live a -
2 Word in speech and deed, We fol - low in the steps of
3 sac - ra - ment of care; The work that Christ be - gan to
4 gain the pil - grim way, And help us to ac - cept with

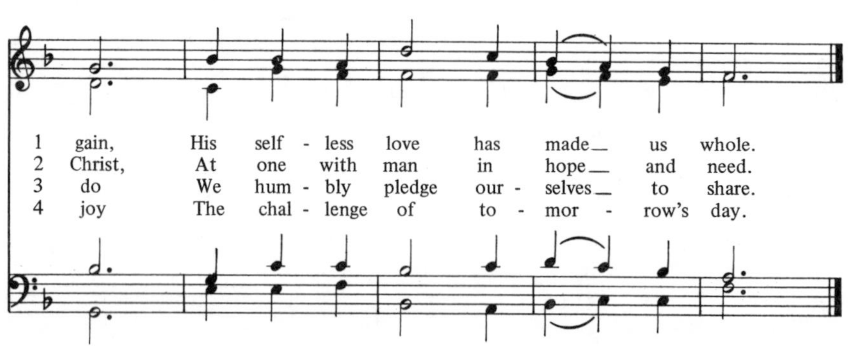
1 gain, His self - less love has made us whole.
2 Christ, At one with man in hope and need.
3 do We hum - bly pledge our - selves to share.
4 joy The chal - lenge of to - mor - row's day.

GO FORTH IN PEACE
J. Smith, 1970
385
ITE IN PACE
C. M.
Dom Gregory Murray, OSB.
1 Go forth in peace, go forth to men, Go forth in peace and joy. The Lamb has tak - en sin a - way, The Lamb who gives us peace.
2 We take his flesh and blood for food, We take his word of peace: We car - ry forth with grate - ful hearts His gra - cious peace to men.
3 We bring the Word as mes - sen - gers A - mid the world of men, To take from him and share with all What he has shared with us.

Alternative Tune: ST. STEPHEN, No. 201.

FOR THE BREAD
Louis FitzGerald Benson, 1855-1930
St. 4 & Chorus, John Henry Hopkins, Jr.,1820-91
386
WERDE MUNTER
87. 87, with Chorus
Johan Schop, 1642
Arr., J. S. Bach, 1716
1 For the bread which you have bro - ken, For the wine which you have poured, For the words which you have spo - ken, Now we give you thanks,- O Lord.
2 By this pledge that you still love us, By your gift of peace re - stored, By your call to joys a - bove us, Sanc - ti - fy our lives O Lord.
3 In your serv - ice, Lord, de - fend us, In our hearts keep watch and ward, In the world where you now send us Let your king - dom come, O Lord.
4 Come with us, O bless - ed Je - sus, Keep your pres - ence ev - er new, And in leav - ing now your al - tar, Let us nev - er more leave you.
O let your an - gel cho - rus Nev - er cease the heav'n - ly strain, But in us, your lov - ing

chil - dren, Bring peace, good will to men.

LORD, WHEN WE BEND
J. D. Carlyle, 1758-1804, alt.

387

ST. BERNARD
C. M.
Tochter Sion, Cologne, 1741

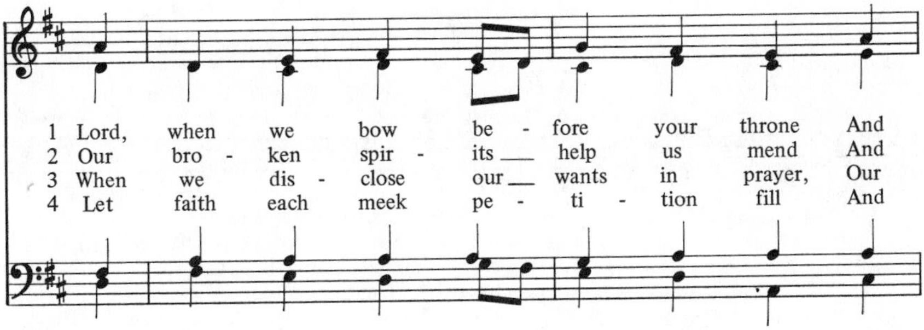

1 Lord, when we bow be - fore your throne And
2 Our bro - ken spir - its help us mend And
3 When we dis - close our wants in prayer, Our
4 Let faith each meek pe - ti - tion fill And

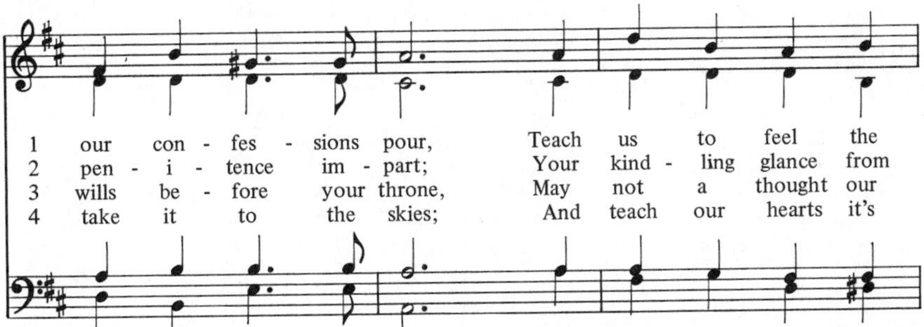

1 our con - fes - sions pour, Teach us to feel the
2 pen - i - tence im - part; Your kind - ling glance from
3 wills be - fore your throne, May not a thought our
4 take it to the skies; And teach our hearts it's

1 sins we own, And hate what we de - plore.
2 heav - en send; Beam hope up - on the heart.
3 bos - oms share That is not yours a - lone.
4 good - ness still That grants it or de - nies.

LORD, AS TO THY DEAR CROSS
John Hampden Gurney, 1938, alt.

388

Higher Key at No. 261 (First tune).

BANGOR
C. M.
William Tans'ur, 1734

1 Lord, as to your dear cross we__ flee And
2 Help us, through good re - port and__ ill, Our
3 Let grace our sel - fish - ness ex - pel, Our
4 Kept peace - ful in the midst of__ strife, For -

1 plead to__ be for - giv'n, So let your life our__
2 dai - ly__ cross to bear; Like you, to do our__
3 earth - li - ness re - fine, That kind - ness in our__
4 giv - ing__ and for - giv'n, O may we lead the__

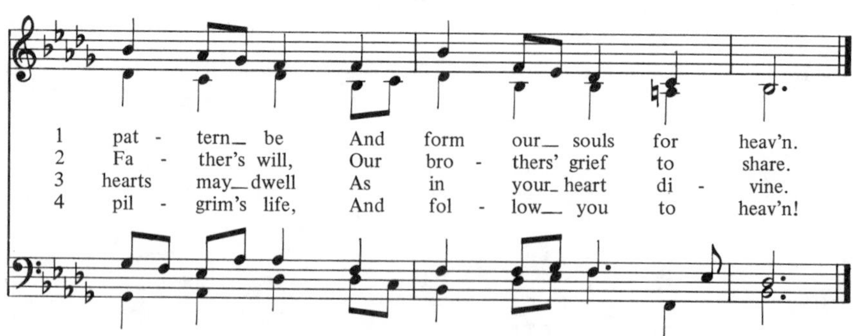
1 pat - tern__ be And form our__ souls for heav'n.
2 Fa - ther's will, Our bro - thers' grief to share.
3 hearts may__ dwell As in your__ heart di - vine.
4 pil - grim's life, And fol - low__ you to heav'n!

OH, FOR A HEART TO PRAISE
Charles Wesley, 1742, alt.

389

KILMARNOCK
C. M.
Neill Dougall, 1831

1 Oh, for a heart to praise my God, A
2 A heart re - signed, sub - mis - sive, meek, My
3 A hum - ble, low - ly, con - trite heart, Be -
4 A heart in ev - 'ry thought re - newed, And
1 heart from sin set free! A heart that's sprin - kled
2 dear Re - deem - er's throne, Where on - ly Christ is
3 liev - ing, true, and clean; Which neith - er life nor
4 full of love di - vine, All per - fect, right, and
1 with the blood So free - ly shed for me;
2 heard to speak, Where Je - sus reigns a - lone;
3 death can part From him that dwells with - in;
4 pure, and good; Your heart, O Lord, as mine!

5 Your nature, gracious Lord, impart;
Come quickly from above;
Write your new name upon my heart,
Your new, best name of Love.

390

Μνώεο Χριστέ
Synesius of Cyrene, d. 430
Tr., Allen William Chatfield, 1876, cento

SOUTHWELL
S. M.
William Damon's *Psalmes,* 1579

1 Lord Je - sus, think on me, And purge a - way my sin; From earth - born pas - sions set me free, And make me pure with - in.
2 Lord Je - sus, think on me, With care and woe op - prest; Let me your lov - ing ser - vant be And taste your prom - ised rest.
3 Lord Je - sus, think on me, A - mid the bat - tle's strife; In all my pain and mis - er - y, O be my health and life.
4 Lord Je - sus, think on me, Nor let me go a - stray; Thru dark - ness and anx - i - e - ty Now point the heav'n - ly way.

5 Lord Jesus, think on me,
That, when the flood is past,
I may th'eternal brightness see
And share your joy at last.

6 Lord Jesus, think on me,
That I may sing above
All glory to the Trinity,
The songs of praise and love.

391

ST. MICHAEL
S. M.

Τῶν ἁμαρτιῶν μου τὴν πληθὺν
Joseph the Hymnographer, c. 860, cento
Tr., John M. Neale, 1862

Melody by Louis Bourgeois, 1551
adapted by William Crotch, 1836

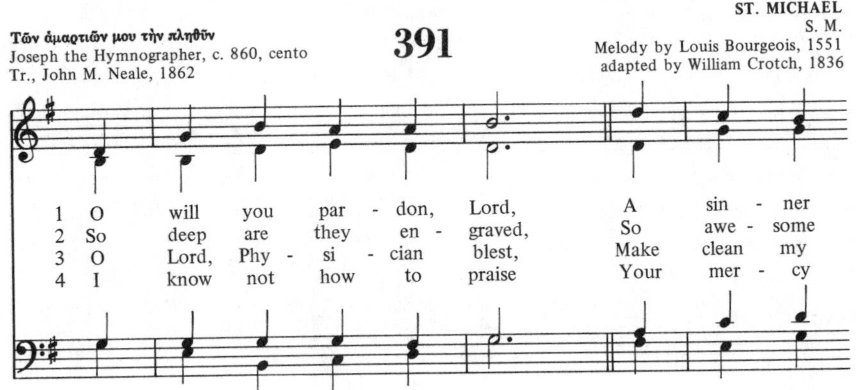
1 O will you par - don, Lord, A sin - ner
2 So deep are they en - graved, So awe - some
3 O Lord, Phy - si - cian blest, Make clean my
4 I know not how to praise Your mer - cy

1 such as I, Al - though your book his
2 is their fear; The right - eous scarce - ly
3 guilt - y soul And me, by man - y
4 and your love; Be pleased my soul from

1 crimes re - cords Of such a crim - son dye.
2 shall be saved, And where shall I ap - pear.
3 sins op - prest, Re - store and keep me whole.
4 earth to raise And learn from you a - bove.

O THOU TO WHOSE
John Wesley, 1703-1791, alt.
Based on the German of
Nicolaus L. von Zinzendorf, 1703-60

392

PARKER
L. M.
Horatio Parker, 1894

1 O Lord, to whose all search - ing sight The
2 Wash out its stains, re - fine its dross, Nail
3 If in this dark - some wild I stray, Please
4 When - e'er your steps come in - to view, I'll
1 dark - ness shines as bright as light,
2 my af - fec - tions to the cross;
3 be my light and be my way;
4 hur - ry, Lord, to fol - low you.
1 Search, prove my heart; it longs to be From
2 Re - fine each thought; Let all with - in Be
3 No foes, no e - vils need I fear, No
4 O let your hand sup - port me still, And
1 sin - ful chains and bonds set free!
2 clean, O Lord, and free from sin.
3 harm, while you, my God, are near.
4 lead me to your ho - ly hill.

393

THOU TO WHOM
G. Thring, 1823-1903

COBLENZ
87. 87. 77
Bremen Melody, 1680

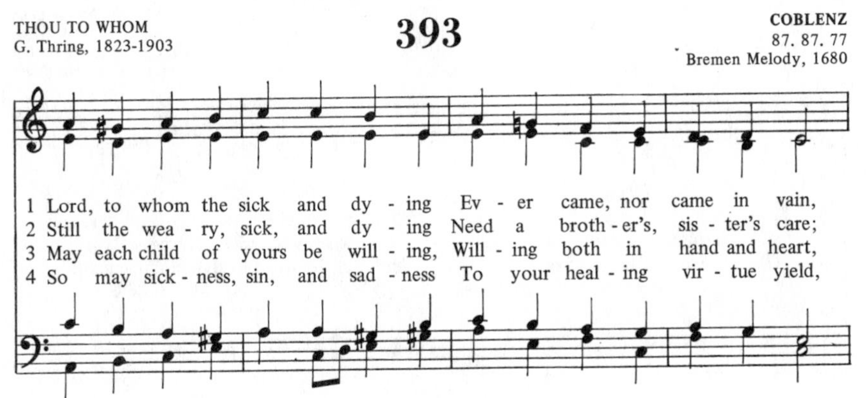
1 Lord, to whom the sick and dy - ing Ev - er came, nor came in vain,
2 Still the wea - ry, sick, and dy - ing Need a broth - er's, sis - ter's care;
3 May each child of yours be will - ing, Will - ing both in hand and heart,
4 So may sick - ness, sin, and sad - ness To your heal - ing vir - tue yield,

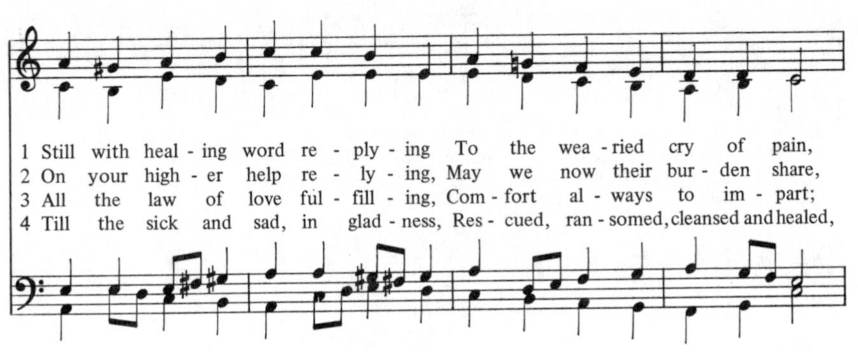
1 Still with heal - ing word re - ply - ing To the wea - ried cry of pain,
2 On your high - er help re - ly - ing, May we now their bur - den share,
3 All the law of love ful - fill - ing, Com - fort al - ways to im - part;
4 Till the sick and sad, in glad - ness, Res - cued, ran - somed, cleansed and healed,

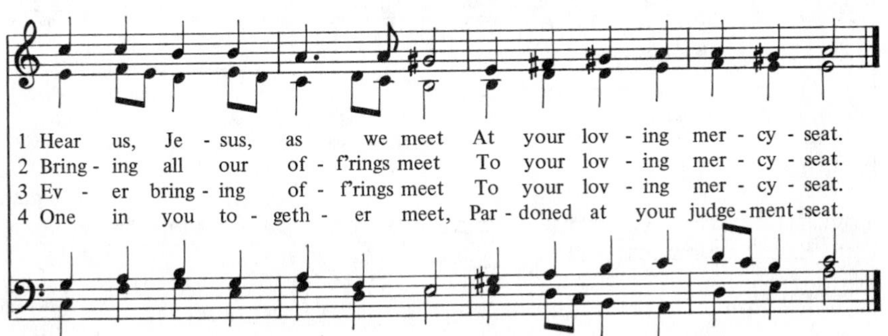
1 Hear us, Je - sus, as we meet At your lov - ing mer - cy - seat.
2 Bring - ing all our of - f'rings meet To your lov - ing mer - cy - seat.
3 Ev - er bring - ing of - f'rings meet To your lov - ing mer - cy - seat.
4 One in you to - geth - er meet, Par - doned at your judge - ment - seat.

394

Greek Office of Anointing
Tr., John Brownlie, 1859-1925

LIGHT OF DAY
66. 66. 88
Traditional Welsh Melody
Harm. by Roger Nachtwey

1 Lord, you have pow'r to heal, And you will quick - ly aid,
2 Send speed - y help, we pray, To him/her who sick now lies,
3 Oh, blind - ed are our eyes, And all are held in night;

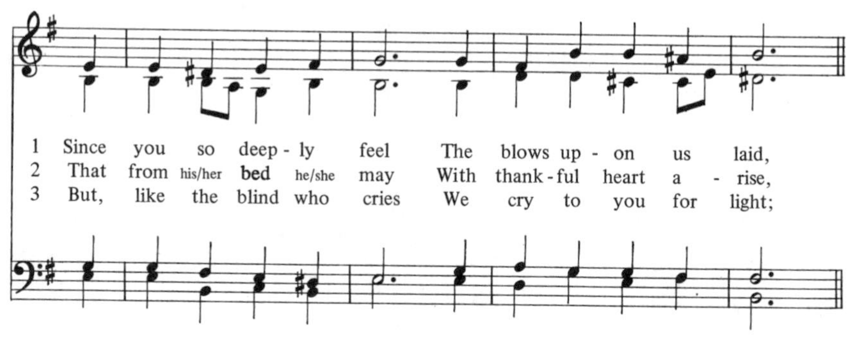
1 Since you so deep - ly feel The blows up - on us laid,
2 That from his/her bed he/she may With thank - ful heart a - rise,
3 But, like the blind who cries We cry to you for light;

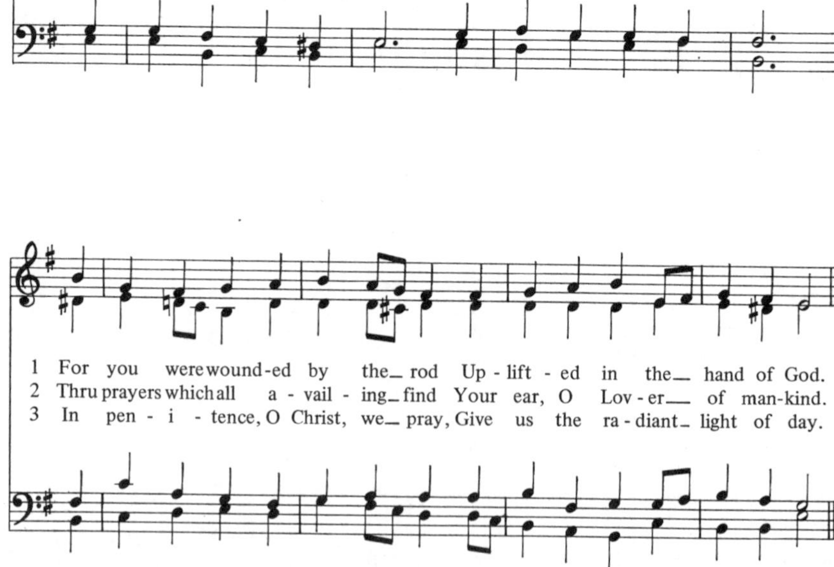
1 For you were wound - ed by the rod Up - lift - ed in the hand of God.
2 Thru prayers which all a - vail - ing find Your ear, O Lov - er of man-kind.
3 In pen - i - tence, O Christ, we pray, Give us the ra - diant light of day.

395

GOD OF THE PROPHETS
Denis Wortman, 1884, alt.

PENITENTIA
10 10. 10 10
Edward Dearle, 1880

1 God of the proph - ets, bless the proph - ets' sons;
2 A - noint them proph - ets! Make their ears at - tent
3 A - noint them priests! Strong in - ter - cess - ors they
4 A - noint them kings! Yes, king - ly kings, O Lord!
1 E - li - jah's man - tle o'er E - li - sha cast:
2 To your most ho - ly speech; their hearts a - wake
3 For par - don and for char - i - ty and peace!
4 A - noint them with the Spir - it of your Son:
1 Each age its sol - emn task may claim but once;
2 To hu - man need; their lips make el - o - quent
3 O that with them, the world, so far a - stray,
4 Theirs not a jew - eled crown, a blood-stained sword;
1 Make each one no - bler, strong - er than the last.
2 For right - eous - ness that shall all e - vil break.
3 Might pass with - in Christ's life of sac - ri - fice!
4 Theirs, by the love of Christ, a king - dom won.

5 Make them apostles, heralds of your cross;
May they go forth to tell all realms your grace:
By you inspired, may they count all but loss,
And stand at last with joy before your face.

LORD OF TRUE LIGHT
Henry R. Moxley, b. 1881

396[1]

Higher Key

ST. WINIFRED
11 10. 11 10
John Bacchus Dykes, 1823-76

1 Lord of true light, we grate - ful - ly a - dore you
2 We praise you, Lord, that now the light is fall - ing
3 Be in his/their mind(s), the truth of all his/their teach - ing;
4 Be in his/their heart(s), the fount of all his/their lov - ing;
5 Be in his/their will(s), his/their strength for self - de - ni - al;

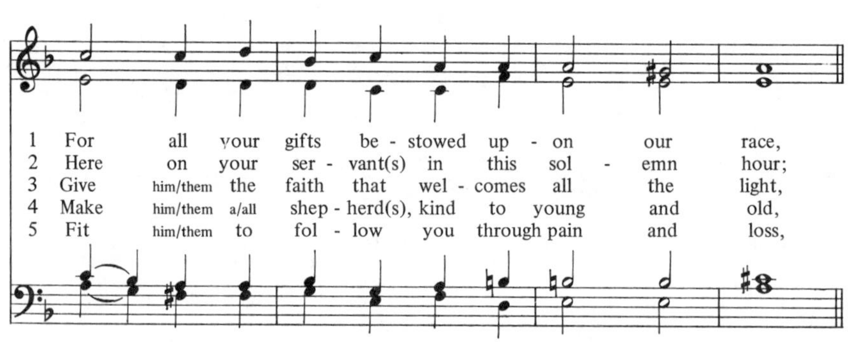
1 For all your gifts be - stowed up - on our race,
2 Here on your ser - vant(s) in this sol - emn hour;
3 Give him/them the faith that wel - comes all the light,
4 Make him/them a/all shep - herd(s), kind to young and old,
5 Fit him/them to fol - low you through pain and loss,

1 For saints of old, who made their vows be - fore you,
2 Strength - en in him/them the high and ho - ly call - ing,
3 Till, from the shad - ows to your pres - ence reach - ing,
4 Pa - tient and watch - ful when your sheep are rov - ing,
5 Serv - ing the world un - til, through ev - 'ry tri - al,

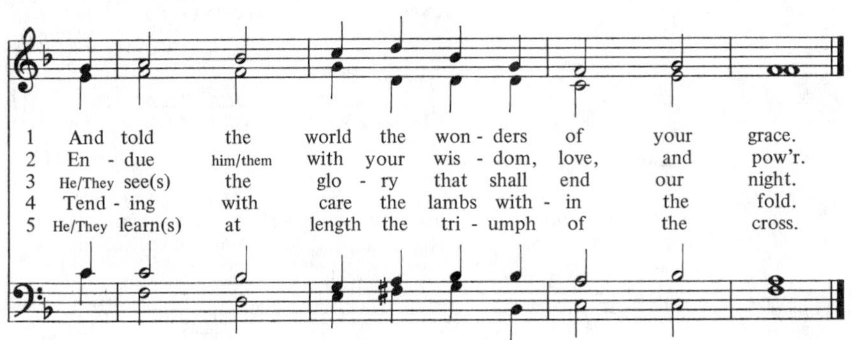
1 And told the world the won - ders of your grace.
2 En - due him/them with your wis - dom, love, and pow'r.
3 He/They see(s) the glo - ry that shall end our night.
4 Tend - ing with care the lambs with - in the fold.
5 He/They learn(s) at length the tri - umph of the cross.

396[2]

Lower Key

LORD OF THE CHURCH
Sts. 1&2, Edward Osler, 1793-1863, alt.
St. 3, Charles Wesley, 1707-88, alt.
397
ALLGÜTIGER
MEIN PREISGESANG (ERFURT)
886. 886
Georg Peter Weimar, 1734-1800
1. Lord of the Church, we hum - bly pray For those who guide us in your way And speak your ho - ly word. With love di - vine their hearts in - spire, And touch their lips with holy fire; Your grace in them be stirred.
2. Their ser - vice bring a ho - ly flood, Re - demp - tion through the Sav - ior's blood. And may they nev - er cease To bring to us the ho - ly Bread And liv - ing Word of Christ, our Head, His life and love and peace.
3. So may they live for you a - lone And serve us too, as you have shown, And take their crown a - bove; And, en - ter - ing their Mas - ter's bliss, En - joy the world that fol - lows this, And live with you in love.

398

LORD OF THE LIVING HARVEST
John S. B. Monsell, 1811-75

Higher Key at No. 472

AURELIA
76. 76. D.
Samuel Sebastian Wesley, 1864

1 Lord of the liv - ing har - vest That whit - ens o'er the plain,
2 As lab - 'rers in your vine - yard, Lord, send them out a - new,
3 Be with them, God the Fa - ther; Be with them, God the Son;
1 Where an - gels soon shall gath - er Their sheaves of gold - en grain,
2 Con - tent to bear the bur - den Of wear - y days for you;
3 And God the Ho - ly Spir - it; Most bless - ed Three in One!
1 Ac - cept these hands to la - bor, These hearts to trust and love;
2 To ask no oth - er wa - ges, When you shall call them home,
3 Make them a roy - al priest - hood You right - ly to a - dore,
1 Be pleased through them to has - ten Your king - dom from a - bove.
2 But to have shared the bur - den Which makes your king - dom come.
3 And fill them with your ful - ness Both now and ev - er - more.

399

O FATHER, ALL CREATING
John Ellerton, 1876

EDEN
76. 76. D.
Sacred Hymns and Tunes, Boston, 1880
Harm. by Roger Nachtwey

1 O Fa - ther, all cre - at - ing, Whose wis - dom, love, and pow'r
2 O Je - sus, who at Ca - na Did as a guest ap - pear,
3 O Spir - it of the Fa - ther, Breathe on them from a - bove,
4 Un - less you build it, Fa - ther, The house is built in vain;
1 First bound two lives to geth - er In E - den's pri - mal hour,
2 Grant these who kneel be - fore you Your gra - cious pres - ence here;
3 So might - y in your pure - ness, So ten - der in your love,
4 Un - less you bless it, Sav - ior, The joy will turn to pain.
1 To - day to these your chil - dren Your ear - liest gifts re - new—
2 Their store of earth - ly glad - ness Trans-form to heav'n - ly wine,
3 That, guard - ed by your pres - ence, From sin and strife set free,
4 But what can break the mar - riage Of hearts in you made one?
1 A home by you made hap - py, A love by you kept true.
2 And teach them, in the test - ing, To see the sa - cred sign.
3 Their hearts and lives be guid - ed Un - til your face they see.
4 The love the Spir - it bless - es Is end - less love be - gun.

Alternative Tune: "AURELIA", No. 472

THE VOICE THAT BREATHED
John Keble, 1857, alt.

400

Higher Key at No. 352

ALL HALLOWS
76. 76. D.
George C. Martin, 1892

1 The voice that breathed o'er E - den That ear - li - est wed - ding day,
2 Be pre - sent, lov - ing Fa - ther, To give a - way this bride
3 Be pre - sent, Ho - ly Spir - it, To bless them as they kneel,
4 To cast their lot be - fore you In hum - ble sac - ri - fice,
1 The pri - mal mar - riage bless - ing— It has not passed a - way.
2 As you gave Eve to Ad - am, A help - mate at his side.
3 Just as for Christ, the Bride - groom, The heav'n - ly Spouse you seal.
4 Till to the home of glad - ness With Christ's own Bride they rise.
1 Still in the pure es - pou - sal Of Chris - tian man and maid
2 Be pre - sent, Son of Mar - y, To join their lov - ing hands
3 O spread your wings a - bove them, Let no ill pow'r find place
4 To Fa - ther, Son, and Spir - it, E - ter - nal One and Three,
1 The Tri - une God is with us, The three - fold grace is said.
2 As you have joined two na - tures In your e - ter - nal bands.
3 When on - ward to your al - tar Their ho - ly path they trace,
4 As was and is for - ev - er, All praise and glo - ry be.
3
3

O PERFECT LOVE
Dorothy F. Gurney, 1883, alt.
401[1]
Higher Key
PERFECT LOVE (SANDRINGHAM)
11 10. 11 10
Joseph Barnby, 1889
1 O per - fect Love, all hu - man thought tran - scend - ing,
2 O per - fect Life, be their one, full as - sur - ance
3 Grant them the joy which bright-ens earth - ly sor - row;
1 Low - ly we kneel in prayer be - fore your throne,
2 Of ten - der char - i - ty and stead - fast faith,
3 Grant them the peace which calms all earth - ly strife,
1 That theirs may be the love that knows no end - ing,
2 Of pa - tient hope, and qui - et, brave en - dur - ance,
3 And to life's day the glo - rious un - known mor - row
1 Whom now for - ev - er - more you join in one.
2 With child - like trust that fears not pain nor death.
3 That dawns up - on e - ter - nal love and life.

401²
Lower Key
MAY THE GRACE
John Newton, 1779, alt.
402
GOTT WILL'S MACHEN
87. 87
Johann Ludwig Steiner, 1735, alt.
1 May the grace of Christ our Sav - ior, And the Fa - ther's bound-less love,
2 Thus may they a - bide in un - ion, Prais - ing Christ, their Lord there - by,
1 With the Ho - ly_ Spir - it's fa - vor_ Rest_ up - on them from a - bove.
2 And pos - sess, in_ sweet com-mun - ion,_ Joys_ the earth can - not sup - ply.

LORD JESU, WHO
Hardwicke Drummond Rawnsley, 1850-1920

403

Higher Key at No. 342

MANNA
886. 886
J. G. Schlicht, 1753-1823

1 Lord Je - sus, who at Laz - 'rus' tomb To weep - ing friends from
2 May we be - hold a - cross the bar The dear im - mor - tals
3 Not fet - tered now by flesh - ly bond, But tire - less in the
4 O Ho - ly Spir - it, strength and guide Of those who to this
1 death's dark womb Brought forth_ new joy to life,
2 as they are, Em - pow'red in act and will,
3 great be - yond, And grow - ing day by day.
4 earth have died, But live_ more near to God,
1 Grant to the friends who stand for - lorn A vis - ion of that
2 With pur - er eyes to see their King, With full - er hearts his
3 Can we not make their glad - ness ours, And share their thoughts, their
4 Give us your grace to fol - low on Till we with them the
1 larg - er morn Where peace_ has con - quered strife.
2 praise to sing With strength to help us still.
3 add - ed pow'rs, And fol - low as we pray?
4 crown have won Who du - ty's paths have trod.

Alternative Tune: ALLGUTIGER, MEIN PREISGESANG, No. 397.

DE PROFUNDIS EXCLAMANTES
Anonymous, 13th cent.
Tr., Richard Frederick Littledale
404
Stanzas 2 & 3 at Mass only
Higher Key at No. 354
SAINT THOMAS
87. 87. 87
J. F. Wade's Cantus Diversi, 1751
1 Christ, en-throned in high - est heav - en, Hear us cry - ing from the deep
2 King of Glo - ry, hear our voic - es: Grant your faith-ful rest, we pray;
3 That which you your - self have of - fered To your Fa - ther, of - fer we;
4 They are yours, O take them quick - ly; Lord, their Hope, O raise them high;
1 For the faith - ful ones de - part - ed, For the souls of all that sleep;
2 We have sinned, and may not stand it If you mark our steps a - stray;
3 Let it win for them a bless - ing; Bless them, Je - sus, set them free:
4 Ev - er hop - ing, ev - er trust - ing, Un - to you they strive and cry;
1 As your lov - ing Church en - treats you, Lis - ten, Shep-herd of the sheep.
2 Yet we plead that sav - ing Vic - tim, Which for them we bring to - day.
3 They are yours, they wait in pa - tience; Mer - ci - ful and gra - cious be.
4 Day and night, both morn and eve - ning, Be, O Christ, their guard - ian nigh.

5 Let your gracious loving-kindness,
As we pray, on them be poured;
Let them through your boundless mercy
From all evil be restored;
Listen to the gentle pleading
Of your Mother, gracious Lord.

6 When, O kind and radiant Jesus,
Kneels the Queen your throne before,
Let the court of saints attending
Mercy for the dead implore;
Listen, loving Friend of sinners,
Whom the cross exalted bore.

7 Hear and answer prayers so humble;
Break, O Lord, each binding chain,
Dash the gates of death asunder,
Crush the devil and his train;
Bring the souls which you have ransomed
Evermore in joy to reign.

Alternative Tune: PICARDY, No. 360

YESU BIN MARIAMU
Swahili Author Unknown
Tr., Edmund S. Palmer, pub. 1906, alt.

405

Stanza 1 at Mass only

ADORO TE DEVOTE
65. 65. 65
Paris Processional, 1695

1 Je - sus, Son of Mar - y, Source of life a - lone, Here we know you
2 Look, O Lord, in mer - cy On the souls of those Who, in faith gone
3 Of - ten were they wound - ed In this earth - ly strife; Heal them, good Phy -
4 Rest e - ter - nal grant_ them, Af - ter wea - ry fight; Shed on them the
1 pres - ent On your al - tar throne. Hum - bly we_ a - dore_ you,
2 from_ us, Now in death re - pose. Here 'mid stress_ and con - flict
3 si - cian; Give them end - less life. Ev - 'ry taint_ of e - vil,
4 ra - diance Of your heav - 'ly light. Lead them on - ward, up - ward,
1 Lord of end - less might, In the mys - tic sym - bols Veiled from earth - ly sight.
2 Toils can nev - er cease; There the war is end - ed; May they rest in peace.
3 Frail - ty and de - cay, Good and gra - cious Sav - ior, Cleanse and purge a - way.
4 To the ho - ly place, Where your saints, made per - fect, Gaze up - on your face.

GOD OF THE LIVING
John Ellerton, 1858, alt.
406
MELITA
88. 88. 88
John B. Dykes, 1861
1 God of the liv - ing, in whose eyes Un - veiled your whole cre -
2 Re - leased from earth - ly toil and strife, With you is hid - den
3 Your word is true, your will is just; To you we leave them,
4 O Breath - er in - to man of breath, O Hold - er of the
1 a - tion lies, All souls are yours; we must not say That
2 still their life; Yours are their thoughts, their works, their pow'rs, All
3 Lord, in trust, And bless you for the love which gave Your
4 keys of death, O Giv - er of the life with - in, Save
1 those are dead who pass a - way; From this our world of
2 yours, and yet most tru - ly ours, For well we know, where -
3 Son to fill a hu - man grave, That none might fear that
4 us from death, the death of sin, That bod - y, soul, and
1 flesh set free, We know they live e - ter - nal - ly.
2 'er they be, Our dead now live e - ter - nal - ly.
3 world to see Where all now live e - ter - nal - ly.
4 spir - it be A - live with you e - ter - nal - ly.

Alternative Tune: ST. CATHERINE, No. 474.

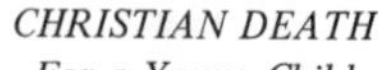

CHRISTIAN DEATH

For a Young Child

IN PARADISE REPOSING
Richard Frederick Littledale, 1833-90

407[1]

Higher Key

CHRISTUS, DER IST MEIN LEBEN
76. 76
Melchior Vulpius, 1609

1 In Par - a - dise re - pos - ing, By life's e - ter - nal well,
2 There palms and ti - ny crown - lets, A - glow with bright - est gem,
3 With them the rose - wreathed ar - my Of chil - dren un - de - filed,
4 With them in peace un - end - ing, With them in joy - ous mirth,
7 O Je - sus, lov - ing Shep - herd, Your lambs you gent - ly bear

1 The ten - der lambs of Je - sus In green - est pas - tures dwell.
2 Be - deck the ba - by mar - tyrs Who died in Beth - le - hem.
3 Who passed through mor - tal tor - ments For love of Christ the Child;
4 Are all the stain - less in - fants Who since have gone from earth.
7 To you bright throne in heav - en; Bring us to join them there.

5 The angels, once their guardians,
Their fellows now in grace,
With them, in love adoring,
See God the Father's face.

6 The lullaby to hush them
In that eternal rest
Is sweet angelic singing,
Their nurse God's Mother blest.

407[2]

Lower Key

408

O LORD, TO WHOM
Richard Frederick Littledale, 1864

ST. CHRYSOSTOM
88. 88. 88
Joseph Barnby, 1871

1 O Lord, to whom the spir - its live Of all the faith - ful
2 Lord, bless the dead who die in you; As you have giv - en
3 In your green, pleas - ant pas - tures feed The sheep that you have
4 Di - rect us with your arm of might, Bring us, per - fect - ed
1 passed a - way, Un - to their path that bright - ness give Which
2 them re - lease, En - liv - en them, since they were true, And
3 sum - moned hence; And by the still, cool wa - ters lead Your
4 then, with them To dwell with - in your ci - ty bright, The
1 leads them to the per - fect day. O Lamb of God, Re -
2 give them ev - er - last - ing peace. O Lamb of God, Re -
3 flock in lov - ing pro - vi - dence. O Lamb of God, Re -
4 heav - en - ly Je - ru - sa - lem. O Lamb of God, Re -
1 deem - er blest, Grant them e - ter - nal light and rest.
2 deem - er blest, Grant them e - ter - nal light and rest.
3 deem - er blest, Grant them e - ter - nal light and rest.
4 deem - er blest, Grant them e - ter - nal light and rest.

Alternative Tune: MELITA, No. 508.

HOLY, HOLY, HOLY
Reginald Heber, 1826
409[1]
Higher Key
NICAEA
11 12. 12 10
John B. Dykes, 1861
1 Ho - ly, ho - ly, ho - ly! Lord God Al - might - y! Early in the morn - ing our song shall rise to thee; Ho - ly, ho - ly, ho - ly! Mer - ci - ful and might - y!
2 Ho - ly, ho - ly, ho - ly! all the a - dore thee, Cast - ing down their gold - en crowns a - round the glass - y sea; Cher - u - bim and ser - a - phim fall - ing down be - fore thee,
3 Ho - ly, ho - ly, ho - ly! though the dark - hide thee, Though the eye of sin - ful man thy glo - ry may not see, On - ly thou art ho - ly; there is none be - side thee,
4 Ho - ly, ho - ly, ho - ly! Lord God Al - might - y! All thy works shall praise thy name, in earth and sky and sea; Ho - ly, ho - ly, ho - ly! Mer - ci - ful and might - y!

1 God in three Per - sons, bless - ed Trin - i - ty!
2 Who wert, and art, and ev - er - more shalt be.
3 Per - fect in pow'r, in love, and pu - ri - ty.
4 God in three Per - sons, bless - ed Trin - i - ty!

409²

Lower Key

410

GOTT VATER, SEI GEPRIESEN
Anonymous
Tr., John Rothensteiner, d. 1936, alt.

MAINZ MELODY
76. 76, with Refrain

1 O God, al - might - y Fa - ther, Cre - a - tor of all things, The
2 O Je - sus, Word In - car - nate, Re - deem-er most a - dored, All
3 O God, the Ho - ly Spir - it, You live_with - in our soul; Send
1 heav - ens stand in won - der, While earth_ your glo - ry sings
2 glo - ry, praise and hon - or Be yours,_O sov - 'reign Lord.
3 forth your light and lead us To our__e - ter - nal goal.
Refrain
O most ho - ly Trin - i - ty, Un - di - vid - ed__ U - ni - ty,
Ho - ly God, might - y God, God im - mor - tal, be a - dored!

COME, THOU ALMIGHTY KING
Anonymous tract, 1757, alt.

411

Lower Key at No. 525

MOSCOW (ITALIAN HYMN)
664. 6664
Felice De Giardini, 1769, alt.

1 Come to us, might - y King, Help us your name to sing, Help us to praise: Fa - ther; all glo - ri - ous, O'er all vic - to - ri - ous, Come, and reign o - ver us, An - cient of Days.
2 Come now, In - car - nate Word, Gird on your might - y sword, Our prayer at - tend: Come, and your peo - ple bless, And give your word suc - cess; Spir - it of ho - li - ness, On us de - scend.
3 Come, Ho - ly Com - fort - er, Your sa - cred wit - ness bear In this glad hour: To all your grace im - part, Now rule in ev - 'ry heart, And nev - er from us part, Spir - it of pow'r.
4 To the great One in Three The high - est prais - es be For - ev - er - more! His sov - 'reign maj - es - ty May we in glo - ry see, And to e - ter - ni - ty Love and a - dore.

THOU, WHOSE ALMIGHTY WORD
John Marriott, 1813, alt.
412
OLIVET
664. 6664
Lowell Mason, 1833
1 God, whose al - might - y word Cha - os and dark - ness heard And took their flight; Hear us, we hum - bly pray, And, where the Gos - pel day Sheds not its glo - rious ray, Let there be light!
2 Sa - vior, who came to bring On your re - deem - ing wing Heal - ing and sight, Health to the sick of mind, Sight to the in - ward blind, O now to all man - kind Let there be light!
3 Spir - it of truth and love, Life - giv - ing ho - ly Dove, Speed forth your flight! Move on the wa - ter's face, Bear - ing your gifts of grace, And in earth's dark - est place Let there be light!
4 Ho - ly and bless - èd Three, Glo - ri - ous Trin - i - ty, Wis - dom, love, might! Bound - less as o - cean's tide Roll - ing in full - est pride, Through the world, far and wide, Let there be light!

BRIGHT THE VISION THAT DELIGHTED
Richard Mant, 1837, alt.
413
Lower Key at No. 302
MOULTRIE
87. 87. D.
Gerald Francis Cobb, 1834-1904
1 Round the Lord in glo - ry seat - ed Cher - u - bim and ser - a - phim
2 Heav'n is still with glo - ry ring - ing; Earth takes up the an - gels' cry:
3 "Lord, your glo - ry fills the heav - en, Earth is with your full-ness stored:
1 Filled his tem - ple and re - peat - ed Each to each the roy - al hymn:
2 "Ho - ly, ho - ly, ho - ly," sing - ing, "Lord of hosts, the Lord most high."
3 Un - to you be glo - ry giv - en, Ho - ly, Ho - ly, Ho - ly Lord."
1 "Lord, your glo - ry fills the heav - en, Earth is with your full - ness stored:
2 With his an - gel hosts be - fore him, With his ho - ly church be - low,
3 Thus your glo - rious name con - fess - ing, With your an - gel hosts we cry,
1 Un - to you be glo - ry giv - en, Ho - ly, ho - ly, ho - ly Lord!"
2 Thus u - nite we to a - dore him, Bid we thus our prais - es flow:
3 "Ho - ly, ho - ly, ho - ly," bless - ing You, the Lord of hosts Most High.

414

Based on "Te Deum Laudamus"
GROSSER GOTT WIR LOBEN DICH
Allgemeines Katholisches Gesangbuch, c. 1774
Tr., Clarence Agustus Walworth, 1853, alt.

TE DEUM
78. 78. 77
Allgemeines Katholisches Gesangbuch, ca. 1774
Alt. in Schicht's Choral-Buch, 1819

1 Ho - ly God, we praise your name; Lord of all, we
2 Hark, the glad ce - les - tial hymn An - gel choirs a -
3 All a - pos - tles join the strain As your sa - cred
4 Ho - ly Fa - ther, Ho - ly Son, Ho - ly Spir - it:
1 bow be - fore you; All on earth your scep - tre claim,
2 bove are rais - ing; Cher - u - bim and ser - a - phim
3 name they hal - low; Pro - phets swell the glad re - frain,
4 Three we name you; While in es - sence on - ly One,
1 All in heav'n a - bove a - dore you. In - fin - ite your
2 In un - ceas - ing cho - rus prais - ing, Cry - ing out with
3 And the bless - èd mar - tyrs fol - low, And from morn to
4 Un - di - vid - ed God we claim you, And a - dor - ing
1 vast do - main, Ev - er - last - ing is your reign!
2 one ac - cord, "Ho - ly, ho - ly, ho - ly Lord!"
3 set of sun Through the church the song goes on.
4 bend the knee While we praise the mys - ter - y. A - men.

O PATER SANCTE, MITIS ATQUE PIE
c. 10th cent.
Tr., A. E. Alston, 1862-1927

415

Lower Key at No. 326

HERR, DEINEN ZORN
11 11. 11 5
Johan Crüger, 1653

1 Fa - ther most ho - ly, mer - ci - ful and lov - ing,
2 Three in a won - drous U - ni - ty un - brok - en,
3 All your cre - a - tion serves its great Cre - a - tor,
4 Lord God Al - might - y, yours be all the glo - ry,
1 Je - sus, Re - deem - er, ev - er to be wor - shipped,
2 One per - fect God - head, love that's nev - er fail - ing,
3 And ev - 'ry crea - ture prais - es with - out ceas - ing;
4 One in three Per - sons, o - ver all ex - alt - ed.
1 Life - giv - ing Spir - it Com - fort - er most
2 Light of the an - gels, Help - er of the
3 We, too, would sing you psalms of true de -
4 Yours, as is fit - ting, be all praise and
1 gra - cious, God ev - er - last - ing.
2 need - y, Hope of all liv - ing.
3 vo - tion: Hear, we im - plore you!
4 bless - ing Now and for - ev - er!
A - men.

DIE PARENTE TEMPORUM
Le Mans Breviary, 1748
Tr., Henry Williams Baker, 1821-77 alt.
416
Lower Key at No. 476
LÜBECK
77. 77
Freylinghausen's
Geistreiches Gesangbuch, 1704
1 On this day, the first of days, God the Father's name we praise, Who, creation's Lord and Spring, Did the world from darkness bring.
2 On this day the loving Son O-ver death his triumph won; On this day the Spirit came With his gifts of living flame.
3 Oh, that fervant love today May in ev-'ry heart have sway, Teaching us to praise aright God, the source of life and light!
4 Father, you created me Image of yourself to be; Fill me with your love divine; May your guiding help be mine.

417

Based on Psalm 117
FROM ALL THAT DWELL
Isaac Watts, 1719, alt.
St. 4, Thomas Ken, 1709

OLD HUNDREDTH
L. M.
Louis Bourgeois, 1551

1 From all that dwell be - low the skies
2 In ev - 'ry land be - gin the song,
3 E - ter - nal are your mer - cies, Lord;
4 Praise God from whom all bless - ings flow;
1 Let praise to the Cre - a - tor rise;
2 To ev - 'ry land the strains be - long;
3 E - ter - nal truth at - tends your word;
4 Praise him, all crea - tures here be - low;
1 Let the Re - deem - er's name be sung Through
2 In cheer - ful sound all voic - es raise And
3 Your praise shall sound from shore to shore, Till
4 Praise him a - bove, O heav'n - ly host; Praise
1 ev - 'ry land, by ev - 'ry tongue.
2 fill the world with joy - ful praise.
3 suns shall rise and set no more.
4 Fa - ther, Son, and Ho - ly Ghost. A - men.

418[1]

Higher Key

יגדל אלהים חי וישתבח
Daniel ben Judah Dayyan, c. 1400
Tr., Sts. 1, 3, 4, Max Landsburg
& Nawton Mann, 1914, alt.
Tr., Sts. 2, 5, Thomas Olivers, c. 1770, alt.

LEONI (YIGDAL)
66. 84. D.
Traditional Hebrew Melody
Transcribed by Meyer Lyon, c. 1770

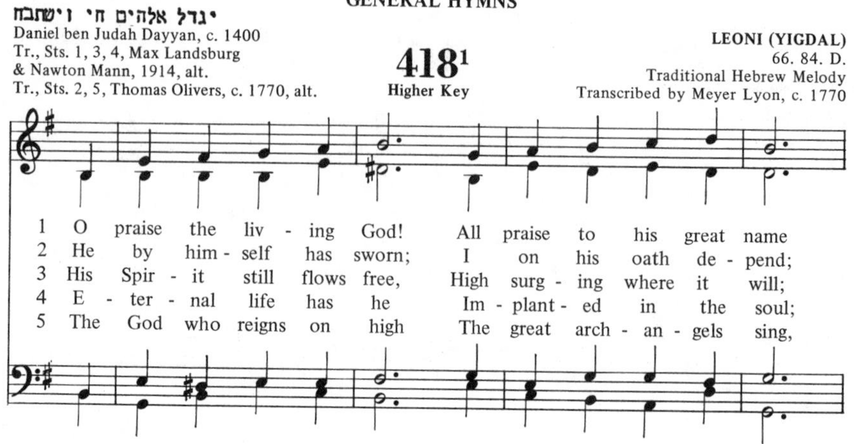
1 O praise the liv - ing God! All praise to his great name
2 He by him - self has sworn; I on his oath de - pend;
3 His Spir - it still flows free, High surg - ing where it will;
4 E - ter - nal life has he Im - plant - ed in the soul;
5 The God who reigns on high The great arch - an - gels sing,

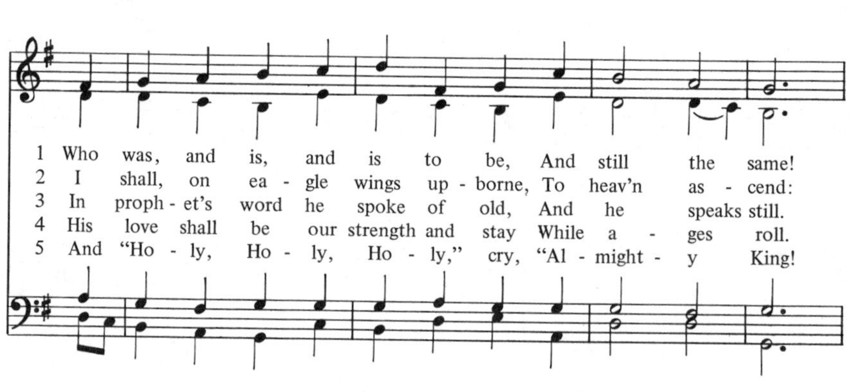
1 Who was, and is, and is to be, And still the same!
2 I shall, on ea - gle wings up - borne, To heav'n as - cend:
3 In proph - et's word he spoke of old, And he speaks still.
4 His love shall be our strength and stay While a - ges roll.
5 And "Ho - ly, Ho - ly, Ho - ly," cry, "Al - might - y King!

1 The one e - ter - nal God be - fore all that ap - pears;
2 I shall be - hold his face, I shall his pow'r a - dore,
3 Es - tab - lished is his law, And change - less shall it stand,
4 O praise the liv - ing God! All praise to his great name
5 Who were, and are, the same, And ev - er - more shall be,

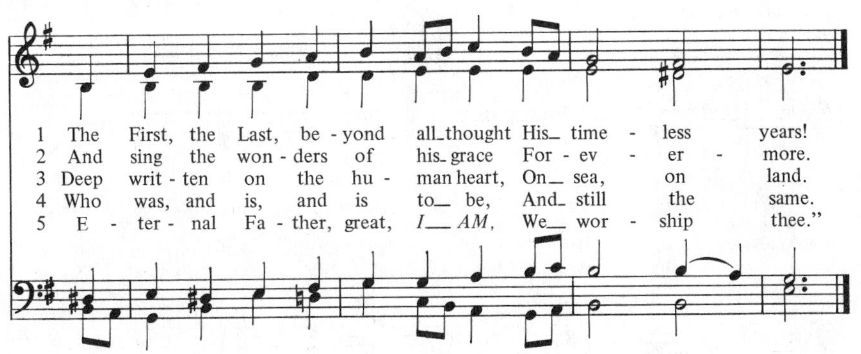
1 The First, the Last, be-yond all thought His time-less years!
2 And sing the won-ders of his grace For-ev-er-more.
3 Deep writ-ten on the hu-man heart, On sea, on land.
4 Who was, and is, and is to be, And still the same.
5 E-ter-nal Fa-ther, great, *I AM,* We wor-ship thee."

418[2]

Lower Key

Based on Psalms 103 & 150
LOBE DEN HERREN
Joachim Neander, 1679
Tr., Catherine Winkworth, 1863, alt.

419

Lower Key at No. 348

PRAISE TO THE LORD
14 14. 478
Straslund Gesangbuch, 1665
The Chorale Book for England, 1863

1 Praise to the Lord, the Al - might - y, the
2 Praise to the Lord, who o'er all things is
3 Praise to the Lord! He shall watch o'er your
4 Praise to the Lord! O let all that is

1 King of cre - a - tion! O my soul,
2 won - drous - ly reign - ing, Shel - t'ring you
3 way and de - fend you; Sure - ly his
4 in me a - dore him! All that have

1 praise him, for he is your health and sal -
2 un - der his wings and so gen - tly sus -
3 good - ness and mer - cy shall ev - er at -
4 life and breath, come now with prais - es be -

1 va - tion! Join the great throng,
2 tain - ing. Have you not seen?
3 tend you! Pon - der a - new
4 fore him! Let the A - men

1 Lift up your voic - es in song,
2 All that is need - ful has been
3 What the Al - might - y can do,
4 Sum all our prais - es a - gain,

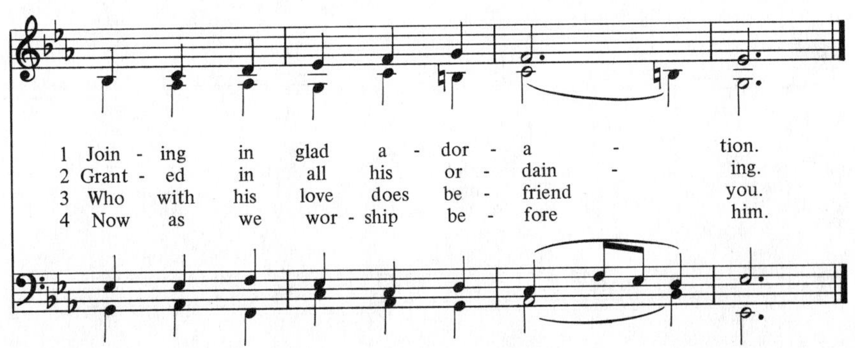
1 Join - ing in glad a - dor - a - tion.
2 Grant - ed in all his or - dain - ing.
3 Who with his love does be - friend you.
4 Now as we wor - ship be - fore him.

Psalm 104
O WORSHIP THE KING
Robert Grant, 1833, alt.
420[1]
Higher Key
HANOVER
10 10. 11 11
William Croft, 1708
1 O wor - ship the King all glo - rious a -
2 O tell of his might! O sing of his
3 The earth with its store of won - ders un -
4 Your boun - ti - ful care, what tongue can re -
1 bove! O grate - ful - ly sing his
2 grace! His robe is the light, his
3 told, Al - might - y, your pow'r has
4 cite? It breathes in the air, it
1 pow'r and his love! Our shield and de -
2 can - o - py space. His char - iots of
3 found - ed of old; Es - tab - lished it
4 shines in the light; It streams from the
1 fend - er, the An - cient of Days,
2 wrath the deep thun - der clouds form,
3 fast by a change - less de - cree,
4 hills, it de - scends to the plain,

1 En - throned in all splen - dor, and clothed with all praise.
2 And dark is his path on the wings of the storm.
3 And round it has cast, like a man - tle, the sea.
4 And sweet - ly dis - tills in the dew and the rain.

5 We children of dust are feeble and frail;
In you do we trust nor find you to fail;
Your mercies how tender, how firm to the end,
Our Maker, Defender, Redeemer and friend!

6 O measure-less Might, ineffable Love,
While angels delight to praise you above,
The humbler creation, tho feeble their lays,
With true adoration shall sing to your praise.

420[2]

Lower Key

Psalm 90:1-5
OUR GOD, OUR HELP
Isaac Watts, 1719, alt.

421

SAINT ANNE
C. M.
William Croft (?), 1708

1 O God, our help in a - ges past, Our hope for years to come, Our shel - ter from the storm - y blast, And our e - ter - nal home:
2 Safe in the shad - ow of your throne Your saints have dwelt se - cure; Suf - fi - cient is your arm a - lone, And our de - fence is sure.
3 Be - fore the hills in or - der stood, Or earth re - ceived her frame, From ev - er - last - ing you are God, To end - less years the same.
4 Your word com - mands our flesh to dust, "Re - turn, O sons of men:" All na - tions rose from earth at first, And turn to earth a - gain.

5 A thousand ages in your sight
Are like an evening gone,
Short as the watch that ends the night
Before the rising sun.

6 The Busy tribes of flesh and blood
With all their lives and cares
Are carried downwards by the flood
And lost in foll'wing years.

7 Time, like an ever-rolling stream,
Bears all its sons away;
They fly, forgotten, as a dream
Dies at the dawn of day.

8 Like flow'ry fields the nations stand
Pleased with the morning light;
The flow'rs beneath the mower's hand
Lie with'ring, come the night.

9 O God, our help in ages past,
Our hope for years to come,
O, be our guide while life shall last,
And our eternal home.

422

Based on Psalm 150
PRAISE THE LORD WITH BLASTS
C. J. Marivoet

LAUDATE DOMINUM
Irregular, with Chorus
Ignace de Sutter
Harm. by Jerry R. Brubaker

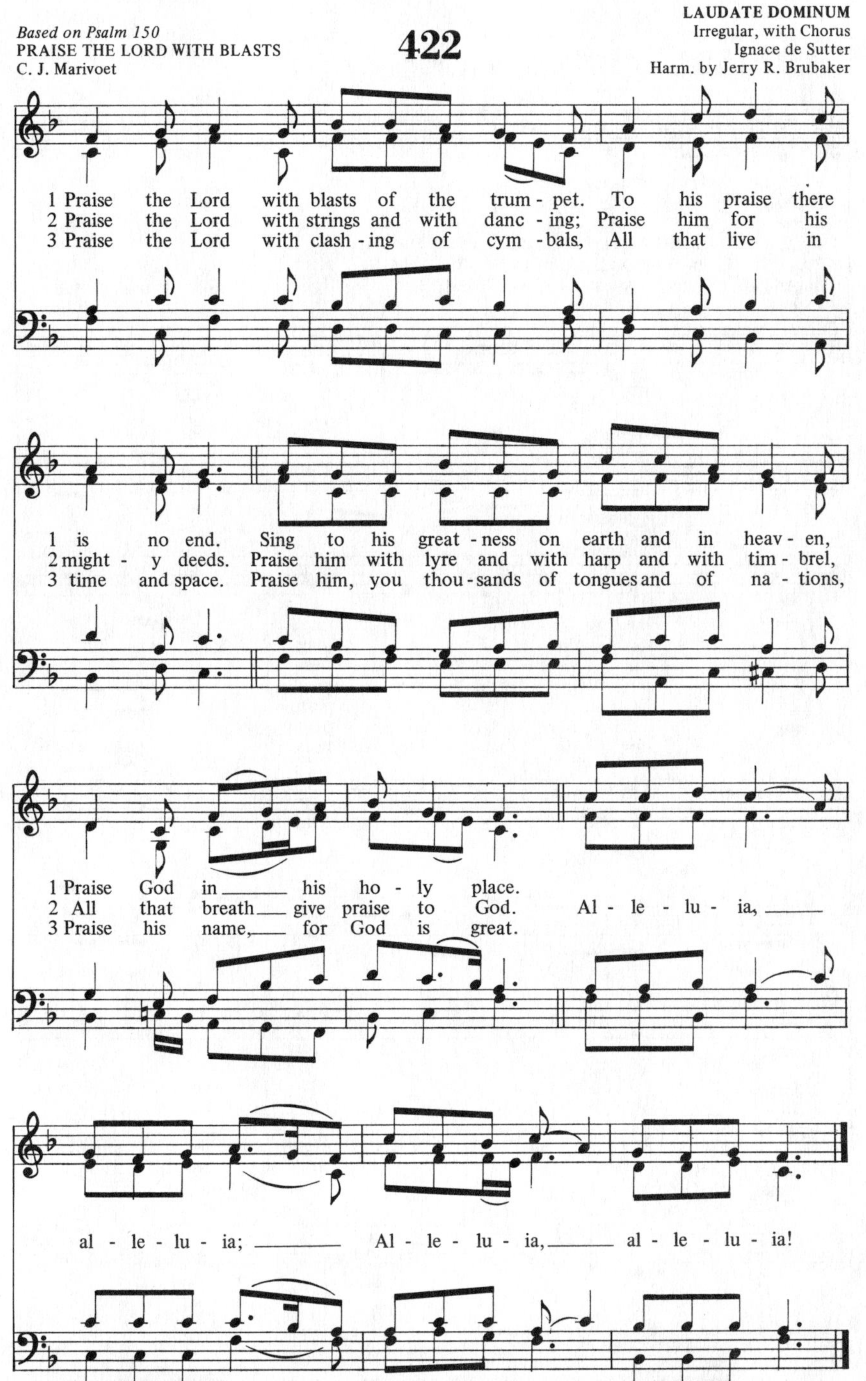
1 Praise the Lord with blasts of the trum - pet. To his praise there
2 Praise the Lord with strings and with danc - ing; Praise him for his
3 Praise the Lord with clash - ing of cym - bals, All that live in
1 is no end. Sing to his great - ness on earth and in heav - en,
2 might - y deeds. Praise him with lyre and with harp and with tim - brel,
3 time and space. Praise him, you thou - sands of tongues and of na - tions,
1 Praise God in his ho - ly place.
2 All that breath give praise to God. Al - le - lu - ia,
3 Praise his name, for God is great.
al - le - lu - ia; Al - le - lu - ia, al - le - lu - ia!

LAUDATO SIA DIO MIO SIGNORE
St. Francis of Assisi, 1225
Tr., William H. Draper, 1855-1933
Adapted by Anthony G. Petti, 1972

423

Higher Key at No. 269

LASST UNS ERFREUEN
L. M. with Alleluias
Ausserlesne Katolische
Geistliche Kirchengesange
Cologne, 1623

1 All cre - tures of our God and king, Lift
2 Great rush - ing winds who are so strong, You
3 Swift flow - ing wa - ter, pure and clear, Make
4 Dear moth - er earth, who day by day Un -
5 You men with mer - cy in your heart, For -
6 And you, most kind and gen - tle death, Wait -
7 Let all things their cre - a - tor bless, And

1 up your voic - es, let us sing: Al - le -
2 clouds a - bove that sail a - long, O ___
3 mu - sic for your Lord to hear, Al - le -
4 fold your bless - ings on our way, O ___
5 giv - ing oth - ers, take your part, O ___
6 ing to hush our fin - al breath, O ___
7 wor - ship him in hum - ble - ness, O ___

1 lu - ia! Al - le - lu - ia! Bright burn - ing sun with gold - en
2 praise him! Al - le - lu - ia! Fair ris - ing morn, with praise re -
3 lu - ia! Al - le - lu - ia! Fire, so in - tense and fierce - ly
4 praise him! Al - le - lu - ia! All flow'rs and fruits that in you
5 sing now: Al - le - lu - ia! All you that pain and sor - row
6 praise him! Al - le - lu - ia! You lead back home the child of
7 praise him! Al - le - lu - ia! Praise God the Fa - ther, praise the

1 beams, Soft sil - ver moon that gen - tly gleams,
2 joice, Stars night - ly shin - ing, find a voice:
3 bright, Who gives to man both warmth and light:
4 grow, Let them his glo - ry al - so show:
5 bear, Praise him, and cast on him your care:
6 God, And Christ our Lord the way has trod:
7 Son, And praise the Spir - it, three in one:
1 O praise him! O praise him! Al - le -
2 O praise him! O praise him! Al - le -
3 O praise him! O praise him! Al - le -
4 O praise him! O praise him! Al - le -
5 O praise him! O praise him! Al - le -
6 O praise him! O praise him! Al - le -
7 O praise him! O praise him! Al - le -
1 lu - ia! Al - le - lu - ia! Al - le - lu - ia!
2 lu - ia! Al - le - lu - ia! Al - le - lu - ia!
3 lu - ia! Al - le - lu - ia! Al - le - lu - ia!
4 lu - ia! Al - le - lu - ia! Al - le - lu - ia!
5 lu - ia! Al - le - lu - ia! Al - le - lu - ia!
6 lu - ia! Al - le - lu - ia! Al - le - lu - ia!
7 lu - ia! Al - le - lu - ia! Al - le - lu - ia!

Based on Psalm 148
PRAISE THE LORD OF HEAVEN
Thomas Brierly Browne, 1850-74, alt..

424[1]
Higher Key

UNE VAINE CRAINTE
65. 65. D.
French Noel

1 Praise the Lord of heav - en; Praise him in the height! Praise him all you an - gels; Praise him, stars and light; Praise him, earth and wa - ters, Praise him, all you skies;
2 Praise the Lord, you foun - tains Of the depths and seas, Rocks and hills and moun - tains, Ce - dars and all trees; Praise him, clouds and va - pors, Snow and hail and fire,
3 Praise him, all you na - tions, Rul - ers and all kings; Praise him, men and maid - ens, All cre - a - ted things. Glo - ri - ous and might - y Is his name a - lone;

1 When his word com-mand - ed, All things did a - rise.
2 Na - ture all ful - fill - ing On - ly his de - sire.
3 All the earth his foot - stool, Heav - en is his throne.

424[2]

Lower Key

Based on Psalm 103
PRAISE, MY SOUL, THE KING
Henry Francis Lyte, 1834, alt.

425[1]
Higher Key

LAUDA, ANIMA (PRAISE, MY SOUL)
87. 87. 87
John Goss, 1869

1 Praise, my soul, the King of heav - en; To his feet your trib - ute bring; Ran - somed, healed, re - stored, for - giv - en, Ev - er - more his prais - es sing: Al - le - lu - ia! Al - le -
2 Praise him for his grace and fa - vor To our fa - thers in dis - tress; Praise him still the same as ev - er, slow to chide, and swift to bless: Al - le - lu - ia! Al - le -
3 Fa - ther - like he tends and spares us; Well our fee - ble frame he knows; In his hands he gen - tly bears us, Res - cues us from all our foes. Al - le - lu - ia! Al - le -
4 Come, then, help us to a - dore him Till we see him face to face; Glad - ly wor - ship we be - fore him, Dwell - ers now in time and space. Al - le - lu - ia! Al - le -

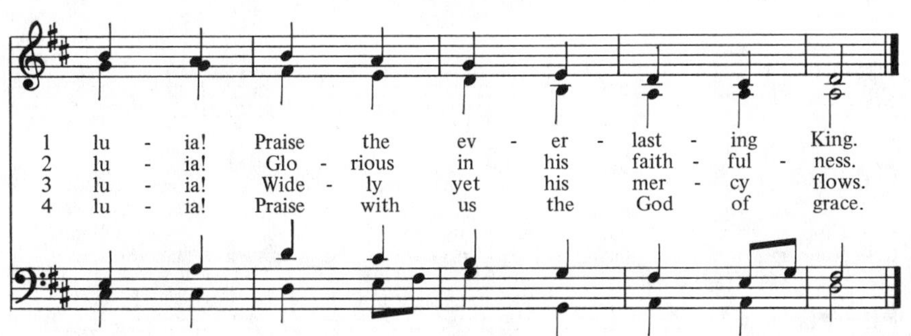
1 lu - ia! Praise the ev - er - last - ing King.
2 lu - ia! Glo - rious in his faith - ful - ness.
3 lu - ia! Wide - ly yet his mer - cy flows.
4 lu - ia! Praise with us the God of grace.

425[2]

Lower Key

426

JOYFUL, JOYFUL, WE ADORE THEE
Henry van Dyke, 1907

HYMN TO JOY
87. 87. D.
Ludwig van Beethoven, 1824
Arr., as hymn tune, 1846

1 Joy - ful, joy - ful, we a - dore thee, God of glo - ry, Lord of love;
2 All thy works with joy sur - round thee, Earth and heav'n re - flect thy rays,
3 Thou art giv - ing and for - giv - ing, Ev - er bless - ing, ev - er blest,
4 Mor - tals, join the hap - py cho - rus Which the morn - ing stars be - gan;
1 Hearts un - fold like flow'rs be - fore thee, O - p'ning to the sun a - bove.
2 Stars and an - gels sing a - round thee, Cen - ter of un - bro - ken praise.
3 Well - spring of the joy of liv - ing, O - cean depth of hap - py rest!
4 Fa - ther love is reign - ing o'er us, Broth - er love binds man to man.
1 Melt the clouds of sin and sad - ness, Drive the dark of doubt a - way; Giv -
2 Field and for - est, vale and moun - tain, Flow - 'ry mead - ow, flash - ing sea, Chant -
3 Thou our Fa - ther, Christ our broth - er, All who live in love are thine; Teach
4 Ev - er sing - ing, march we on - ward, Vic - tors in the midst of strife; Joy -
1 - er of im - mor - tal glad - ness, Fill us with the light of day.
2 - ing bird and flow - ing foun - tain, Call us to re - joice in thee.
3 us how to love each oth - er, Lift us to the joy di - vine.
4 - ful mu - sic leads us sun - ward In the tri - umph song of life.

427

WILT HEDEN NU TREDEN
Anonymous, 1625
Tr., Theodore Baker, 1917, alt.

KREMSER
12 11. 12 11
Netherlands Folk Song, pub. 1625
Arr., Edward Kremser, 1877

1 We gath - er to - geth - er to ask the Lord's bless - ing;
2 Be - side us to guide us, our God with us join - ing,
3 We all do ex - tol you, O lead - er tri - um - phant,
1 He chas - tens and has - tens his will to make known;
2 Or - dain - ing, main - tain - ing his king - dom al - ways;
3 And pray that you still our de - fend - er will be.
1 The wick - ed op - press - ing now cease from dis - tress - ing.
2 So from the be - gin - ning the fight we were win - ning;
3 Let your con - gre - ga - tion es - cape trib - u - la - tion.
1 Sing prais - es to his name; he for - gets not his own.
2 You, Lord, were at our side, to you be all praise.
3 Your name be ev - er praised! O Lord, make us free!

WE PRAISE YOU, O GOD, OUR REDEEMER
Julia Cady Cory, 1902, 1956, alt.

428

ST. CATHERINE'S COURT
12 11. 12 11
R. Strutt, 1848-1927

1 We praise you, O God, our Re - deem - er, Cre - a - tor,
2 We wor - ship you, God of our fa - thers, we bless you;
3 With voic - es u - nit - ed our prais - es we of - fer,
1 In grate - ful de - vo - tion our trib - ute we bring.
2 Through life's storm and tem - pest our guide you have been.
3 And glad - ly our songs of true wor - ship we raise.
1 We lay it be - fore you, we kneel and a - dore you,
2 When per - ils o'er - take us, you will not for - sake us,
3 Our sins now con - fess - ing, we pray for your bless - ing;
1 We bless your ho - ly name, glad prais - es we sing.
2 And with your help, O Lord, life's bat - tles we win.
3 To you, our great Re - deem - er, for - ev - er be praise!

Based on Sirach 50:22-24
NUN DANKET ALLE GOTT
Martin Rinckart, 1636
Tr., Catherine Winkworth, 1858, alt.
429
NUN DANKET
67. 67. 66. 66
Johann Crüger, 1647
Adapted by Felix Mendelssohn, 1840
1 Now thank we all our God With heart and hands and voic - es,
2 O may this gra - cious God Thru all our life be near us,
3 All praise and thanks to God The Fa - ther now be giv - en,
1 Who won-drous things has done, In whom his world re - joic - es;
2 With ev - er - joy - ful hearts And bless - ed peace to cheer us;
3 The Son and Spir - it blest, Who reign in high - est heav - en,
1 Who from our moth-er's arms Has blessed us on our way
2 And keep us in his grace, And guide us when per - plext,
3 E - ter - nal, Tri - une God, Whom earth and heav'n a - dore,
1 With count - less gifts of love, And still is ours to - day.
2 And free us from all ills In this world and the next.
3 For thus it was, is now, And shall be ev - er - more. A-men.

430

ALL THINGS BRIGHT AND BEAUTIFUL
Cecil Frances Alexander, 1848

ROYAL OAK
76. 76, with Refrain
Traditional English Melody
Adapted by Martin Shaw, 1915

Refrain
All things bright and beau - ti - ful, All crea - tures great and_ small,
All things wise and won - der - ful, The Lord God made them all.
1 Each lit - tle flow'r that_ o - pens, Each lit - tle bird_ that sings,
2 The pur - ple head - ed_ moun - tain, The riv - er run - ning by,
3 The cold wind in the_ win - ter, The pleas-ant sum-mer sun,
4 He gave us eyes to_ see them, And lips_ that we_ might tell

1 He made their glow - ing col - ors, He made their ti - ny wings.
2 The sun - set, and the morn - ing That bright - ens up the sky,
3 The ripe fruits in the gar - den, He made them ev - 'ry one.
4 How great is God Al - might - y, Who has made all things well.
Based on 1 Timothy 1:17
IMMORTAL, INVISIBLE, GOD ONLY WISE
Walter Chalmers Smith, 1867
Adapted by Anthony G. Petti, 1971
431
Lower Key at No. 290
ST. DENIO (JOANNA)
11 11. 11 11
Welsh Melody
Adapted, 1839
1 Im - mor - tal, in - vis - i - ble, God on - ly wise, In light in - ac -
2 Un - rest - ing, un - hast - ing, and si - lent as light, Not want - ing or
3 To all things life giv - ing, to great and to small, In all ev - er -
4 Great Fa - ther of glo - ry, pure Fa - ther of Light, Your an - gels a -
1 ces - si - ble, hid from our eyes, Most bless - ed and glo - rious, the
2 wast - ing, you rule in your might, Your jus - tice like moun - tains high
3 liv - ing, the true life of all; We blos - som, then per - ish, as
4 dore you, all veil - ing their sight; All praise we shall ren - der; make
1 An - cient of Days, Al - might - y, vic - to - rious, your great name we praise.
2 soar - ing a - bove, Like tor - rents your foun - tains of good - ness and love.
3 leaves on the tree, But you ev - er flour - ish and al - ways shall be.
4 this your de - cree: That you in your splen - dor we ev - er shall see.

432

SONGS OF PRAISE
James Montgomery, 1819, alt.

Lower Key at No. 489

RILEY
77. 77. D.
Martin Shaw, 1915

1 Songs of praise the an - gels sang, Heav'n with al - le - lu - ias rang,
2 Heav'n and earth must pass a - way; Songs of praise shall crown that day:
3 Saints be - low, with heart and voice, Still in songs of praise re - joice,
1 When cre - a - tion was be - gun, When God spoke and it was done.
2 God will make new heav'ns and earth; Songs of praise shall hail their birth.
3 Learn - ing here, by faith and love, Songs of praise to sing a - bove.
1 Songs of praise a - woke the morn When the Prince of Peace was born;
2 And shall man a - lone be dumb Till that glo - rious king - dom come?
3 Borne up - on their fi - nal breath, Songs of praise shall con - quer death;
1 Songs of praise a - rose when he Cap - tive led cap - tiv - i - ty.
2 No; the Church de - lights to raise Psalms and hymns and songs of praise.
3 Then, a - midst e - ter - nal joy, Songs of praise their pow'rs em - ploy.

MONKLAND
77. 77
Anonymous Melody, Manchester, 1824
arr., John Bernard Wilkes, 1861

433

Based on Psalm 136
LET US WITH A GLADSOME MIND
John Milton, 1623, alt.

Lower Key at No. 313

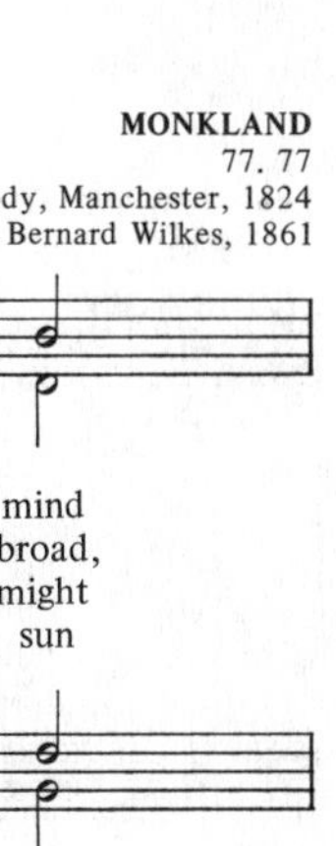

1 Let us with a glad - some— mind
2 Let us sound his name— a - broad,
3 He with all - com - mand - ing— might
4 He the bright and gold - en— sun

1 Praise the Lord, for he is kind:
2 For of gods he is the God:
3 Filled the new - made world with light:
4 Caused all day its course to run:

For his— mer - cies shall en - dure,

Ev - er— faith - ful, ev - er sure.

5 Caused the moon to shine by night
'Mid her sparkling sisters bright:

For his mercies shall endure,
Ever faithful, ever sure.

6 All things living does he feed;
His full hand supplies their need:

For his mercies shall endure,
Ever faithful, ever sure.

7 Let us, then, with gladsome mind
Praise the Lord, for he is kind:

For his mercies shall endure,
Ever faithful, ever sure.

434

Based on Luke 1:46-55
TELL OUT, MY SOUL
T. Dudley-Smith, b. 1926

BIRMINGHAM
10 10. 10 10
Francis Cunningham's
A Selection of Psalm Tunes, 1834

1 Tell out, my soul, the great - ness of the Lord! Un - num - bered bless - ings give my spir - it voice;
2 Tell out, my soul, the great - ness of his name! Make known his might, the deeds his arm has done;
3 Tell out, my soul, the great - ness of his might! Pow'rs and do - min - ions lay their glo - ry by
4 Tell out, my soul, the glo - ries of his word! Firm is his prom - ise, and his mer - cy sure.
1 Ten - der to me the prom - ise of his word; In God my Sav - ior shall my heart re - joice.
2 His mer - cy sure, from age to age the same; His ho - ly name— the Lord, the might - y One.
3 Proud hearts and stub - born wills are put to flight, The hun - gry fed, the hum - ble lift - ed high.
4 Tell out, my soul, the great - ness of the Lord To chil - dren's chil - dren and for - ev - er - more!

435

Based on Psalm 103
O BLESS THE LORD, MY SOUL
James Montgomery, 1819, alt.

Higher Key at No. 209

WILLIAMS (ST. THOMAS)
S. M.
Aaron Williams, 1763

1 O bless the Lord, my_ soul! His_ grace to_
2 O bless the Lord, my_ soul! His_ mer - cies_
3 He will not al - ways_ chide; He_ will with_
4 He par - dons all your_ sins, Pro - longs your_
1 you pro - claim! And all that is with -
2 bear in mind! For - get not all his
3 pa - tience wait; His wrath is ev - er
4 fee - ble breath; He heals all your in -
1 in_ me_ join To bless his_ ho - ly name!
2 ben - e - fits! The Lord to_ you is kind.
3 slow_ to_ rise, And read - y_ to a - bate.
4 firm - i - ties And ran - soms_ you from death.

5 He clothes you with his love.
Upholds you with his truth;
And like the eagle he renews
The vigor of your youth.

6 Then bless his holy name,
Whose grace has made you whole,
Whose loving kindness crowns your days!
O bless the Lord, my soul!

Based on Psalm 95
O COME AND SING UNTO THE LORD
The Psalter, 1912, alt.

436

Lower Key at No. 531

ST. PETER
C. M.
Alexander R. Reinagle, 1836

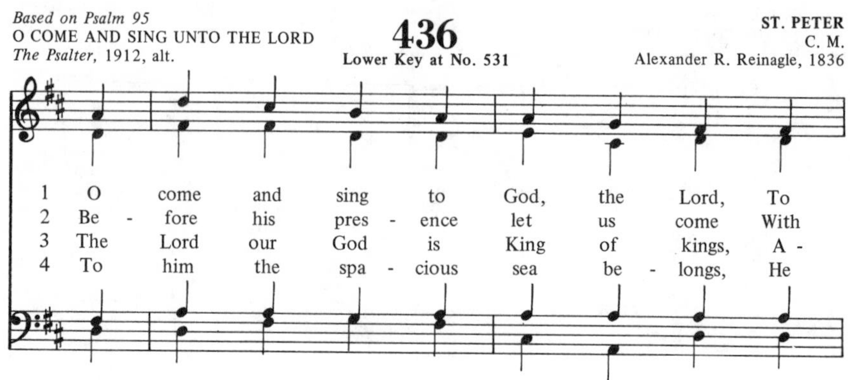
1 O come and sing to God, the Lord, To
2 Be - fore his pres - ence let us come With
3 The Lord our God is King of kings, A -
4 To him the spa - cious sea be - longs, He

1 him our voic - es raise; Let us in our most
2 praise and thank - ful voice; Let us sing joy - ful
3 bove all gods his throne; The depths of earth are
4 made its waves and tides; And by his hand the

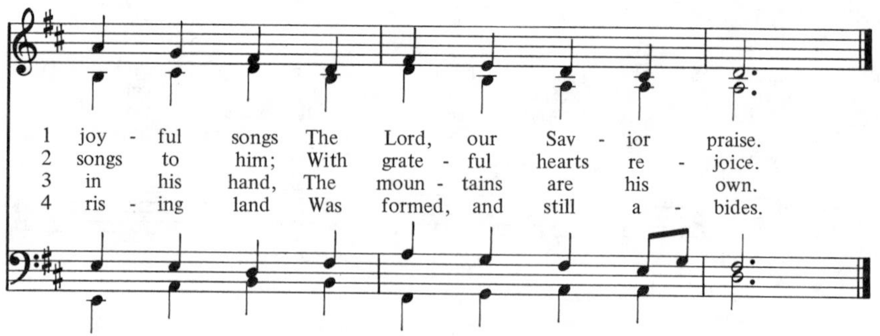
1 joy - ful songs The Lord, our Sav - ior praise.
2 songs to him; With grate - ful hearts re - joice.
3 in his hand, The moun - tains are his own.
4 ris - ing land Was formed, and still a - bides.

5 O come and, bowing down to him,
Our worship let us bring;
O let us praise the gracious Lord,
Our Maker and our King.

437

THERE'S A WIDENESS IN GOD'S MERCY
From "Souls of Men, Why Will Ye Scatter"
Frederick William Faber, 1862

Lower Key at No. 240

BEECHER
87. 87. D.
John Zundel, 1870

1 There's a wide-ness in God's mer-cy Like the wide-ness of the_ sea;
2 There is no place where earth's sor-rows Are more felt than up in_ heav'n;
3 For the love of God is_ broad-er Than the meas-ure of man's mind,
4 There is grace e-nough for_ thou-sands Of new worlds as great as_ this;
1 There's a kind-ness in his_ jus-tice Which is more than lib-er-ty.
2 There is no place where earth's fail-ings Have such kind-ly judge-ment giv'n.
3 And the heart of the e-ter-nal Is most won-der-ful-ly_ kind.
4 There is room for fresh cre-a-tions In that up-per room of_ bliss.
1 There is wel-come for the_ sin-ner And more gra-ces for the_ good;
2 There is plen-ti-ful re-demp-tion In the blood that has been shed;
3 But we make his love too_ nar-row By false lim-its of our_ own;
4 If our love were just more sim-ple, We would take him at his_ word,
1 There is mer-cy with the_ Sav-ior; There is heal-ing in his_ blood.
2 There is joy for all the_ mem-bers In the sor-rows of the_ Head.
3 And we mag-ni-fy his_ strict-ness With a zeal un-like his_ own.
4 And our lives would be all_ sun-shine In the sweet-ness of the_ Lord.

438

GOD MOVES IN A MYSTERIOUS WAY
William Cowper, 1774, alt.

ST. BERNARD
C. M.
Cologne, 1741
arr. by John Richardson, 1851

1 God moves in a mys - ter - ious way His won - ders to per - form:
2 Deep down in rich mys - ter - ious mines, With nev - er - fail - ing skill,
3 O fear - ful souls, fresh cour - age take; The clouds you so much dread
4 Judge not the Lord by fee - ble sense, But trust him for his grace;

1 He plants his foot - steps in the sea, And rides up - on the storm.
2 He treas - ures up his bright de - signs And works his sov - 'reign will.
3 Are big with mer - cy, and shall break In bless - ings on your head.
4 Be - hind a frown - ing pro - vi - dence He hides a smil - ing face.

5 His purposes will ripen fast,
Unfolding ev'ry hour:
The bud may have a bitter taste,
But sweet will be the flow'r.

6 Blind unbelief is sure to err
And scan his work in vain;
God is his own interpreter,
And he will make it plain.

439

Psalm 145
PRAISE GOD, PRAISE GOD
Gary Ault, 1973

PRAISE GOD, PRAISE GOD
Irregular
Gary Ault, 1973
Harm. by Jerry R. Brubaker

C G Am F C G
Praise God, praise God; Let his love re - mind us of the
F G G7 C G Am F
pow - er of his name. Praise God, praise God;

THE PRAISE OF GOD

C
G7
C
Fine
All cre - a - tion sings its song of praise.
G
C
G
C
1. I will praise you, God and King, each and ev - 'ry day.
2. Lord, you're high - ly to be praised; your great - ness o - ver - whelms.
3. The splen - dor of your maj - es - ty is joy - ful - ly re - told;
4. The Lord is kind and mer - ci - ful; his an - ger slow to rise.
E7
Am
F
G7
1. My mouth shall nev - er cease to sing, and I will bless your name for - ev - er.
2. Age on age will praise your works and I will bless your name for - ev - er.
3. The fame of your a - bun - dant good and jus - tice we will sing for - ev - er.
4. The Lord is good to all his works; his gra - cious - ness re - mains for - ev - er.

5 Let the faithful bless you, Lord,
And all your works give thanks.
Let them sing the glory of your kingdom
And your might forever.

6 We will share with all the World
Your splendor and your might;
Your kingdom is a kingdom for
All ages and will last forever.

7 The Lord is faithful in his words
And holy in his works.
He raises up the lowly and
He lifts the falling up forever.

8 Your people look to you in hope;
You give them food in time.
You satisfy the longing of your
People in their need forever.

9 The Lord is just in all his ways
And holy in his works;
To all who call in truth upon him
He will stay with them forever.

10 He hears their cry and makes them safe;
He satisfies their needs.
The wicked he will banish,
But the faithful he will keep forever.

11 May my mouth be quick to speak
The praises of the Lord;
May all flesh be quick to bless
His holy name now and forever.

Based on Psalm 148
PRAISE THE LORD, YE HEAVENS
Sts. 1, 2, anon., c. 1801, alt.
St. 3, Edward Osler, 1836, alt.
440
Higher Key at No. 463
HYFRYDOL
87. 87. D
Rowland Hugh Prichard, c. 1830
1 Praise the Lord, you heav - 'ns a - dore him; Praise him, an - gels
2 Praise the Lord, for he is glo - ri - ous; Nev - er shall his
3 Wor - ship, hon - or, glo - ry, bless - ing, Lord, we of - fer
1 in the height; Sun and moon, re - joice be - fore him,
2 prom - ise fail. God has made his saints vic - to - ri - ous;
3 as our gift. Young and old, your praise ex - press - ing,
1 Praise him, all you stars of light. Praise the Lord, for he has
2 Sin and death shall not pre - vail. Praise the God of our sal -
3 Our glad songs to you we lift. All the saints in heav'n a -
1 spo - ken; Worlds his might - y voice o - beyed; Laws which
2 va - tion! Hosts on high, his pow'r pro - claim; Heav'n and
3 dore you, We would join their glad ac - claim; As your

1 nev - er shall be bro - ken For their guid-ance he has made.
2 earth and all cre - a - tion, Praise and mag - ni - fy his name.
3 an - gels serve be - fore you, So on earth we praise your name.

Based on the Epistle to Diognetus, c. 150
THE GREAT CREATOR OF THE WORLDS
F. Bland Tucker, 1939

441

Higher Key at No. 492

SAINT FULBERT
C. M.
H. J. Gauntlett, 1805-76

1 The great Cre - a - tor of the worlds, The sov - 'reign God of heav'n,
2 He sent no an - gel of his host To bear his might - y word,
3 He sent him not in wrath and pow'r, But grace and peace to bring;
4 He sent him down as send - ing God; As man he came to men;

1 His ho - ly and im - mor - tal truth To men on earth has giv'n.
2 But him thru whom the worlds were made, The ev - er - last - ing Lord.
3 In kind - ness, as a king might send His son, him - self a king.
4 As one with us he dwelt with us, And died and lives a - gain.

5 He came as Savior to his own,
The way of love he trod;
He came to win men by good will,
For force is not of God.

6 Not to oppress, but summon men
Their truest life to find,
In love God sent his Son to save,
Not to condemn mankind.

CORDE NATUS EX PARENTIS
Aurelius Clemens Prudentius, 348-413
Tr., J. M. Neale, 1851, & H. W. Baker, 1859
442[1]
Higher Key
DIVINUM MYSTERIUM
87. 87. 877
Plainsong Melody, 12th cent.
1 Of the Fa - ther's love be - got - ten, Ere the
2 O that birth for - ev - er bless - ed, When the
3 O you heights of heav'n, a - dore him; An - gel
4 Let the old men, let the young men, Let the
5 Christ, to you, with God the Fa - ther, And the
1 worlds be - gan to be, He is Al - pha
2 Vir - gin, full of grace, By the Love of
3 hosts, his prais - es sing; Pow'rs, Do - min - ions,
4 boys in cho - rus sing; Moth - ers, maid - ens,
5 Spir - it, one in three, Hymn and chant and
1 and O - me - ga, He the Source, the
2 God con - ceiv - ing, Bore the Sav - ior
3 bow be - fore him, And ex - tol our
4 and the young girls, With glad voic - es
5 high thanks - giv - ing And un - wea - ried

1 End - ing he, Of the things that are, that
2 of___ our race; And the Babe, the world's Re -
3 God___ and King; Let no tongue on earth be
4 an - swer - ing: Let their guile - less songs re -
5 prais - es be: Hon - or, glo - ry, and do -
1 have___ been, And that fu - ture
2 deem - er, First re - vealed his
3 si - lent, Ev - 'ry voice in
4 ech - o, And the heart its
5 min - ion, And e - ter - nal
1 years shall see, Ev - er - more and ev - er - more!___
2 sa - cred face, Ev - er - more and ev - er - more!___
3 con - cert ring, Ev - er - more and ev - er - more!___
4 mu - sic bring, Ev - er - more and ev - er - more!___
5 vic - to - ry, Ev - er - more and ev - er - more!___

442[2]

Lower Key

443

Lower Key at No. 460

WIE SCHÖN LEUCHTET
Phillip Nicolai, 1599
Tr., Catherine Winkworth, 1863, alt.

WIE SCHÖN LEUCHTET (FRANKFORT)
887. 887. 484. 8
Philip Nicolai, 1599
arr. by J. S. Bach, c. 1730

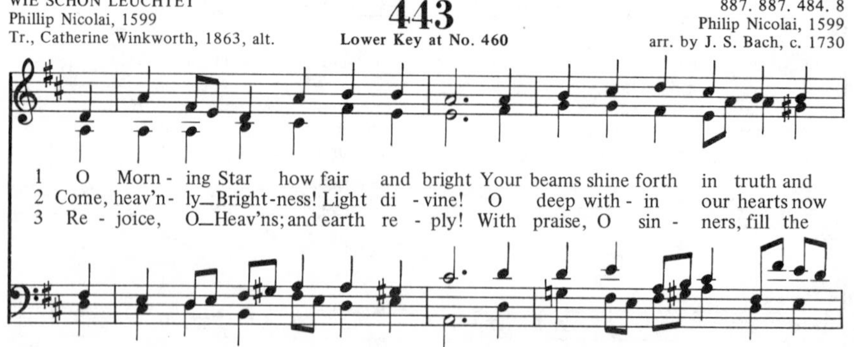
1 O Morn - ing Star how fair and bright Your beams shine forth in truth and
2 Come, heav'n - ly_Bright - ness! Light di - vine! O deep with - in our hearts now
3 Re - joice, O_Heav'ns; and earth re - ply! With praise, O sin - ners, fill the

1 light! O Sov - 'reign meek and low - ly! O Root of_Jes - se, Da - vid's
2 shine, And make you there an al - tar! Fill us with joy and strength to
3 sky, For this, his In - car - na - tion. In - car - nate God, put forth your
1 Son, Our Lord and Mas - ter, you have won Our hearts to serve you
2 be Your mem - bers joined with u - ni - ty In love that can - not
3 pow'r; Ride on, ride on, great Con - quer - or, Till all know your sal -
1 sole - ly! You are ho - ly, Fair and glo - rious, all - vic - to - rious,
2 fal - ter! Toward you long - ing Does pos - sess us; turn and bless us;
3 va - tion. A - men! A - men! Al - le - lu - ia! Al - le - lu - ia!
1 Rich in bless - ing, Rule and might o'er all pos - sess - ing.
2 Here in sad - ness Eye and heart long for your glad - ness!
3 Praise be giv - en Ev - er - more by earth and heav - en.

HERR JESU, LICHT DER HEIDEN
Johann Franck, 1674
Tr., Catherine Winkworth, 1863, alt.
444
DAY OF REST
76. 76. D.
James William Elliott, 1874
1 O Light of Gen - tile_ na - tions, O Sav - ior_ from a - bove,
2 Yes, Lord, your ser vants_ meet you In ev - 'ry_ ho - ly place
3 Let us, O Lord, be_ faith - ful Like Sim - eon_ to the end,
1 Drawn by your Spir - it's_ lead - ing, We come with joy and love
2 Where your true word has_ prom - ised That we should see your face.
3 So that his prayer ex - ul - tant May from our hearts as - cend:
1 To en - ter now your tem - ple And wait with ear - nest mind
2 And still to - day you grant_ us Who gath - er 'round you here
3 "O Lord, now let your ser - vant De - part in peace, I pray,
Unison
Harmony
1 As_ Sim - eon once had wait - ed His God and_Lord to find.
2 In_ arms of faith to bear_ you As did that_ a - gèd seer.
3 Since_ I have seen my Sav - ior And here be - held his day."

HAIL TO THE LORD WHO COMES
John Ellerton, 1880, alt.

445[1]

Higher Key

OLD HUNDRED TWENTIETH
66. 66. 66
T. Est's *Whole Book of Psalmes,* 1592

1 Hail to the Lord who comes, Comes to his tem - ple gate,
2 But borne up - on the throne Of Mar - y's gen - tle breast,
3 There Jo - seph at her side In rev - 'rent won - der stands,
4 O Light of all the earth, Your glo - ry let us see;
1 Not with his an - gel host, Not in his king - ly state;
2 Watched by her ten - der love, In her fond arms at rest;
3 And, filled with ho - ly joy, Old Sim - eon in his hands
4 Come to your tem - ples here, That we, from sin set free,
1 No shouts pro - claim him near, No crowds his com - ing wait;
2 So to his Fa - ther's house He comes, the heav'n-ly guest.
3 Takes up the prom - ised child, The glo - ry of all lands.
4 Be - fore your Fa - ther's face May all pre - sent - ed be.
445[2]
Lower Key

IN HIS TEMPLE NOW BEHOLD HIM
Henry J. Pye, 1851, alt.

446

Higher Key at No. 256

ST, NICHOLAS (ELLIS)
87. 87. 87
W. Ellis, 1868-1947

1 In his tem - ple__ now be - hold_him, See the_ long - ex -
2 In the arms_ of__ her who_ bore_him, Vir - gin_pure, be -
3 Je - sus, by__ your__ pre - sen - ta - tion, Suf - f'ring will - ling
1 pect - ed Lord; An - cient proph-ets__ had fore - told_him;
2 hold him lie, While his a - gèd__ saints a - dore_him—
3 to en - dure, Make us see__ your__ great sal - va - tion,
1 God has now ful - filled his word. Now, to__ praise him,
2 Bless - èd sight be - fore they die. Al - le - lu - ia!
3 Seal us with your prom - ise sure, And pre - sent us
1 his re - deemed ones Shall_ break forth in one ac - cord.
2 Al - le - lu - ia! See__ the__ in - fant God most high!
3 in your_ glo - ry To__ your_Fa - ther, cleansed and pure.

YE SERVANTS OF GOD
Charles Wesley, 1744, alt.
447[1]
Higher Key
LYONS
10 10. 11 11
Arranged 1822
from J. Michael Hayden
1 You servants of God, your Master proclaim,
And publish abroad his wonderful name:
The name, all-victorious, of Jesus extol;
His kingdom is glorious, and rules o'er all.
2 Our God rules on high, almighty to save;
And still he is nigh, his presence we have.
The great congregation his triumph shall sing,
Ascribing salvation to Jesus, our King.
3 Salvation to God, who sits on the throne!
Let all cry aloud and honor the Son.
The praises of Jesus the angels proclaim,
Fall down on their faces and worship the Lamb.
4 Then let us adore, and give him his right,
All glory and pow'r, and wisdom and might,
All honor and blessing, with angels above,
And thanks never ceasing, and infinite love.

447[2]
Lower Key
Based on Philippians 2:9-10
AT THE NAME OF JESUS
Caroline Maria Noel, 1870
448
KING'S WESTON
65. 65. D.
Ralph Vaughan Williams, 1925
1 At the name of Je - sus Ev - 'ry knee shall bow,
2 Hum-bled for a sea - son, To re - ceive a Name
3 Bore it up tri - umph - ant, With its hu - man light,
4 In your hearts en - throne him; There let him sub - due

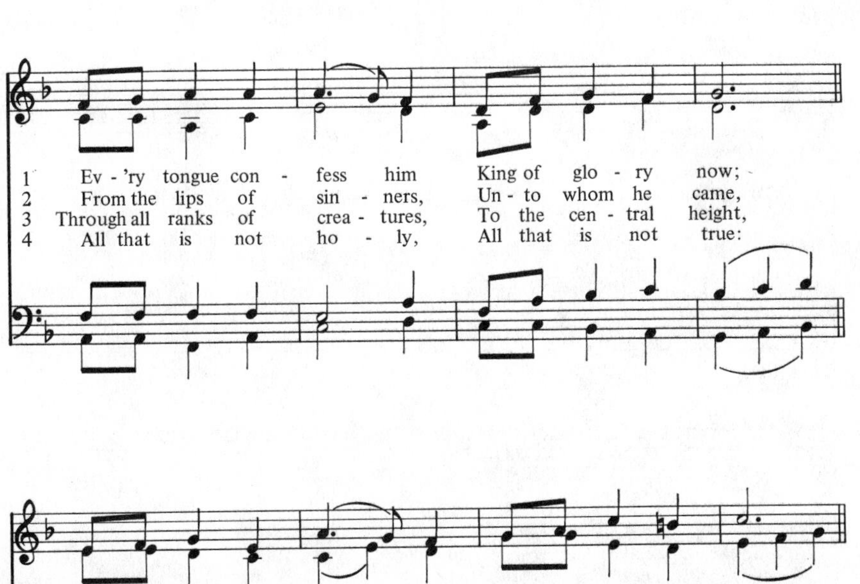
1 Ev - 'ry tongue con - fess him King of glo - ry now;
2 From the lips of sin - ners, Un - to whom he came,
3 Through all ranks of crea - tures, To the cen - tral height,
4 All that is not ho - ly, All that is not true:

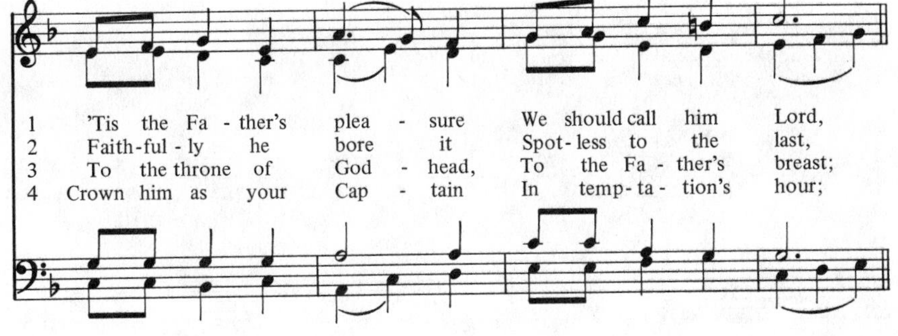
1 'Tis the Fa - ther's plea - sure We should call him Lord,
2 Faith-ful - ly he bore it Spot - less to the last,
3 To the throne of God - head, To the Fa - ther's breast;
4 Crown him as your Cap - tain In temp - ta - tion's hour;

1 Who from the be - gin - ing Was the might - y Word.
2 Brought it back vic - to - rious, When from death he passed;
3 Filled it with the glo - ry Of that per - fect rest.
4 Let his will en - fold you In its light and pow'r.

5 Brothers, this Lord Jesus
Shall return again,
With his Father's glory
O'er the earth to reign;

For all wreaths of empire
Meet upon his brow,
And our hearts confess him
King of glory now.

GLORIOSI SALVATORIS
c. 15th cent.
Tr., J. M. Neale, et al.
449
ORIEL
87. 87. 87
Caspar Ett, 1840
1 To the name of our sal - va - tion Praise and hon - or
2 Je - sus is the name we treas-ure, Name be - yond what
3 Name that who - so - ev - er preach-es Speaks like mu - sic
4 There - fore we in love a - dor - ing The most bless - èd
1 let us pay, Which for ma - ny a gen - er - a - tion
2 words can tell; Name of glad - ness, name of pleas - ure,
3 to the ear; Who in prayer this name be - seech - es
4 name re - vere, Ho - ly Je - sus, you im - plor - ing
1 Hid in God's fore - knowl - edge lay, But with ho - ly
2 Ear and heart de - light - ing well; Name of sweet - ness
3 Finds the sweet - est com - fort near; Who its per - fect
4 So to write it in us here, That here - af - ter
1 ex - ul - ta - tion We may sing a - loud to - day.
2 pass - ing meas-ure, Sav - ing us from sin and hell.
3 wis - dom reach-es Heav'n - ly joy pos - ses - ses here.
4 heav'n - ward soar - ing We may sing with an - gels there.

QUICUMQUE CERTUM QUAERITIS
Anonymous, 18th cent.
Tr., Edward Caswall, 1814-78, alt.
450
Lower Key at No. 491
KINGSFOLD (LAZARUS)
C. M. D.
Traditional English Melody
1 All_ you who seek a com-fort sure In_ sad-ness and_ dis-tress,
2 Now_ hear him as he speaks to us Those words for-ev-er blest:
1 What-ev-er sor-row bur-dens you, What-ev-er griefs op-press:
2 "All_ you who la-bor, come to me, And_ I will give_ you rest."
1 When Je-sus gave_ him-self for men And died up-on the_ tree,
2 O heart a-dored_ by saints on high, And hope of_ sin-ners_ here,
1 His_ heart was pierced for_ love of us; He_ died to set_ us free.
2 We_ place our ev-'ry_ trust in you And_ lift to you_ our prayer.

VIVA! VIVA! GESU!
18th cent.
Tr., Edward Caswall, 1857, alt.

451

WEM IN LEIDENSTAGEN (CASWALL)
65. 65
Friedrich Filitz, 1847

1 Glo - ry be to Je - sus,
2 Grace and life e - ter - nal
3 Blest through end - less a - ges
4 A - bel's blood for ven - geance

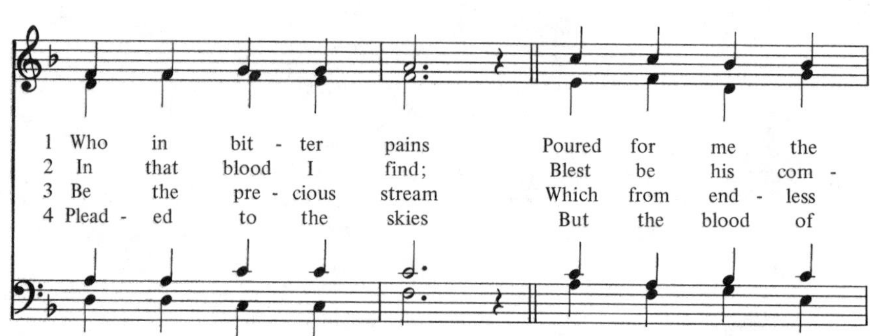
1 Who in bit - ter pains Poured for me the
2 In that blood I find; Blest be his com -
3 Be the pre - cious stream Which from end - less
4 Plead - ed to the skies But the blood of

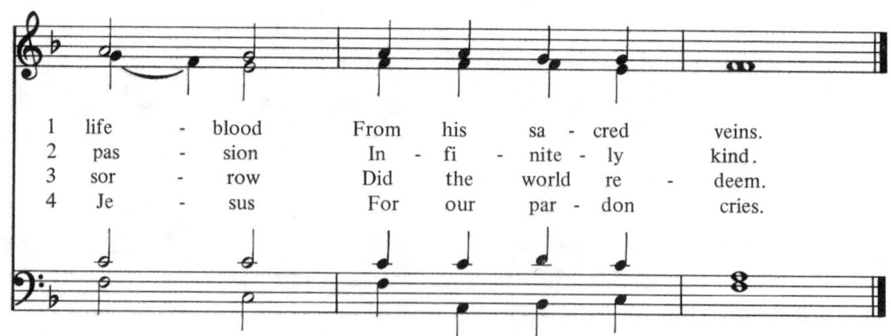
1 life - blood From his sa - cred veins.
2 pas - sion In - fi - nite - ly kind.
3 sor - row Did the world re - deem.
4 Je - sus For our par - don cries.

5 O then lift your voices,
Swell the mighty flood;
Louder still and louder
Praise the precious blood!

TO JESUS CHRIST, OUR SOVEREIGN KING
Martin B. Hellriegel, 1942

452

Lower Key at No. 495

ICH GLAUB AN GOTT
87. 87, with Chorus
Mainz *Gesangbuch*, 1870

1 To Je - sus Christ, our Sov - 'reign King, Who is the world's sal - va - tion, All praise and hom-age do we bring And thanks and ad - o - ra - tion.
2 Your reign ex - tend, O King be - nign, To ev - 'ry land and na - tion; For in your king-dom, Lord di - vine, A - lone we find sal - va - tion.
3 To you and to your Church, great King, We pledge our heart's ob - la - tion; Un - til be - fore your throne we sing In end - less ju - bi - la - tion.
Christ Je - sus, Vic - tor! Christ Je - sus, Rul - er! Christ Je - sus, Lord and Re - deem - er!

ALL HAIL THE POWER OF JESUS' NAME
Edward Perronet, 1779, alt.

453

CORONATION
86. 86. 86
Oliver Holden, 1793

1 All hail the pow'r of Je - sus' Name! Let an - gels pros - trate fall;
2 Hail him, the Heir of Da - vid's line, Whom Da - vid Lord did call,
3 Let ev - 'ry kin - dred, ev - 'ry tribe On this ter - res - trial ball
4 O that with yon - der sa - cred throng We at his feet may fall;
1 Bring forth the roy - al di - a - dem, And crown him Lord of all.
2 The God in - car - nate, Man di - vine, And crown him Lord of all.
3 To him all maj - es - ty as - cribe, And crown him Lord of all.
4 We'll join the ev - er - last - ing song, And crown him Lord of all.
1 Bring forth the roy - al di - a - dem, And crown him Lord of all.
2 The God in - car - nate, Man di - vine, And crown him Lord of all.
3 To him all maj - es - ty as - cribe, And crown him Lord of all.
4 We'll join the ev - er - last - ing song And crown him Lord of all.

5 Crown him, O morning stars of light,
Who fixed this earthly ball;
Now hail the strength of Israel's might,
And crown him Lord of all.
Now hail the strength of Israel's might,
And crown him Lord of all.

6 Crown him, O martyrs of our God
Who from his altar call:
Praise him whose way of pain you trod,
And crown him Lord of all.
Praise him whose way of pain you trod,
And crown him Lord of all.

7 O sinners, who can ne'er forget
The wormwood and the gall,
Go spread your trophies at his feet,
And crown him Lord of all.
Go spread your trophies at his feet
And crown him Lord of all.

8 O seed of Israel's chosen race,
You ransomed of the fall,
Hail him who saves you by his grace
And crown him Lord of all.
Hail him who saves you by his grace,
And crown him Lord of all.

454

THE KING OF GLORY
W.F. Jabusch, pub. 1966

THE KING OF GLORY
Irregular
Traditional Israeli Folk Song
Harm. by Jerry R. Brubaker

Em C Em
The King___ of glo - ry comes, the na - tion___ re - joic - es;
Em C Em
O - pen___ the gates be - fore him, lift up___ your voic - es.
G Em G
1 Who is___ the King of glo - ry; how shall___ we call him?
2 In all___ of Gal - i - lee, in cit - y___ or vil - lage,
3 Sing, then,___ of Da - vid's Son, our Sav - ior___ and broth - er;
4 He gave___ his life for us, the pledge of___ sal - va - tion,
5 He con - quered sin and death; he tru - ly___ has ris - en;
G Em G
1 He is___ Em - man - u - el, the prom - ised___ of a - ges.
2 He goes___ a - mong his peo - ple cur - ing___ their ill - ness.
3 In all___ of Gal - i - lee was nev - er___ an - oth - er.
4 He took___ up - on him - self the sins of___ the na - tion.
5 And he___ will share with us his heav - en - ly vi - sion.

CAELESTIS FORMAM GLORIAE
15th cent.
Tr., John Mason Neale, 1854, alt.

455

Higher Key at No. 353

WAREHAM
L. M.
William Knapp, 1738

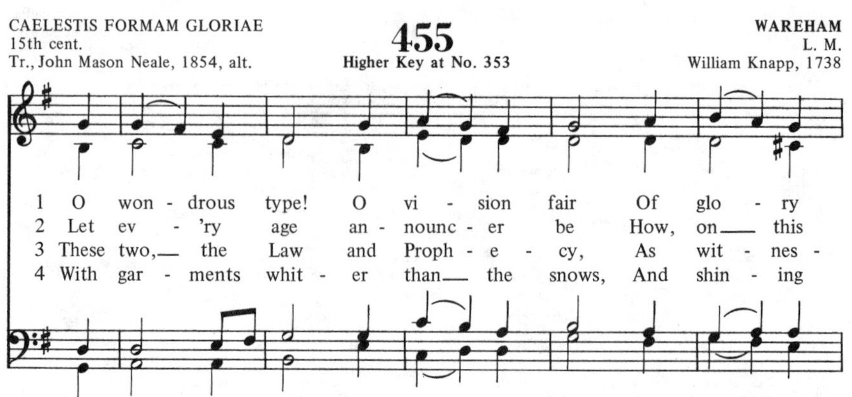
1 O won - drous type! O vi - sion fair Of glo - ry
2 Let ev - 'ry age an - nounc - er be How, on__ this
3 These two,__ the Law and Proph - e - cy, As wit - nes -
4 With gar - ments whit - er than__ the snows, And shin - ing

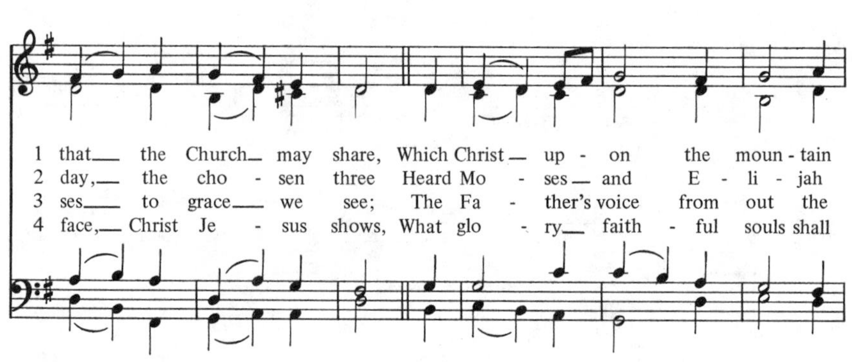
1 that__ the Church__ may share, Which Christ__ up - on the moun - tain
2 day,__ the cho - sen three Heard Mo - ses__ and E - li - jah
3 ses__ to grace__ we see; The Fa - ther's voice from out the
4 face,__ Christ Je - sus shows, What glo - ry__ faith - ful souls shall

1 shows, Where__ bright - er than__ the sun__ he glows!
2 speak With__ Christ__ our Lord,__ the great,__ the meek.
3 cloud Pro - claims__ his on - ly Son__ a - loud.
4 see With__ God__ for all__ e - ter - ni - ty.

5 And faithful souls exultantly
Behold the vision's mystery;
So on this joyful day we raise
The voice of prayer, the hymn of praise.

6 O God the Father, God the Son,
And Holy Spirit, three in one,
Be pleased to bring us by your grace
To see your glory face to face.

456

IT'S GOOD TO BE HERE, LORD
Joseph Armitage Robinson, 1888, alt.

CARLISLE
S. M.
Charles Lockhart, 1769

1 It's good to be here, Lord! Your
2 It's good to be here, Lord, Your
3 Ful - fil - ler of the past! Our
4 Be - fore we taste of death, We
1 glo ry fills the night; Your face and gar - ments,
2 boun - ty to be - hold, Where Mo - ses and E -
3 Pledge of things to be! We hail your bod - y
4 see your king - dom come; We'd love to keep the
1 like the sun Shine with un - bor - rowed light!
2 li - jah stand, Your mes - sen - gers of old.
3 glo - ri - fied And our re - demp - tion see.
4 vi - sion bright And make this hill our home.

5 It's good to be here, Lord,
Yet we may not remain,
But, since we have to leave the mount,
Come with us to the plain.

IN THE CROSS OF CHRIST I GLORY
John Bowring, 1825

457

RATHBUN
87. 87
Ithamar Conkey, 1849

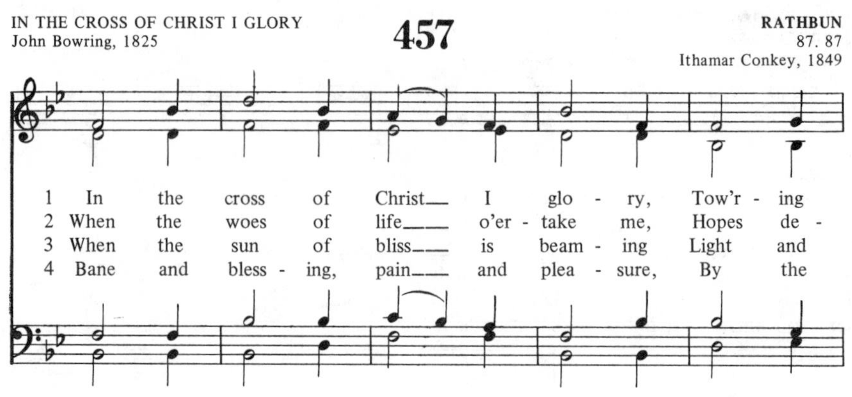
1 In the cross of Christ I glo - ry, Tow'r - ing
2 When the woes of life o'er - take me, Hopes de -
3 When the sun of bliss is beam - ing Light and
4 Bane and bless - ing, pain and plea - sure, By the

1 o'er the wrecks of time; All the light of sa - cred
2 ceive, or foes an - noy, Nev - er shall the cross for -
3 love up - on my way, From the cross the ra - diance
4 cross are sanc - ti - fied; Peace is theirs that knows no

1 sto - ry Gath - ers round its head sub - lime.
2 sake me: See! it glows with peace and joy.
3 stream - ing Adds more lus - ter to the day.
4 mea - sure, Joys that through all time a - bide.

5 In the cross of Christ I glory,
Tow'ring o'er the wrecks of time;
All the light of sacred story
Gathers round its head sublime.

458

WHEN I SURVEY THE WONDROUS CROSS
Isaac Watts, 1707, 1709, alt.

HAMBURG
L. M.
Comp. or Arr. by Lowell Mason, 1825

1 When I be - hold the won - drous cross
2 For - bid it, Lord, that I should boast,
3 See, from his head, his hands, his feet,
4 Were all the realm of na - ture mine,
1 On which the Prince of glo - ry died,
2 Save in the death of Christ, my God.
3 Sor - row and love flow min - gled down.
4 It would be of - f'ring far too small;
1 My rich - est gain I count but loss,
2 All those vain things that charm me most,
3 Did e'er such love and sor - row meet,
4 Love so a - maz - ing, so di - vine,
1 And pour con - tempt on all my pride.
2 I sac - ri - fice them to his blood.
3 Or thorns com - pose so rich a crown?
4 De - mands my soul, my life, my all.

PRAISE TO THE HOLIEST
John Henry Newman, 1865
459[1]
Higher Key
BILLING (NEWMAN)
C. M.
Richard Runciman Terry, 1912
1 Praise to the Ho - liest in the
2 O lov - ing wis - dom of our
3 O wis - est love! that flesh and
4 And that a high - er gift than
1 height, And in the depth be
2 God! When all was sin and
3 blood, Which did in Ad - am
4 grace Should flesh and blood re -
1 praise; In all his
2 shame, A sec - ond
3 fail, Should strive a -
4 fine: God's pres - ence
1 words most won - der - ful, Most
2 A - dam to the fight And
3 fresh a - gainst the foe, Should
4 and his ver - y self, And

1 sure in all his ways!
2 to the res - cue came.
3 strive, and should pre - vail;
4 es - sence all - di - vine.

5 O gen'rous love! that he who smote
In man for man the foe,
The double agony in Man
For man should undergo;

6 And in the garden secretly,
And on the cross on high,
Should teach his brethren, and inspire
To suffer and to die.

7 Praise to the Holiest in the height,
And in the depth be praise;
In all his words most wonderful,
Most sure in all his ways!

459²

Lower Key

460

Based on Eph. 1:3-14; Col. 1:19-20
WITH HEARTS RENEWED
John May, 1964

Higher Key at No. 443

WIE SCHÖN LEUCHTET (FRANKFORT)
887. 887. 484. 8
Philip Nicolai, 1599
arr. by J. S. Bach, c. 1730

1 With hearts re - newed by liv - ing faith, We lift our thoughts in grate - ful
2 So rich God's grace in Je - sus Christ, That we are called as sons of
1 prayer To God our gra - cious Fa - ther, Whose plan it was to make us
2 light To bear the pledge of glo - ry. Through him in whom all full - ness
1 sons Through his own son's re - demp - tive death, That res - cued us from
2 dwells We of - fer God our gift of self In un - ion with the
1 dark - ness.
2 Spir - it.
Lord God, Sav - ior! Give us strength to mold our hearts in

your true like - ness, Sons and serv - ants of our Fa - ther.
TODAY WE CELEBRATE
Sister G. S.
461
TODAY WE CELEBRATE
88, with Alleluias
Traditional Melody
Harm. by Jerry R. Brubaker
1 To - day we cel - e - brate the Lord, Al -
2 He con - quered death and saved us all, Al -
3 He tru - ly rose and lives now on Al -
4 What - e'er I do, wher - e'er I go, Al -
1 le - lu - ia, And sing his praise in one ac - cord, Al -
2 le - lu - ia, A - way with sin and Ad - am's fall, Al -
3 le - lu - ia, The source of joy, e - ter - nal dawn, Al -
4 le - lu - ia, This song keeps ring - ing high and low, Al -
le - lu - ia, al - le - lu - ia, al - le - lu - ia!

5 This is the day of great delight,
Alleluia,
About which David prophesied,
Alleluia, alleluia, alleluia!

CROWN HIM WITH MANY CROWNS
Sts. 1, 2, 3, 5, 6, Matthew Bridges, 1851, alt.
St. 4, Godfrey Thring, 1874

462[1]
Higher Key

DIADEMATA
S. M. D.
George J. Elvey, 1868

1 Crown him with man - y crowns, The Lamb up - on his throne;
2 Crown him the Vir - gin's Son! The God in - car - nate born,
3 Crown him the Lord of love! Be - hold his hands and side;
4 Crown him the Lord of life, Who tri - umphed o'er the grave,

1 Hark! how the heav'n - ly an - them drowns all mu - sic but its own!
2 Whose arm those crim - son tro - phies won Which now his brow a - dorn!
3 Rich wounds, yet vis - i - ble a - bove, In beau - ty glo - ri - fied;
4 And rose vic - to - rious in the strife For those he came to save.

1 I raise my voice and sing Of him who died for me
2 Fruit of the mys - tic Rose As of that Rose the stem:
3 No an - gel in the sky Can ful - ly bear that sight,
4 His glo - ries now we sing Who died and rose on high,

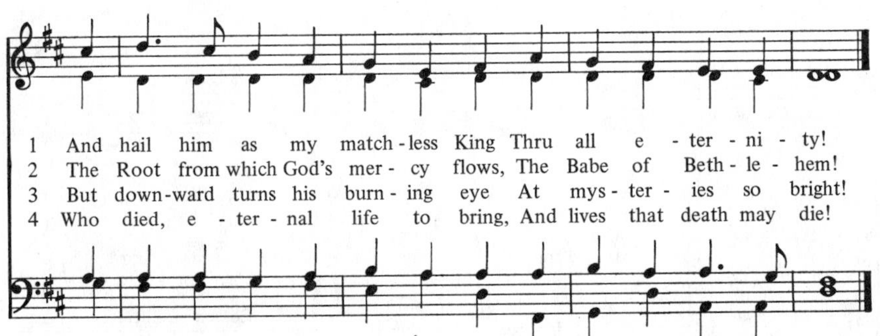
1 And hail him as my match-less King Thru all e - ter - ni - ty!
2 The Root from which God's mer - cy flows, The Babe of Beth - le - hem!
3 But down-ward turns his burn - ing eye At mys - ter - ies so bright!
4 Who died, e - ter - nal life to bring, And lives that death may die!

5 Crown him the Lord of Peace!
Whose pow'r a scepter sways
From pole to pole, that wars may cease,
Absorbed in prayer and praise:
His reign shall have no end,
And round his holy feet
Fair flow'rs of paradise extend
Their fragrance ever sweet.

6 Crown him the Lord of years!
The Potentate of time,
Creator of the rolling spheres,
Ineffably sublime!
All hail, Redeemer, hail!
For you have died for me;
Your praise shall never, never fail
Through all eternity!

462²

Lower Key

ALLELUIA! SING TO JESUS
William Chatterton Dix, 1866, alt.

463

Lower Key at No. 440

HYFRYDOL
87. 87. D.
Rowland H. Prichard, c. 1830

1 Al - le - lu - ia! Sing to Je - sus! His the scep - ter, his the throne; Al - le - lu - ia! His the tri - umph, His the vic - to - ry a - lone. Hark! the songs of peace - ful Zi - on Thun - der like a might - y flood: Je - sus out of
2 Al - le - lu - ia! Not as or - phans Are we left in sor - row now. Al - le - lu - ia! He is near us; Faith be - lieves, nor ques - tions how: Though the cloud from sight re - ceived him When the for - ty days were o'er, Shall our hearts for -
3 Al - le - lu - ia! Bread of heav - en, You on earth our food and stay! Al - le - lu - ia! Here the sin - ful Turn to you from day to day. In - ter - ces - sor, friend of sin - ers, Earth's Re - deem - er, plead for us Where the sing - ing
4 Al - le - lu - ia! King e - ter - nal, You the Lord of lords we own. Al - le - lu - ia! Born of Mar - y, Earth's your foot - stool, heav'n your throne. You with - in the veil have en - tered, Robed in flesh, our great High Priest: You on earth both

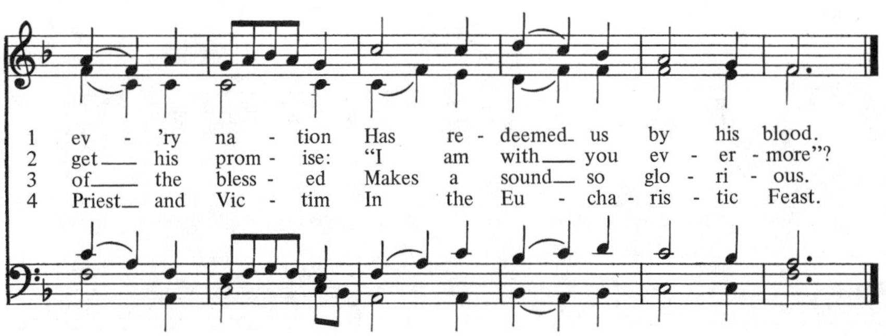
1 ev - 'ry na - tion Has re - deemed us by his blood.
2 get his prom - ise: "I am with you ev - er - more"?
3 of the bless - ed Makes a sound so glo - ri - ous.
4 Priest and Vic - tim In the Eu - cha - ris - tic Feast.

Based on Hebrews 2:10
THE HEAD THAT ONCE
Thomas Kelly, 1820

464

ST. MAGNUS
C. M.
Jeremiah Clark, 1709

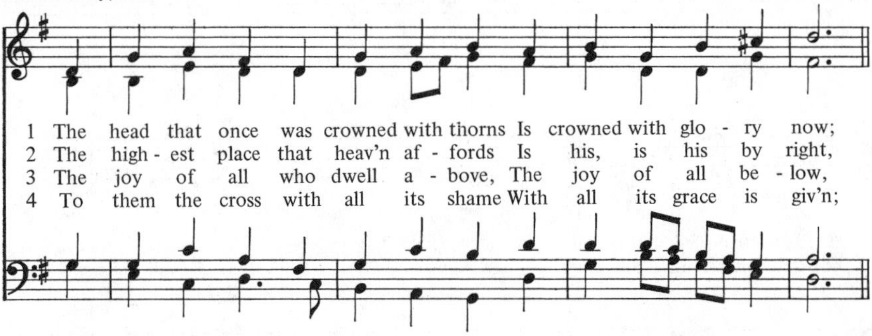

1 The head that once was crowned with thorns Is crowned with glo - ry now;
2 The high - est place that heav'n af - fords Is his, is his by right,
3 The joy of all who dwell a - bove, The joy of all be - low,
4 To them the cross with all its shame With all its grace is giv'n;

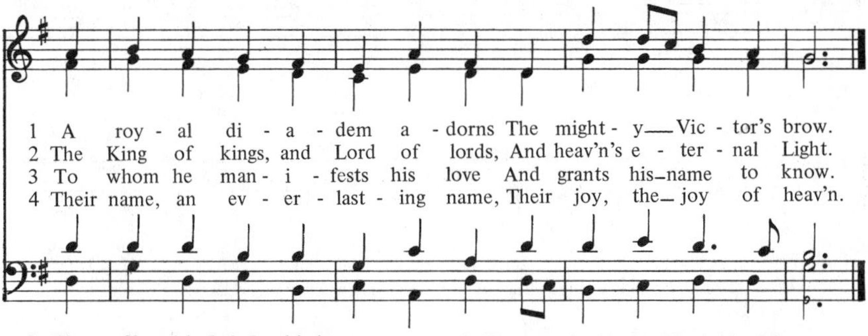

1 A roy - al di - a - dem a - dorns The might - y Vic - tor's brow.
2 The King of kings, and Lord of lords, And heav'n's e - ter - nal Light.
3 To whom he man - i - fests his love And grants his name to know.
4 Their name, an ev - er - last - ing name, Their joy, the joy of heav'n.

5 They suffer with their Lord below,
They reign with him above,
Their profit and their joy to know
The myst'ry of his love.

6 The cross he bore is life and health,
Though shame and death to him:
His people's hope, his people's wealth,
Their everlasting hymn.

465

AND HAVE THE BRIGHT IMMENSITIES
Howard Chandler Robbins, 1932

HALIFAX
C. M. D.
George Frederick Handel, 1748

Lower Key at No. 477

1 And have the bright im - men - si - ties Re - ceived our_ ris - en_ Lord,
2 The heav'n that hides him from_our sight Knows nei - ther_ near nor_ far:
1 Where light - years frame the Plei - a - des And point O - ri - on's_ sword?
2 An al - tar can - dle sheds its light As sure - ly_ as a_ star;
1 Do flam - ing suns_his foot - steps trace Thru cor - ri - dors_ sub - lime,_
2 And where_ his lov - ing peo - ple meet To share the_ gift_ di - vine,_
1 The Lord of in - ter - stel - lar space And Con - quer - or of_ time?
2 There stands he with un - hur - rying feet; There heav'n - ly_ splen - dors shine.

466

LORD OF ALL HOPEFULNESS
Jan Struther, 1933

SLANE
10 11. 11 12
Traditional Irish Melody

1 Lord of all hope-ful-ness, Lord of all joy, Whose trust, ev-er child-like, no cares could des-troy, Be there at our wak-ing, and give us, we pray, Your bliss in our hearts, Lord, at the break of the day.
2 Lord of all ea-ger-ness, Lord of all faith, Whose strong hands were skilled at the plane and the lathe, Be there at our la-bors, and give us, we pray, Your strength in our hearts, Lord, at the noon of the day.
3 Lord of all kind-li-ness, Lord of all grace, Your hands swift to wel-come, your arms to em-brace, Be there at our hom-ing, and give us, we pray, Your love in our hearts, Lord, at the eve of the day.
4 Lord of all gen-tle-ness, Lord of all calm, Whose voice is con-tent-ment, whose pres-ence is balm, Be there at our sleep-ing, and give us, we pray, Your peace in our hearts, Lord, at the end of the day.

IN THE MIDST OF DEATH
Muus Jacobse
David Smith

467[1]

Higher Key

IN THE MIDST OF DEATH
56. 56. 5
Rik Veelenturf
Harm. by Jerry R. Brubaker

1 We who once were dead now live ful - ly know - ing Je - sus at our
2 We were lost in night, but you sought and found us. Give us strength to
3 He be - came our bread Je - sus dies to save us. On him we are
4 Let us share the pain you en - dured in dy - ing. We shall then re -

1 head. Life is o - ver - flow - ing when he breaks the bread.
2 fight. Death is all a - round us. Je - sus be our light.
3 fed eat - ing what he gave us, ris - ing from the dead.
4 main liv - ing death de - fy - ing, we shall rise a - gain.

5 Jesus, you were dead,
but you rose and living
made yourself our bread,
in your goodness giving
life though we were dead.

6 This is our design
in this meal we meet you.
Be our bread and wine,
Jesus we entreat you.
Let this be our sign.

467[2]

Lower Key

468

HE DID NOT WANT TO BE FAR
C. Michael de Vries, 1966, alt.
From the Dutch of Huub Oosterhuis

HUIJBERS
76. 76 (Trochaic), with Chorus
Bernard Huijbers
Harm. by Jerry R. Brubaker

1 He did not want to be far; Near - ness he in - tend - ed.
2 Ev - 'ry - where he's at our side, Hu - man 'midst the hu - man;
3 God of God and Light of Light, Keep - er of cre - a - tion,
4 There-fore, that the world might know, Christ be - came our broth - er;
5 Let's re - joice and sing and cheer: God, to whom be giv - en
Am
C
F
C
1 There-fore in - to what we are Christ the Lord de - scend - ed.
2 No - where is he rec - og - nized, No one sees the new Man.
3 He as - sumed the hu - man plight, Joined our gen - er - a - tion.
4 No man an - y - thing we owe But to love each oth - er.
5 Praise, is in - fi - nite - ly near; Dwells where we are liv - ing.
F
G
C
A - mong you is stand - ing He whom you don't know.
Am
C
Dm
Am
A - mong you is stand - ing He whom you don't know.
Dm
C
F
Dm
F
E

469

BEIM FRÜHEN MORGENLICHT
Anonymous, 18th (?) cent.
Tr., Edward Caswall, 1854, 1858, alt.

LAUDES DOMINI
666. D.
Joseph Barnby, 1868

1 When morn - ing gilds the skies, My heart a - wak - ing cries:
2 Does sad - ness fill my mind? A sol - ace here I find:
3 To God the Word on high The host of an - gels cry:
4 Let earth's wide cir - cle round In joy - ful notes re - sound:
1 May Je - sus Christ be praised! A - like at work and prayer
2 May Je - sus Christ be praised! Or fades my earth - ly bliss?
3 May Je - sus Christ be praised! Let mor - tals, too, up - raise
4 May Je - sus Christ be praised! Let air and sea and sky,
1 To Je - sus I re - pair: May Je - sus Christ be praised!
2 My com - fort still is this: May Je - sus Christ be praised!
3 Their voice in hymns of praise: May Je - sus Christ be praised!
4 From depth to height, re - ply: May Je - sus Christ be praised!

5 Be this, while life is mine,
My canticle divine:
May Jesus Christ be praised!
Be this th'eternal song,
Thru all the ages long:
May Jesus Christ be praised!

O WHERE ARE KINGS
Cento from *Christian Ballads*
Arthur Cleveland Coxe, 1839
470
Higher Key at No. 479
McKEE
C. M.
Black Melody adapted by
Harry T, Burleigh, 1939
1 O where are kings and em - pires now Of
2 We see her state - ly walls and spires And
3 For not like king - doms of the world Your
4 Un - shak - en as e - ter - nal hills, Im -
1 old, that went and came?
2 her foun - da - tions strong;
3 ho - ly Church, O God,
4 mov - a - ble she stands,
1 But, Lord, your Church is
2 We hear, with - in, the
3 Tho earth - quake shocks are
4 A moun - tain that shall
1 pray - ing yet, Two thou - sand years the same.
2 sol - emn voice Of her un - end - ing song.
3 threat - 'ning her, And tem - pests are a - broad;
4 fill the earth, A house not made by hands.

Based on Isaiah 33:20-21 & Psalm 87:3
GLOURIOUS THINGS OF THEE ARE SPOKEN **471**
John Newton, 1779, alt.
Lower Key at No. 530

AUSTRIA (HAYDN)
87. 87. D.
Franz Joseph Haydn, 1797

1 Glo - rious things of you are spo - ken,
2 See, the streams of liv - ing wa - ters,
3 Round each hab - i - ta - tion hov - 'ring,
4 Blest in - hab - i - tants of Zi - on,
1 Zi - on, cit - y of our God;
2 Spring - ing from e - ter - nal Love,
3 See the cloud and fire ap - pear
4 Washed in the Re - deem - er's blood!
1 He whose word can - not be bro - ken
2 Well sup - ply your sons and daugh - ters,
3 For a glo - ry and a cov - 'ring
4 Je - sus, whom their souls re - ly on,
1 Formed you for his own a - bode.
2 And all fears of want re - move:
3 Show - ing that the Lord is near:
4 Makes them kings and priests to God.

1 On the rock of A - ges found - ed,
2 Who can faint, while such a riv - er
3 Thus de - riv - ing from their ban - ner
4 It's his love his peo - ple rais - es
1 What can shake your sure re - pose?
2 Flows their thirst to sat - is - fy?
3 Light by night, and shade by day,
4 O - ver self to reign as kings:
1 With sal - va - tion's walls sur - round - ed,
2 Grace, which like the Lord, the giv - er,
3 Safe they feed up - on the man - na
4 And, as priests, his sol - emn prais - es
1 You may smile at all your foes.
2 Nev - er fails; he does sup - ply.
3 Which he gives them when they pray.
4 Each for a thank - of - f'ring brings.

THE CHURCH'S ONE FOUNDATION
Samuel John Stone, 1866, alt

472

Lower Key at No. 398

AURELIA
76. 76. D.
Samuel Sebastian Wesley, 1864

1 The Church-'s one foun-da-tion Is Je-sus Christ, her Lord;
2 E-lect from ev-'ry na-tion, Yet one o'er all the earth,
3 Though with a scorn-ful won-der Men see her sore op-prest,
4 Mid toil and trib-u-la-tion, And tu-mult of her war,
1 She is his new cre-a-tion By wa-ter and the word:
2 Her char-ter of sal-va-tion: One Lord, one faith, one birth;
3 By dis-cord torn a-sun-der, By age-old wounds dis-trest,
4 She waits the con-sum-ma-tion Of peace for ev-er-more;
1 From heav'n he came and sought her To be his ho-ly bride;
2 One ho-ly name she bless-es, Par-takes one ho-ly food,
3 Yet saints their watch are keep-ing; Their cry goes up: "How long?"
4 Till with the vi-sion glo-rious Her long-ing eyes are blest,
1 With his own blood he bought her, And for her life he died.
2 And to one hope she press-es, With ev-'ry grace en-dued.
3 And soon the night of weep-ing Shall be the morn of song.
4 And then the church vic-to-rious Shall be the church at rest.

5 Yet she on earth has union
With God, the Three in One,
And mystic sweet communion
With those whose rest is won:

O happy ones and holy!
Lord, give us grace that we,
Like them, the meek and lowly,
May live eternally.

ANGULARIS FUNDAMENTUM
From *Urbs Beata Jerusalem*
c. 7th cent.
Tr., John Mason Neale, 1851, alt

473[1]

First Tune

WESTMINSTER ABBEY (BELVILLE)
87. 87. 87
Anthem by Henry Purcell, 1659-95
Adapted by Ernest Hawkins, 1802-68

1 Christ is made the sure foun - da - tion, Christ the head ___ and
2 To this tem - ple where we call you, Come, O Lord ___ of
3 Give, we pray, to all your peo - ple What they ask ___ of
4 Praise and hon - or to the Fa - ther, Praise and hon - or
1 cor - ner - stone, Cho - sen of the Lord and pre - cious,
2 hosts to - day! Come with all your lov - ing - kind - ness,
3 you to gain: What they gain from you, for - ev - er
4 to the Son, Praise and hon - or to the Spir - it,
1 Bind - ing all ___ the church in one; Ho - ly Zi - on's
2 Hear your peo - ple as ___ they pray, And your full - est
3 With the bless - ed to ___ re - tain, And here - af - ter
4 Ev - er Three ___ and ev - er One; One in might, and
1 help for - ev - er, And her con - fi - dence a - lone.
2 ben - e - dic - tion Shed in all its bright - est ray.
3 in your glo - ry Ev - er - more with you to reign.
4 One in glo - ry, While un - end - ing a - ges run.

ANGULARIS FUNDAMENTUM
From Urbs Beata Jerusalem
c. 7th cent.
Tr., John Mason Neale, 1851, alt.
473[2]
Second Tune
Higher Key at No. 211
REGENT SQUARE
87. 87. 87
Henry Smart, 1867
1 Christ is made the sure foun - da - tion, Christ the head and
2 To this tem - ple where we call you, Come, O Lord of
3 Give, we pray, to all your peo - ple What they ask of
4 Praise and hon - or to the Fa - ther, Praise and hon - or
1 cor - ner - stone, Cho - sen of the Lord and pre - cious,
2 hosts to - day! Come with all your lov - ing - kind - ness,
3 you to - gain: What they gain from you, for - ev - er
4 to the Son, Praise and hon - or to the Spir - it,
1 Bind - ing all the church in one; Ho - ly Zi - on's
2 Hear your peo - ple as they pray, And your full - est
3 With the bless - ed to re - tain, And here - af - ter
4 Ev - er Three and ev - er One; One in might, and
1 help for - ev - er, And her con - fi - dence a - lone.
2 ben - e - dic - tion Shed in all its bright - est ray.
3 in your glo - ry Ev - er - more with you to reign.
4 One in glo - ry, While un - end - ing a - ges run.

474

FAITH OF OUR FATHERS
Frederick William Faber, 1849, alt.

Lower Key at No. 341

ST. CATHERINE
88. 88. 88
Henri F. Hemy, 1864
and James G. Walton, 1870

1 Faith of our fa - thers, liv - ing still In spite of dun - geon,
2 Our Fa - thers, chained_ in pris - ons dark, Were still in heart and
3 Faith of our fa - thers, Mar - y's prayers Shall win all na - tions
4 Faith of our fa - thers, we_ will love Both friend and foe in
1 fire,_ and sword: O how our hearts_ beat high_ with joy
2 con - science free: And tru - ly blest_ would be_ our fate,
3 un - to thee; And through the truth_ that comes_ from God,
4 all_ our strife: And preach thee, too,_ as love_ knows how,
1 When - e'er we hear that glo - rious word:
2 If we, like them, should die_ for thee.
3 Man - kind shall then in - deed_ be free.
4 By kind - ly deeds and vir - tuous life.
Faith of our fa - thers,
ho - ly faith! We will be true to thee till death.

RISE, CROWNED WITH LIGHT
Alexander Pope, 1712

475

NATIONAL HYMN
10 10. 10 10
George William Warren, 1892

1 Rise, crowned with light, O holy Church, arise!
2 See a long race your spacious courts adorn:
3 See all the nations at your gates attend,
4 The seas shall waste, the skies to smoke decay,
1 Exalt your tow'ring head and lift your eyes!
2 See future sons and daughters yet unborn,
3 Walk in your light, and in your temple bend:
4 Rocks fall to dust, and mountains melt away;
1 See heav'n its sparkling portals wide display,
2 In crowding ranks on ev'ry side arise,
3 See your bright altars thronged with kneeling kings,
4 But fixed his word, his saving pow'r remains;
1 And break upon you in a flood of day.
2 Demanding life, impatient for the skies.
3 While ev'ry land its joyous tribute brings.
4 Your realm shall last; your own Messiah reigns.

WALTE, WALTE NAH UND FERN
Jonathan Friedrich Bahnmaier, 1827
Tr., Arthur W. Farlander
& Winfred Douglas, 1938, alt.

476

Higher Key at No. 416

LÜBECK
77. 77
Freylinghausen's
Geistreiches Gesangbuch, 1704

1 Spread, O spread the might - y word,
2 Word of how the Fa - ther's will
3 Word of how the Sav - ior's love
4 Might - y word God's Spir - it gave,
1 Spread the king - dom of the Lord,
2 Made the world, and keeps it still;
3 Earth's sore bur - den does re - move;
4 All for heav'n - ly life to save;
1 That to earth's re - mot - est bound
2 How his on - ly Son he gave,
3 How for - ev - er, in its need,
4 Word through whose all - ho - ly might
1 All may heed the joy - ful sound.
2 All from sin and death to save.
3 Through his death the world is freed.
4 We can will and do the right.

5 Word of life, most pure and strong,
Word for which the nations long
Spread abroad, until from night
All the world awakes to light.

ETERNAL GOD, WHOSE POWER
Henry Hallam Tweedy, 1929, alt.

477

Higher Key at No. 465

HALIFAX
C. M. D.
George Frederick Handel, 1748

1 E - ter - nal God, whose pow'r up - holds Both flow'r and flam - ing star,
2 O God of truth, whom sci - ence seeks And rev - 'rent souls a - dore,
3 O God of beau - ty, oft re - vealed In dreams of hu - man art,
4 O God of right - eous - ness and grace, Seen in the Christ, your Son,
1 To whom there is no here nor there, No time, no near or far,
2 En - light - en ev - 'ry ear - nest mind Of ev - 'ry clime and shore;
3 In speech that flows to mel - o - dy, In ho - li - ness of heart,
4 Whose life and death re - veal your face, By whom your will was done,
1 No a - lien race, no for - eign shore, No child un - sought, un - known,
2 Dis - pel the gloom of er - ror's night, Of ig - nor - ance and fear,
3 Teach us to ban all ug - li - ness And all dis - har - mo - ny,
4 Help us to spread your gra - cious reign Till greed and hate shall cease,
1 O send us forth, your proph - ets true, To make all lands your own!
2 Un - til true wis - dom from a - bove Shall make life's path - way clear!
3 Till all shall know the lov - li - ness Of lives made fair and free!
4 And kind - ness dwell in hu - man hearts, And all the earth find peace!

WEISSE FLAGGEN
87. 87. D.
Tochter Sion, Cologne, 1741, alt.
Harm. by Jerry R. Brubaker

478

LORD, WE THANK THEE
Roger K. Powell, 1914-

1 Lord, we thank you for our broth - ers Keep - ing faith with us and you,
2 God be praised for con - gre - ga - tions Join - ing now in char - i - ty;
3 May your name be praised for - ev - er! Heal our dif - f'renc - es of old;
1 Join - ing heart to heart with oth - ers, Thus our one - ness to re - new.
2 Man - y tongues of man - y na - tions Sing the great - er u - ni - ty.
3 Bless your Church-'s new en - deav - or; For your king - dom make us bold.
1 With the cross our on - ly stand - ard Let us sing with one great voice,
2 Wel - come sound of psalm and car - ol When our song is raised as one.
3 One our Christ, and one our Gos - pel; Make us one, we now im - plore.
1 Glo - ry, glo - ry, yours the king - dom; Church - es in your Church re - joice!
2 Glo - ry, glo - ry, yours the pow - er, As in heav'n your will be done.
3 Glo - ry, glo - ry, yours the glo - ry Through the a - ges ev - er - more!

479

IN CHRIST THERE IS
John Oxenham, 1908

Lower Key at No. 470

McKEE
Black Melody adapted by
Harry T. Burleigh, 1939

1 In Christ there is no East or West, In him no South or North, But one great fellowship of love Thro'out the whole wide earth.
2 In him shall true hearts ev'ry-where Their high communion find; His service is the golden chord Close-binding all mankind.
3 Join hands, then, brothers of the faith, What-e'er your race may be! Who serves my Father as a son Is surely kin to me.
4 In Christ now meet both East and West, in him meet South and North; All Christly souls are one in him Thro'out the whole wide earth.

AND IS THE TIME APPROACHING
Jane Borthwick, 1859, alt.
480
ZOAN
76. 76. D.
William H. Havergal, 1859
1 O haste the time ap - point - ed, By proph - ets long fore - told,
2 Let Jew and Gen - tile, meet - ing From ev - 'ry dis - tant shore,
3 Let all that now u - nites us More sweet and last - ing prove,
4 O long - ex - pect - ed dawn - ing, Come with your cheer - ing ray!
1 When all shall dwell to - geth - er, One Shep - herd and one fold.
2 A - round one al - tar kneel - ing, One com - mon Lord a - dore.
3 A clos - er bond of un - ion, In one blest land of love.
4 When shall the morn - ing bright - en And shad - ows flee a - way?
1 Let ev - 'ry i - dol per - ish; Your truth to all make known
2 Let all that now di - vides us De - part and pass a - way,
3 Let war be learned no long - er, Let strife and dis - cord cease,
4 O great an - tic - i - pa - tion! It cheers God's peo - ple on
1 Till ev - 'ry prayer be of - fered To God in Christ a - lone.
2 Like shad - ows of the morn - ing Be - fore the light of day.
3 All earth his bless - èd king - dom, The Lord and Prince of Peace.
4 To pray and hope and la - bor Till our dark night be gone!

O WORD OF GOD INCARNATE
William Walsham How, 1867, alt.

481

MUNICH
76. 76. D.
Meiningen Gesangbuch, 1693

1 O_ Word of God in - car - nate, O Wis - dom_from on high,
2 The_Church from her dear fa - thers Re - ceived the_ gift di - vine,
3 It's_ wav - ing like a ban - ner Be - fore God's host un - furled;
4 O_ make your Church, dear Sav - ior, A lamp of_ pur - est gold
1 O_ Truth un - changed, un - chang - ing, O Light of_ our dark sky,
2 And_ still that light is lift - ing O'er all the_earth to shine;
3 It's_ shin - ing like a bea - con A - bove a_ dark-ened world;
4 To_ bring be - fore the na - tions Your true light_ as of old.
1 We praise you for the ra - diance That from the sa - cred page,
2 It is the pre - cious strong - hold Where gems of truth are stored;
3 It is the chart and com - pass That o - ver life's rough sea,
4 O teach your wan -d'ring pil - grims By this their path to trace
1 A lan - tern to our foot - steps, Shines on from age to age.
2 It is the heav'n - drawn pic - ture Of Christ, the liv - ing Word.
3 'Mid fog and rocks and ice - bergs, Still guides us faith - ful - ly.
4 Till, clouds and dark - ness end - ed, They see you face to face.

BOOK OF BOOKS
Percy Dearmer, 1925
482
Higher Key at No. 331
LIEBSTER JESU, WIR SIND HEIR
78. 78. 88
Johann R. Ahle, 1664
1 Book of books, our peo - ple's strength, States-man's, teach-er's, he - ro's treas - ure, Bring - ing free - dom, spread - ing truth, Shed - ding light that none can meas - ure, Wis - dom comes to those who know you, All the best we have we owe you.
2 Thank we those who toiled in thought, Man - y dif - f'rent scrolls com - plet - ing, Po - ets, proph - ets, schol - ars saints, Each his word from God re - peat - ing, Till they came, who told the sto - ry Of the Word, and showed his glo - ry.
3 Praise we God, who has in - spired Those whose wis - dom still di - rects us; Praise him for the Word - made - flesh, For the Spir - it who pro - tects us. Light of knowl-edge, ev - er burn - ing, Shed on us your end - less learn - ing.

483

GUDS ORD DET ER VORT ARVEGODS
Nikolai F. S. Grundtvig, 1817
Tr., Ole G. Belsheim, 1909, alt.

EIN' FESTE BURG
87. 87. 66. 667
Melody, Martin Luther, 1529

God's word is our great her - i - tage And shall be ours for - ev - er;
To spread its light from age to age Shall be our chief en - deav - or.
Through life it guards our way;
In death it is our stay.
Lord, grant, while worlds en - dure,
We keep its teach-ings pure Through-out all gen - er - a - tions.

AMAZING GRACE
C. M.
American Folk Hymn
Arr., Edwin O. Excell, 1900
Harm. by Jerry R. Brubaker

484

AMAZING GRACE
John Newton, 1779

F F7 B♭ F C7 F C7 F F7 B♭ F Dm C7 F

1 Amazing grace! How sweet the sound!
That saved a wretch like me!
I once was lost, but now am found,
Was blind but now I see.

2 'Twas grace that taught my heart to fear,
And grace my fears relieved;
How precious did that grace appear
The hour I first believed!

3 Through many dangers, toils and snares
I have already come;
'Tis grace has brought me safe thus far,
And grace will lead me home.

4 The Lord has promised good to me,
His word my hope secures;
He will my shield and portion be
As long as life endures.

LORD, TEACH US HOW TO PRAY
James Montgomery, 1771-1854, alt.

485

BEATITUDO
C. M.
John B. Dykes, 1875

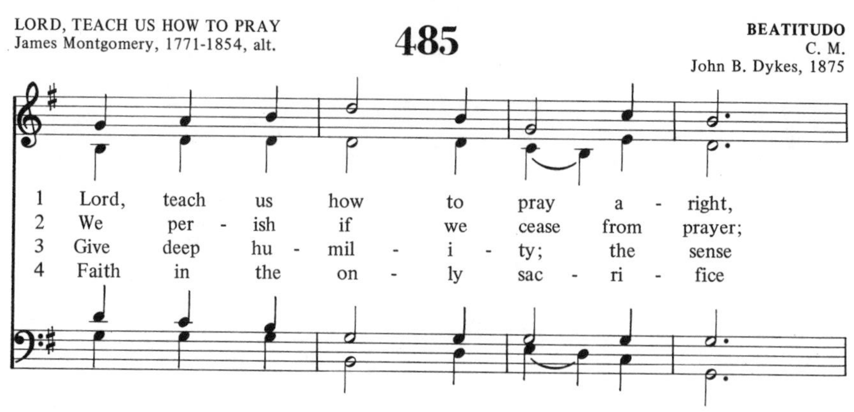
1 Lord, teach us how to pray a - right,
2 We per - ish if we cease from prayer;
3 Give deep hu - mil - i - ty; the sense
4 Faith in the on - ly sac - ri - fice

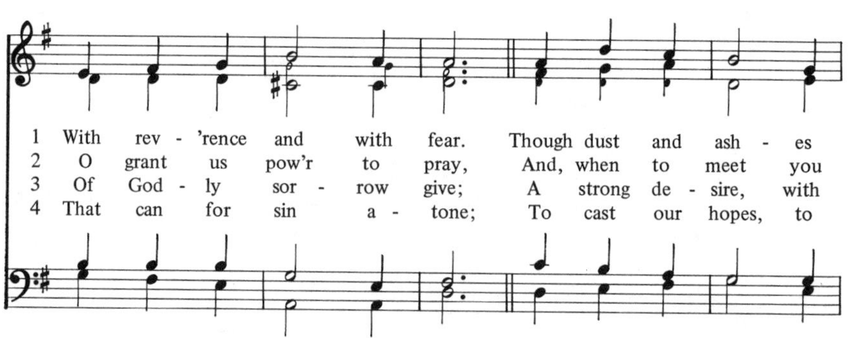
1 With rev - 'rence and with fear. Though dust and ash - es
2 O grant us pow'r to pray, And, when to meet you
3 Of God - ly sor - row give; A strong de - sire, with
4 That can for sin a - tone; To cast our hopes, to

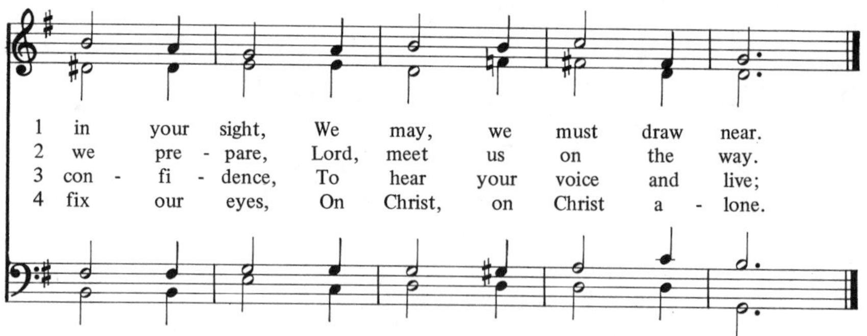
1 in your sight, We may, we must draw near.
2 we pre - pare, Lord, meet us on the way.
3 con - fi - dence, To hear your voice and live;
4 fix our eyes, On Christ, on Christ a - lone.

5 Give these, and then your will be done;
Thus strengthened with all might,
We, through your Spirit and your Son,
Shall pray, and pray aright.

I KNOW NOT WHERE
Evelyn Atwater Cummins, 1922, alt.

486

CAITHNESS
C. M.
Melody in *Scottish Psalter,* 1635

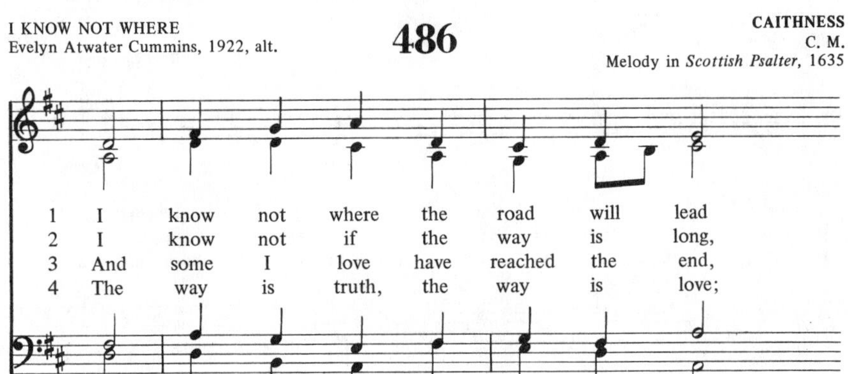
1 I know not where the road will lead
2 I know not if the way is long,
3 And some I love have reached the end,
4 The way is truth, the way is love;

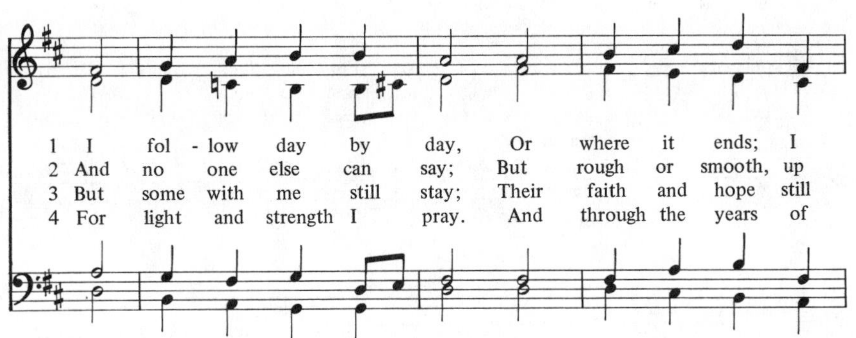
1 I fol - low day by day, Or where it ends; I
2 And no one else can say; But rough or smooth, up
3 But some with me still stay; Their faith and hope still
4 For light and strength I pray. And through the years of

1 on - ly know I walk the King's high - way.
2 hill or down, I walk the King's high - way.
3 guid - ing me, I walk the King's high - way.
4 life, to God, I walk the King's high - way.

5 The countless hosts lead on before;
I must not fear nor stray.
With them, the pilgrims of the faith,
I walk the King's highway.

6 Through light and dark the road leads on
Till dawn the endless day
When I shall know why in this life
I walk the King's highway.

IN HEAVENLY LOVE ABIDING
Anna Laetitia Waring, 1850, alt.
487
Higher Key at No. 260
HERZLICH TUT MICH
(O HAUPT VOLL BLUDT)
(PASSION CHORALE)
76. 76. D.
Hans Leo Hassler, 1601
Adapt. & Harm., J. S. Bach
1 In heav - 'nly love a - bid - ing, No change my heart shall fear,
2 Where - ev - er he may guide me, No want shall turn me back;
3 Green pas - tures are be - fore me, Which yet I have not seen;
1 And safe is such con - fid - ing, For no - thing chang - es here.
2 My Shep - herd is be - side me, And no - thing can I lack.
3 Bright skies will soon be o'er me, Where those dark clouds have been.
1 The storm may roar with - out me, My heart may be a - fraid,
2 His wis - dom's ev - er wak - ing, His sight is nev - er dim;
3 My hope I can - not meas - ure; The path to life is free.
1 But God is round a - bout me; How can I be dis - mayed?
2 He knows the way he's tak - ing, And I will walk with him.
3 My Sav - ior has my treas - ure, And he will walk with me.

488

HOW CAN I KEEP FROM SINGING
Quaker Hymn

HOW CAN I KEEP FROM SINGING
87.87. D. (Iambic)
Quaker Hymn
Harm., D.F., 1977

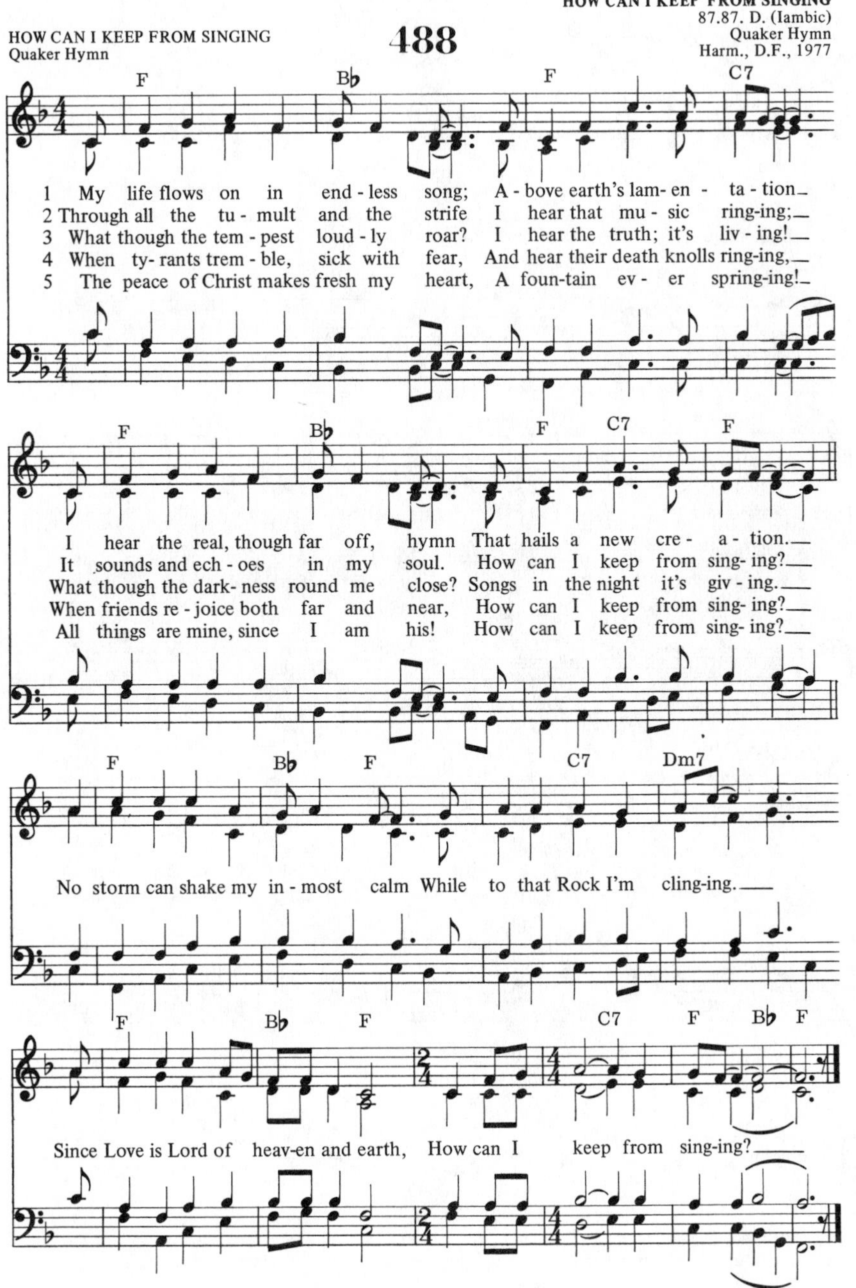

F Bb F C7
1 My life flows on in end - less song; A - bove earth's lam- en - ta - tion
2 Through all the tu - mult and the strife I hear that mu - sic ring-ing;
3 What though the tem - pest loud - ly roar? I hear the truth; it's liv - ing!
4 When ty- rants trem - ble, sick with fear, And hear their death knolls ring-ing,
5 The peace of Christ makes fresh my heart, A foun-tain ev - er spring-ing!
F Bb F C7 F
I hear the real, though far off, hymn That hails a new cre - a - tion.
It sounds and ech - oes in my soul. How can I keep from sing- ing?
What though the dark- ness round me close? Songs in the night it's giv - ing.
When friends re - joice both far and near, How can I keep from sing- ing?
All things are mine, since I am his! How can I keep from sing- ing?
F Bb F C7 Dm7
No storm can shake my in - most calm While to that Rock I'm cling-ing.
F Bb F C7 F Bb F
Since Love is Lord of heav-en and earth, How can I keep from sing-ing?

Based on Psalm 131
LORD, FOREVER AT THY SIDE
James Montgomery, 1819, alt.

489

Higher Key at No. 432

RILEY
77. 77. D.
Martin Shaw, 1915

1 Lord, for - ev - er at your side Let my place and por - tion be.
2 Hum-ble as a lit - tle child Rest - ing on its moth - er's breast,
1 Strip me of the robe of__pride; Clothe me with hu - mil - i - ty.
2 By no sub - tle - ties be - guiled, On your faith - ful word I rest.
1 Meek - ly may my soul re - ceive All your Spir - it has re - vealed.
2 Is - ra - el, for - ev - er - more In the faith - ful Yah - weh trust;
1 You have spo - ken; I be - lieve, Though the or - a - cle__ is sealed.
2 Him in all your ways a - dore, Wise and won - der - ful__ and just.

Psalm 23
THE KING OF LOVE
Henry W. Baker, 1868, alt.

490[1]

Higher Key

SAINT COLUMBA
87. 87 (Iambic)
Ancient Irish Melody

1 The king of love my shep - herd is, Whose
2 Where streams of liv - ing wa - ter flow My
3 Per - verse and fool - ish oft I strayed, But
4 In death's dark vale I fear no ill With

3
1 good - ness fails me nev - er; I noth - ing lack if
2 ran - somed soul he's lead - ing, And where the ver - dant
3 yet in love he sought me, And on his shoul - der
4 you, dear Lord, be - side me; Your rod and staff my
3

1 I am his, And he is mine for - ev - er.
2 pas - tures grow With food ce - les - tial feed - ing.
3 gen - tly laid, And home, re - joic - ing, brought me.
4 com - fort still, Your cross be - fore to guide me.

5 You spread a table in my sight;
Your grace so rich bestowing;
And, Oh, what transports of delight
From your pure cup is flowing!

6 And so through all the length of days
Your goodness fails me never;
Good Shepherd, may I sing your praise
Within your house forever.

490²

Lower Key

OH, FOR A FAITH
William H. Bathurst, 1831, alt.

491

Higher Key at No. 450

KINGSFOLD (LAZARUS)
C. M. D.
Traditional English Melody

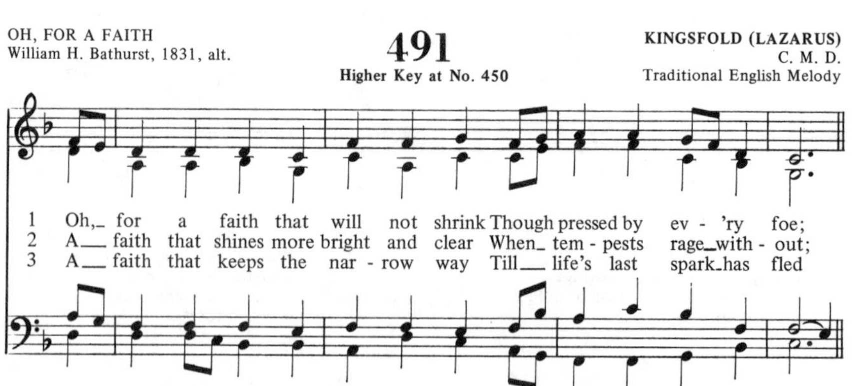
1 Oh,_ for a faith that will not shrink Though pressed by ev - 'ry foe;
2 A_ faith that shines more bright and clear When_ tem - pests rage_with - out;
3 A_ faith that keeps the nar - row way Till_ life's last spark_has fled

1 That_ will not trem - ble on the brink Of_ pov - er - ty_ or
2 That,_ when in dan - ger, knows no fear, In_ dark - ness feels no
3 And_ with a pure and heav - 'nly ray Lights up the dy - ing
1 woe; That_ will not mur - mur nor com - plain Be -
2 doubt; That_ bears un - moved_ the world's dread frown Nor_
3 bed. Lord,_ give us such_ a faith as this; And_
1 neath the_ chast - 'ning rod, But_ in the hour_ of_
2 heeds its_ scorn - ful smile; That_ sin's wild o - cean_
3 then, what - e'er may come, We'll_ know right now_ the_
1 grief and pain Can_ lean up - on_ its God;
2 can - not drown Nor_ Sa - tan's arts_ be - guile.
3 ho - ly bliss Of_ an e - ter - nal home.

O DEUS, EGO AMO TE
Cæleste Palmetum, Cologne, 1669

492

Lower Key at No. 441

ST. FULBERT
C. M.
Henry J. Gauntlett, 1852

1 My God, I love you not be - cause I
2 But that you willed up - on the cross All
3 And griefs and tor - ments num - ber - less, And
4 Then why, most lov - ing Je - sus Christ, Should

1 hope for heav'n there - by, Nor yet for fear that
2 peo - ple to em - brace; And for us bore the
3 sweat of ag - o - ny; Yes, death it - self; and
4 I not love you well, Not for the sake of

1 lov - ing not I might for - ev - er die;
2 nails and spear, And man - i - fold dis - grace,
3 all for man Who was your en - e - my.
4 win - ning heav'n, Nor an - y fear of hell;

5 Not with the hope of any gain,
Not seeking a reward,
But only since you first loved me,
O ever-loving Lord!

6 Above all, Lord, I love you so,
And in your praise will sing,
Yes, just because you are my God
And my eternal King!

ABIDE WITH ME
Henry Francis Lyte, 1847

493

EVENTIDE
10 10. 10 10
William H. Monk, 1861

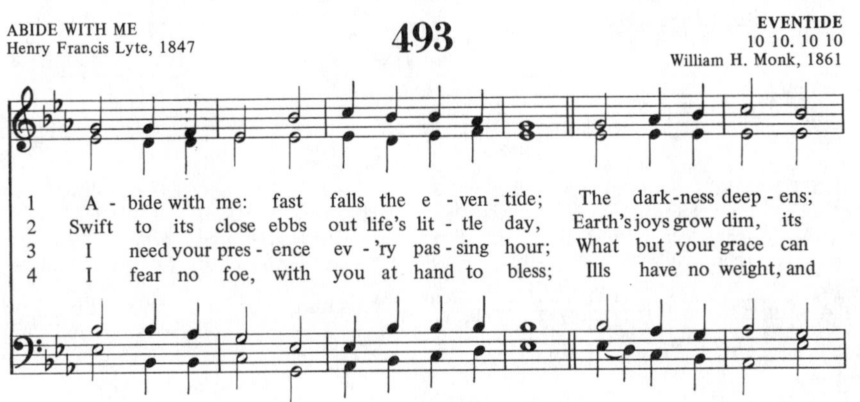
1 A - bide with me: fast falls the e - ven - tide; The dark-ness deep - ens;
2 Swift to its close ebbs out life's lit - tle day, Earth's joys grow dim, its
3 I need your pres - ence ev - 'ry pas - sing hour; What but your grace can
4 I fear no foe, with you at hand to bless; Ills have no weight, and

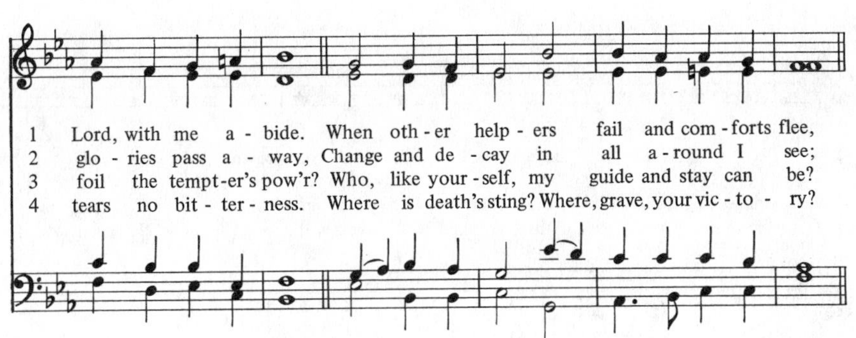
1 Lord, with me a - bide. When oth - er help - ers fail and com - forts flee,
2 glo - ries pass a - way, Change and de - cay in all a - round I see;
3 foil the tempt-er's pow'r? Who, like your - self, my guide and stay can be?
4 tears no bit - ter - ness. Where is death's sting? Where, grave, your vic - to - ry?

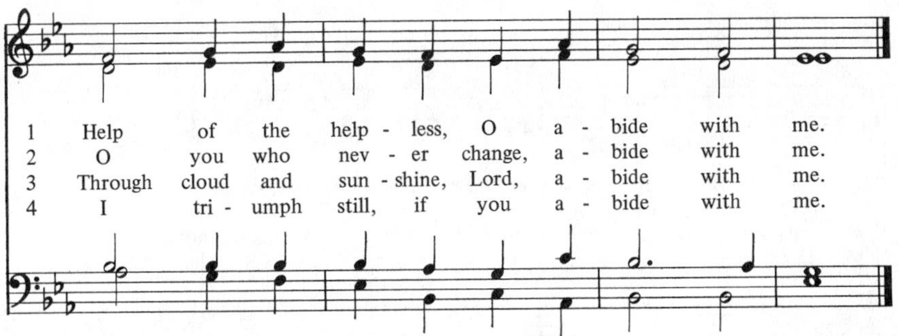
1 Help of the help - less, O a - bide with me.
2 O you who nev - er change, a - bide with me.
3 Through cloud and sun - shine, Lord, a - bide with me.
4 I tri - umph still, if you a - bide with me.

5 Lord, hold your cross before my closing eyes;
Shine through the gloom, and point me to the skies;
Heav'n's morning breaks, and earth's vain shadows flee;
In life, in death, O Lord, abide with me.

PRAISE AND THANKSGIVING
Albert F. Bayly, b. 1901
494
Higher Key at No. 323
BUNESSAN
55. 54. D.
Old Gaelic Melody
1 Praise and thanks-giv - ing, Fa - ther, we of - fer For all things
2 Lord, bless the la - bor We bring to serve you, That with our
3 Fa - ther, pro - vid - ing Food for your chil - dren, Your wis - dom
4 Then will your bless - ing Reach ev - 'ry peo - ple; All men con -
1 liv - ing Which you made good; Har - vest of sown fields, Fruits of the
2 neigh - bor We may be fed. Sow - ing or til - ling, We would work
3 guid - ing Teach - es us share One with an - oth - er, So that, re -
4 fes - sing Your gra - cious hand. Where your will's reign - ing No man will
1 or - chard, Hay from the mown fields, Blos - som and wood.
2 with you, Har - vest - ing, mil - ling, For dai - ly bread.
3 joic - ing With us, our broth - er May know your care.
4 hun - ger, Your love sus - tain - ing, Fruit - ful the land.

THE MASTER CAME
Gabriel Huck, 1965
495
Higher Key at No. 452
ICH GLAUB AN GOTT
87. 87, with Chorus
Mainz Gesangbuch, 1870
1 The Mas - ter came to bring good news, The news of love and
2 The Law's ful - filled through Je - sus Christ, The man who lived for
3 To seek the sin - ners Je - sus came, To live a - mong the
4 For - give us, Lord, as we for - give And seek to help each
1 free - dom, To heal the sick and seek the poor, To
2 oth - ers. The law of Christ is love a - lone, To
3 friend - less, To show them love that they might share The
4 oth - er. For - give us, Lord, and we shall live To
1 build the peace - ful king - dom. Fa - ther, for - give us!
2 serve now all our broth - ers. Fa - ther, for - give us!
3 king - dom that is end - less. Fa - ther, for - give us!
4 pray and work to - geth - er. Fa - ther, for - give us!
1 Through Je - sus hear us! As we for - give one an - oth - er!
2 Through Je - sus hear us! As we for - give one an - oth - er!
3 Through Je - sus hear us! As we for - give one an - oth - er!
4 Through Je - sus hear us! As we for - give one an - oth - er!

496

O HOLY CITY, SEEN OF JOHN
Walter Russell Bowie, 1909, alt.

MORNING SONG
86. 86. 86
Kentucky Harmony, c. 1815

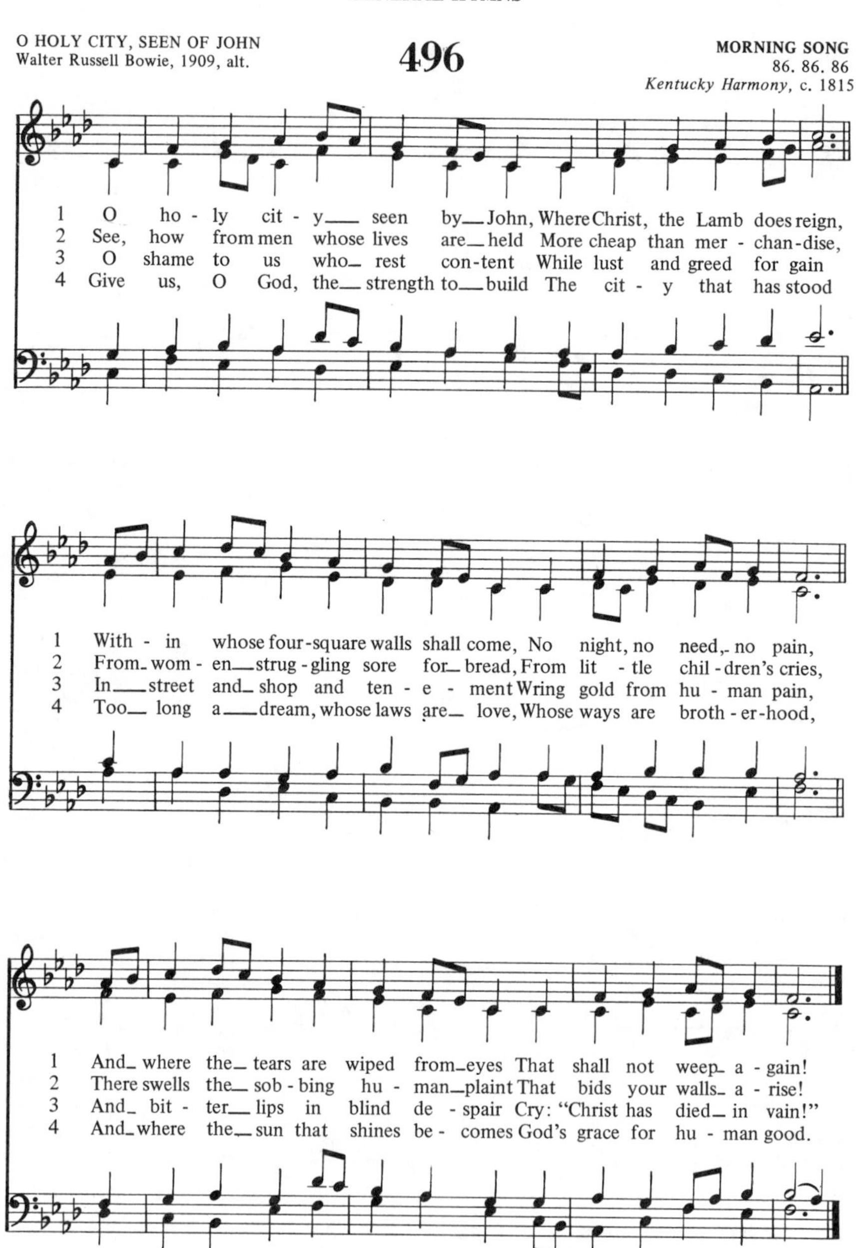
1 O ho - ly cit - y__ seen by__ John, Where Christ, the Lamb does reign,
2 See, how from men whose lives are__ held More cheap than mer - chan-dise,
3 O shame to us who__ rest con-tent While lust and greed for gain
4 Give us, O God, the__ strength to__ build The cit - y that has stood
1 With - in whose four-square walls shall come, No night, no need,_ no pain,
2 From_ wom - en__ strug - gling sore for__ bread, From lit - tle chil - dren's cries,
3 In__ street and__ shop and ten - e - ment Wring gold from hu - man pain,
4 Too__ long a__ dream, whose laws are__ love, Whose ways are broth - er-hood,
1 And_ where the_ tears are wiped from_eyes That shall not weep_ a - gain!
2 There swells the__ sob - bing hu - man__plaint That bids your walls_ a - rise!
3 And_ bit - ter__ lips in blind de - spair Cry: "Christ has died__ in vain!"
4 And_where the__sun that shines be - comes God's grace for hu - man good.

5 Already in the mind of God
That city rises fair:
See how its splendor challenges
The souls that greatly dare,
And bids us seize the whole of life
And build its glory there.

FORGIVE OUR SINS
Rosamond E. Herklots, b. 1905
497
BURFORD
C. M.
Chetham's Psalmody, 1718
1 "For - give our sins as we for - give" You taught us, Lord, to pray,
2 How can your par - don reach and bless The un - for - giv - ing heart
3 In blaz - ing light your cross re - veals The truth we dim - ly knew:
4 Lord, cleanse the depths with - in our souls, And bid re - sent - ment cease;
1 But you a - lone can grant us grace To live the words we say.
2 That broods on wrongs, and will not let Old bit - ter - ness de - part?
3 How small the debts men owe to us, How great our debt to you.
4 Then, rec - on - ciled to God and man, Our lives will spread your peace.

WHERE CROSS THE CROWDED WAYS
Frank Mason North, 1905, alt

498

ST. VINCENT
L. M.
Sigismund Neukomm
arr. by James Uglow, 1868

1 On all the crowd - ed ways of life, A - mid the
2 In slums of wretch - ed - ness and need, On shad - owed
3 From ten - der child - hood's help - less - ness, From wo - man's
4 The cup of wa - ter giv'n for you Still holds the

1 cries of race and clan, A - bove the noise of
2 thresh - olds dark with fears, From paths of hid - den
3 grief, man's bur - dened day, From hun - gry souls, from
4 fresh - ness of your grace, Yet all these peo - ple

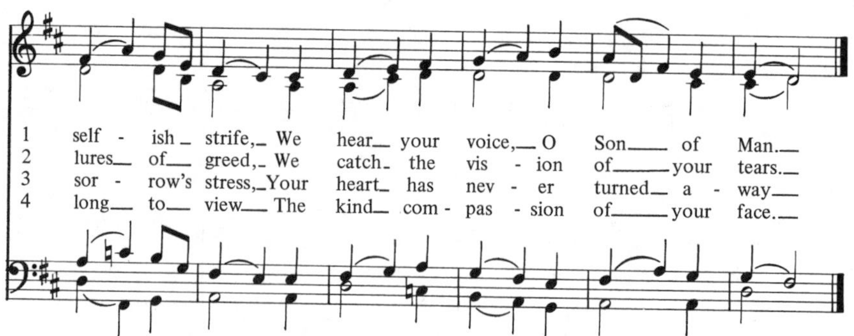
1 self - ish strife, We hear your voice, O Son of Man.
2 lures of greed, We catch the vis - ion of your tears.
3 sor - row's stress, Your heart has nev - er turned a - way.
4 long to view The kind com - pas - sion of your face.

5 O Master, from the mountainside
Come down to heal these hearts, and then
Among these restless crowds abide,
And walk our city's streets again,

6 Till all mankind shall learn your love
And follow where your feet have trod,
Till glorious from your heav'n above
Shall come the city of our God.

AU SANG QU'UN DIEU
87. 87. D.
Traditional French melody
Adapted from G. B. Pergolesi, 1710-36

SON OF GOD, ETERNAL SAVIOR
Somerset Corry Lowry, 1893, alt.

499

1 Son of God, e - ter - nal Sav - ior, Source of life and truth and grace,
2 Lord, as you have lived for oth - ers, So may we for oth - ers live;
3 Come, O Christ, and reign a - mong us, King of love and Prince of peace;
4 Bind us all as one to - geth - er In your Church-'s sa - cred fold,
1 Son of Man, whose birth in - car - nate Sanc - ti - fies our hu - man race,
2 Free - ly have your gifts been grant - ed, Free - ly may your ser - vants give.
3 Hush the storm of strife and pas - sion, Bid its cru - el dis - cords cease.
4 Weak and health - y, poor and wealth - y, Sad and joy - ful, young and old.
1 You, our Head, who, throned in glo - ry, For your own now ev - er plead,
2 Yours the gold and yours the sil - ver, Yours the wealth that can en - sue;
3 By your pa - tient years of toil - ing, By your si - lent hours of pain,
4 Is there pain or want or sor - row? Make us all the bur - den share.
1 Fill us with your love and pit - y, Heal our wrongs and help our need.
2 We but stew - ards of your boun - ty, Held in sol - emn trust for you.
3 Quench our burn - ing thirst of pleas - ure, Shame our self - ish greed of gain.
4 Are there spir - its crushed or bro - ken? Teach us, Lord, to soothe and care.

5 Dark the path that lies behind us,
Filled with cruel pain and blood,
But before us glows the vision
Of the coming brotherhood.

As you prayed it; as you willed it—
That your people should be one,
Grant, O grant our hope's fulfillment:
Here on earth your will be done!

AM I MY BROTHER'S KEEPER
Ian Ferguson, 1967

500

Higher Key at No. 515

LLANGLOFFAN
76. 76. D.
Welsh Melody
Evans' *Hymnau a Thonau,* 1865

1 "Am I my broth - er's keep - er?" The mut - tered cry was drowned
2 The rul - er called for wa - ter And thought his hands were clean.
3 As long as peo - ple hun - ger, As long as peo - ple thirst,
1 By A - bel's life - blood shout - ing In si - lence from the ground.
2 Christ count - ed less than or - der, The man than the ma - chine.
3 And ig - no - rance and ill - ness And war - fare do their worst,
1 For no man is an is - land Di - vid - ed from the main—
2 The crowd cried, "Cru - ci - fy him," Their mal - ice would - n't budge,
3 As long as there's in - just - ice In an - y of God's lands,
1 The bell which tolled for A - bel Tolled e - qual - ly for Cain.
2 So Pi - late called for wa - ter, And his - t'ry is his judge.
3 I am my broth - er's keep - er; I dare not wash my hands!

HELP US TO HELP EACH OTHER
Charles Wesley, 1707-88, cento
501
RICHMOND
C. M.
Thomas Haweis, 1792
1 Help us to help each other, Lord, Each other's cross to bear; Let each his friendly aid afford, And feel his brother's care.
2 Lord, in to thee, our living Head, Let us in all things grow, And by thy sacrifice be led The fruits of love to show.
3 Drawn by the magnet of thy love Let all our hearts agree; And ever towards each other move, And ever move towards thee.
4 This is the bond of perfectness, Thy spotless charity. O let us still, we pray, possess The mind that was in thee.

SING A SONG OF HIGH REVOLT
Fred Kaan, b. 1929, alt.
502
Lower Key at No. 207
TRURO
L. M.
Melody from *Psalmodia Evangelica,* 1789
1 Sing we a song of high re - volt; Make
2 Sing we of him who deep - ly cares And
3 By him the poor are lift - ed up; He
4 He calls us to re - volt and fight With
1 great the Lord, his name ex - alt: Sing
2 still with us our bur - den shares; He,
3 sat - is - fies with bread and cup The
4 him for what is just and right, To
1 we the words of Mar - y's song Of
2 who with strength the proud dis - owns, Brings
3 hun - gry men of man - y lands; The
4 sing and live *Mag - nif - i - cat* To
1 God at war with hu - man wrong.
2 down the might - y from their thrones.
3 rich are left with emp - ty hands.
4 ease his peo - ple's sor - ry lot.

O GOD IN HEAVEN
Hugh Martin, 1890-1964,alt.
503
WRESTLING JACOB
88. 88. 88
S. S. Wesley, 1810-76
1 O God in heav'n, whose lov - ing plan Or - dained for us our
2 May young and old to - geth - er find In Christ the Lord of
3 The sins that mar our homes for - give; From all self - seek - ing
4 O Fa - ther, in our homes pre - side, Their du - ties shared as
1 par - ents' care, And, from the time our life be - gan, The
2 ev - 'ry day, That fel - low - ship our homes may bind In
3 set us free; May par - ents, chil - dren ev - er live In
4 in thy sight; O be in kind - ly ways our guide; On
1 shel - ter of a home to share.
2 joy and sor - row, work and play.
3 glad o - be - di - ence to thee.
4 joy and troub - le shed thy light.
Our Fa - ther, on the
homes we love Send down thy bless - ings from a - bove.

OUR FATHER, BY WHOSE NAME
F. Bland Tucker, 1941, alt.

504

RHOSYMEDRE
66. 66. 888
John David Edwards, c. 1840

1 Our Fa - ther, by whose Name All fa - ther - hood is known,
2 O Christ, your - self a child With - in an earth - ly home,
3 O Ho - ly Spir - it, bind Our hearts in u - ni - ty,
1 In love do you pro - claim Each fam - i - ly your own;
2 With heart still un - de - filed You did to man - hood come;
3 And teach us all to find The love from self set free;
1 O bless all par - ents, guard - ing well, With con - stant love as
2 Our chil - dren bless, in ev - 'ry place, That they may all be -
3 In all our hearts such love in - crease, That ev - 'ry home, by
1 sen - ti - nel, The homes in which your peo - ple dwell.
2 hold your face, And know - ing you may grow in grace.
3 this re - lease, May be the dwell - ing place of peace.

505

O THOU WHOSE FEET
Louis Fitzgerald Benson, 1894

IRISH
C.M.
Melody Pub. Dublin, 1749

1 O Lord, whose feet have climbed life's hill, And trod the path of youth, Our Sav - ior and our broth - er still, Now lead us in - to truth.
2 The call is yours; O be the Way, And give us men to guide; Let wis - dom broad - en with the day, Let hu - man faith a - bide.
3 Who learn of you, the truth shall find; Who fol - low, gain the goal; With rev - 'rence crown the ear - nest mind, And speak with - in the soul.
4 A - wake the pur - pose high which strives, And, fal - ling, stands a - gain; Con - firm the will of ea - ger lives To prove that they are men.

5 Your life the bond of fellowship,
Your love the law that rules,
Your Name, proclaimed by ev'ry lip,
The Master of our schools.

HELP US, O LORD, TO LEARN
William Watkins Reid, b. 1923

506

YATTENDON 46
S. M.
Harry Ellis Wooldridge, 1899

1 Help us, O Lord, to learn
2 Help us, O Lord, to live
3 Help us, O Lord, to teach
1 The truths your Word im - parts:
2 The faith which we pro - claim,
3 The beau - ty of your ways,
1 To stud - y, that your laws may be
2 That all our thoughts and words and deeds
3 That yearn - ing souls may find the Christ
1 In - scribed up - on our hearts.
2 May glo - ri - fy your name.
3 And sing a - loud his praise.

JESUS, THOU DIVINE COMPANION
Henry Van Dyke, 1909, alt.
507
Higher Key at No. 307
PLEADING SAVIOR
87. 87. D.
Leavitt's Christian Lyre, 1830
1 Je - sus, our di - vine Com - pan - ion, By your low - ly hu - man birth
2 Where the man - y work to - geth - er, You are there a - mong your own;
3 Ev - 'ry task, how - ev - er sim - ple, Sets the soul that does it free;
1 You have come to join the work - ers, Bur - den - bear - ers of the earth.
2 Where the wea - ry work - man's sleep - ing, You are there with him a - lone:
3 Ev - 'ry deed of love and kind - ness Done to man is done to thee.
1 You, the car - pen - ter of Naz - 'reth, Work - ing for your dai - ly food,
2 You, the peace that pas - ses knowl - edge, Dwel - ling in the dai - ly strife;
3 Je - sus, our di - vine Com - pan - ion, Help us all to work our best;
1 By your pa - tience and your cour - age, You have taught us work is good.
2 You, the Bread of heav'n are bro - ken In the sac - ra - ment of life.
3 Bless us in our dai - ly la - bor, Lead us to our Sab - bath rest.

ETERNAL FATHER, STRONG TO SAVE
Sts. 1, 4, William Whiting, 1860, alt.
Sts. 2, 3, Robert Nelson Spencer, 1937, alt.

508

MELITA
88. 88. 88
John B. Dykes, 1861

1 E - ter - nal Fa - ther, strong to save, Whose arm has bound the
2 O Christ, the Lord of hill and plain O'er which our traf - fic
3 O Spir - it, whom the Fa - ther sent To spread a - broad the
4 O Trin - i - ty of love and pow'r, Our broth - ers shield in
1 rest - less wave, Who bid the might - y o - cean deep Its
2 runs a - main By moun - tain pass or val - ley low; Wher -
3 fir - ma - ment; O Wind of heav - en, by your might Save
4 dan - ger's hour; From rock and tem - pest, fire and foe, Pro -
1 own ap - point - ed lim - its keep: To you we pray most
2 ev - er, Lord, your peo - ple go, Pro - tect them by your
3 all who dare the ea - gle's flight, And keep them by your
4 tect them ev - 'ry - where they go; Thus ev - er - more with
1 ear - nest - ly For those in per - il on the sea.
2 guard - ing hand From ev - 'ry per - il on the land.
3 watch - ful care From ev - 'ry per - il in the air.
4 thanks shall we Give praise from air and land and sea. A - men.

509
THINE ARM, O LORD
Edward Hayes Plumptre, 1864, alt.
WEYMOUTH
C. M. D.
Theodore P. Ferris, 1941
1 Your arm, O Lord, in days of old Was strong to heal and save;
2 Praise God! Your touch brought life and health, Gave speech, and strength and sight;
3 Christ, be our great de - liv - er - er, O Lord of life and death;
1 It con - quered both dis - ease and death, Both dark - ness and the grave.
2 And youth re - newed and fren - zy calmed Hailed you the Lord of light.
3 Re - store, en - liv - en, soothe and bless With your al - might - y breath.
1 To you they went, the blind, the dumb, The pal - sied and the lame,
2 And now, O Lord, be near to bless, Al - might - y as of yore,
3 To hands that work and eyes that see Give wis - dom's ho - ly lore,
1 The lep - er with his taint - ed life, The sick with fe - vered frame.
2 In crowd - ed street, by pain - ful bed, As by Gen - es - 'reth's shore.
3 That sound and sick, and weak and strong May praise you ev - er - more.

O GOD, BY WHOSE ALMIGHTY PLAN
H. C. A. Gaunt, b. 1902

510

DAVID'S HARP
88. 88. 88
Robert King, 1722

1 O God, by whose al - might - y plan First or - der out of
2 O Christ, whose touch un - veiled the blind, Whose pres - ence warmed the
3 O Ho - ly Spir - it, by whose grace Our skills a - bide, our
1 cha - os stirred, And life, pro - gres - sive at your word,
2 lone - ly soul; Your love made bro - ken sin - ners whole,
3 wis - dom grow, In ev - 'ry heal - ing work dis - close
1 Ma - tured through na - ture up to man; Grant us in
2 Your faith cast dev - ils from the mind. Grant us your
3 New paths to probe, new thoughts to trace. Grant us your
1 light and love to grow, Your sov - 'reign truth to seek and know.
2 faith, your love, your care To bring to suf - f'rers ev - ry - where.
3 wis - est ways to go In all we think, or speak, or do.

Alternative Tune: MELITA, No. 508

511

O GOD, WHOSE WILL
H. D. Rawnsley, 1851-1920, alt.

DUNDEE
C. M.
Scottish Psalter, 1615

1 O God, whose will is life and good For
2 Make strong their hands and hearts and wills To
3 Wher - e'er they heal the sick and blind, Christ's
4 Be - fore them set your ho - ly will, That

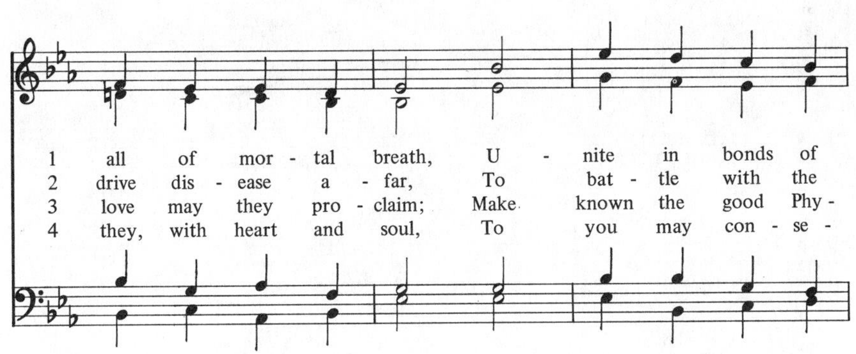
1 all of mor - tal breath, U - nite in bonds of
2 drive dis - ease a - far, To bat - tle with the
3 love may they pro - claim; Make known the good Phy -
4 they, with heart and soul, To you may con - se -

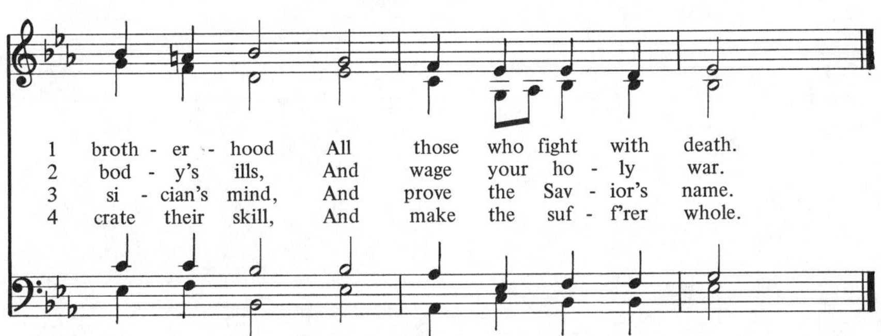
1 broth - er - hood All those who fight with death.
2 bod - y's ills, And wage your ho - ly war.
3 si - cian's mind, And prove the Sav - ior's name.
4 crate their skill, And make the suf - f'rer whole.

FROM THEE ALL SKILL
Charles Kingsley, 1819-75, alt.

512

ST COLUMBA
C. M.
Traditional Irish Melody

1 From you all skill and science flow,
2 And give them, Lord, to each and all,
3 And hasten, Lord, that perfect day
4 When ever-blue the sky shall gleam,
1 All pity, care, and love,
2 As each and all shall need
3 When pain and death shall cease,
4 And ever-green the sod,
1 All calm and courage, faith and hope—
2 To rise like incense, each to you,
3 And your just rule shall fill the earth
4 And man's rude work deface no more
1 O pour them from above!
2 In noble thought and deed.
3 With health, and light, and peace,
4 The Paradise of God.

513

ONCE TO EVERY MAN AND NATION
From *The Present Crisis*
James Russell Lowell, 1845, alt.

EBENEZER (TON-Y-BOTEL)
87. 87. D.
Thomas John Williams, 1890

1 Once to_ ev - 'ry man and_ na - tion Comes the_ mo - ment to_ de - cide
2 Then to_ side with truth is_ no - ble, When we_ share_ her wretch - ed crust,
3 By the_ light of burn - ing_ mar - tyrs, Christ, your bleed - ing feet_ we track,
4 Though the_ cause of e - vil_ pros - per, Yet 'tis_ truth_ a - lone_ is strong;
1 In the_ strife of truth and_ false - hood, For the_ good_ or e - vil side;
2 Ere her_ cause bring fame and_ prof - it, And 'tis_ pros - p'rous to_ be just;
3 Toil - ing_ up new Cal - v'ries_ ev - er With the_ cross_ that turns not back;
4 Though her_ por - tion be the_ scaf - fold, And up - on_ the throne_ be wrong,
1 Some great cause, God's new Mes - si - ah, Of - f'ring_ each the bloom or_ blight,
2 Then it_ is the brave man_ choos - es While the_ cow - ard stands a - side,
3 New oc - ca - sions teach new_ du - ties, Time makes_ an - cient good un - couth;
4 Yet that_ scaf - fold sways the_ fu - ture, And, be - hind the dim un - known,
2
1 And the choice goes by for - ev - er 'Twixt that_ dark - ness and_ that light.
2 Till the_ mul - ti - tude make_ vir - tue Of the_ faith_ they had_ de - nied.
3 They must up - ward still and_ on - ward, Who would keep_ a - breast_ of truth.
4 Stands our_ God with - in the_ shad - ow Keep - ing_ watch a - bove_ his own.

514

LORD CHRIST, WHEN FIRST
Walter Russell Bowie, 1928, alt.

Lower Key at No. 336

MIT FREUDEN ZART
(BOHEMIAN BRETHREN)
87. 87. 887
Genevan Psalter, 1551
Adapted by Unitas Fratrum, 1566

1 Lord Christ, when first you came to men, Up - on a cross they
2 O won - drous love, which found no room In life where sin de -
3 New com - ing of the love of Christ, Shall we a - gain re -
4 O wound - ed hands of Je - sus, build In us your new cre -
1 bound you, And mocked your sav - ing king - ship then By thorns with which they
2 nied you, And doomed to death, must bring to doom The pow'r which cru - ci -
3 fuse you, Till in the night of hate and war We per - ish as we
4 a - tion; Our pride is dust, our boast is stilled, We wait your rev - e -
1 crowned you: And still our wrongs may weave you now New
2 fied you, Till not a stone was left on stone, And
3 lose you? From old un - faith our souls re - lease To
4 la - tion: O love that tri - umphs o - ver loss, We
1 thornes to pierce that stead - y brow, And robe of sor - row round you.
2 all a na - tion's pride, o'er-thrown, Went down to dust be - side you!
3 seek the king - dom of your peace, By which a - lone we choose you.
4 bring our hearts be - fore your cross, To fin - ish your sal - va - tion.

O GOD OF EARTH AND ALTAR
Gilbert K. Chesterton, 1906

515

Lower Key at No. 500

LLANGLOFFAN
76. 76. D.
Welsh Melody
Evans' *Hymnau a Thonau,* 1865

1 O God of earth and al - tar, Bow down and hear our cry;
2 From all that ter - ror teach - es, From lies of tongue and pen,
3 Tie in a liv - ing teth - er The priest and prince and thrall;
1 Our earth - ly rul - ers fal - ter; Our peo - ple drift and die;
2 From all the eas - y speech - es That com - fort cru - el men,
3 Bind all our lives to - geth - er; Smite us and save us all;
1 The walls of gold en - tomb us; The swords of scorn di - vide;
2 From sale and prof - a - na - tion Of hon - or and the sword,
3 In ire and ex - ul - ta - tion, A - flame with faith, and free,
1 Take not thy thun - der from __ us, But take a - way our pride.
2 From sleep and from dam - na - tion, De - liv - er us, good Lord!
3 Lift up a liv - ing na - tion, A sin - gle sword to thee.

O GOD OF EVERY NATION
William W. Reid, Jr., 1958, alt.
516
KING'S LYNN
76. 76. D.
Traditional English Melody,
Arr. by R. Vaughan Williams, 1906
1 O God of ev - 'ry na - tion, Of__ ev - 'ry race and land,
2 From search for wealth and pow - er And__ scorn of truth and right,
3 Lord, strength-en all who la - bor That__ men may find re - lease
4 Keep bright in us the vi - sion Of__ days when war shall cease,
1 Re - deem the whole cre - a - tion With your al - might - y hand;
2 From_trust in bombs that_show - er De - struc - tion through the night,
3 From_fear of rat - tling_ sa - ber, From dread of war's in - crease;
4 When_ha - tred and di - vi - sion Give way to love and peace,
1 Where_ hate and fear di - vide us And bit - ter threats are hurled,
2 From_ pride of race and_ na - tion And blind - ness to your way,
3 When_ hope and cour - age_ fal - ter, Your still small voice be heard;
4 Till___ dawns the morn - ing_ glo - rious When broth - er - hood shall reign
1 In love and mer - cy guide__ us And__ heal our strife - torn world.
2 De - liv - er ev - 'ry na - tion, E - ter - nal God, we pray!
3 With faith that none can al - ter, Your_ ser - vants un - der - gird.
4 And Christ shall rule vic - tor - i - ous O'er__ all the world's do - main.

PEACE IN OUR TIME, O LORD
John Oxenham, 1938
517[1]
Higher Key
CORONA
S. M. D.
Richard R. Terry, 1865-1938
1 Peace in our time, O Lord, To all the peo - ples— peace!
2 Too long mis - trust and fear Have held our souls in thrall;
3 Oh, shall we nev - er learn The truth all time has taught,
4 Peace in our time, O Lord, To all the peo - ples – peace!
1 Peace sure - ly based up - on your will And built in right - eous - ness.
2 Sweep through the earth, keen breath of heav'n, And sound a no - bler call!
3 That with - out God as ar - chi - tect Our build - ing comes to naught?
4 Peace that shall build a glad new world And make for life's in - crease.
1 Your pow'r a - lone can break The fet - ters that en - chain
2 Come, as you did of old, In love so great that men
3 Lord, help us and in - spire Our hearts and lives a - gain,
4 O liv - ing Christ, who still Our heav - y bur - dens share,
1 The sore - ly - strick - en soul of life, And make it live a - gain.
2 Shall cast a - side all oth - er gods And turn to you a - gain!
3 That we may build, with all your gifts, Your king - dom here for men.
4 Come now and dwell with - in the hearts Of all men ev - 'ry - where!

517[2]

Lower Key

GIVE PEACE, O GOD
John W. Norris, 1939, alt.

518

ARLINGTON
C. M.
Thomas A. Arne, 1762

1 Give peace, O God, the na - tions cry, From
2 Yet not your peace, O God, they ask, The
3 But peace they ask from war's a - larms, Re -
4 We need the peace of heart and mind In
5 O cleanse all hearts of pride and greed, Re -

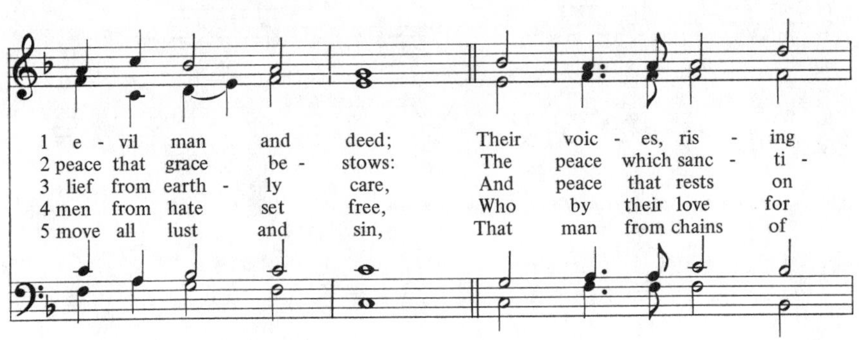
1 e - vil man and deed; Their voic - es, ris - ing
2 peace that grace be - stows: The peace which sanc - ti -
3 lief from earth - ly care, And peace that rests on
4 men from hate set free, Who by their love for
5 move all lust and sin, That man from chains of

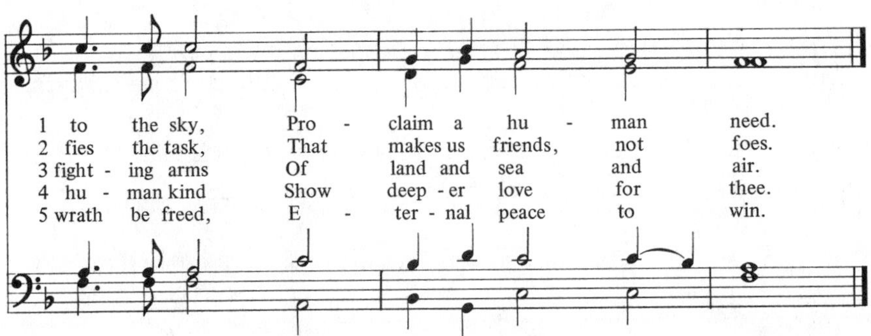
1 to the sky, Pro - claim a hu - man need.
2 fies the task, That makes us friends, not foes.
3 fight - ing arms Of land and sea and air.
4 hu - man kind Show deep - er love for thee.
5 wrath be freed, E - ter - nal peace to win.

519

MAKE ME A CHANNEL
Adapted from the *Prayer of St. Francis*
Sebastian Temple, 1967

PRAYER OF ST. FRANCIS
Irregular
Sebastian Temple, 1967
Harm., D.F., 1977

D
1. Make me a chan - nel of your peace. Where
2. Make me a chan - nel of your peace. Where
A7
1. there is ha - tred, let me bring your love. Where
2. there's des - pair in life, let me bring hope. Where
1. there is in - ju - ry, your par - don Lord. And
2. there is dark - ness, on - ly light, And
1
D
2
D
D7
1. where there's doubt, true faith in you.
2. where there's sad - ness, ev - er joy.
G
D
O Mas - ter, grant that I may nev - er seek So

D
much to be con - soled as to con - sole. To be
G
D
un - der - stood as to un - der - stand. To be
E7
A7
loved as to love, with all my soul.
D
Make me a chan-nel of your peace. It is in par-don-
A7
ing that we are par - doned; In giv - ing to all men that we re - ceive,
D
And in dy - ing that we're born to e - ter - nal life.

O DAY OF GOD, DRAW NIGH
R. B. Y. Scott, 1937, alt.

520

FESTAL SONG
S. M.
William H. Walter, 1894

1 O Day of God, draw nigh In beau - ty and in pow'r, Come with your_ time - less judg - ment now To match_ our pre - sent hour.
2 Bring to our troub - led mind, Un - cer - tain and a - fraid, The qui - et of a stead - fast faith, Calm of_ a call o - beyed.
3 Bring jus - tice to our land, That all_ may dwell se - cure, And fine - ly_ build for days to come Foun - da - tions that en - dure.
4 Bring to our world of strife Your sov - 'reign word of peace, That war may haunt the earth no more And des - o - la - tion cease.

5 O Day of God, draw nigh;
As at creation's birth
Let there be light again, and set
Your judgments on the earth.

O GOD OF LOVE
Henry Williams Baker, 1861, alt.

521

Higher Key at No. 247

ERHALT UNS, HERR (SPIRES)
L. M.
J. Klug's *Geistliche Lieder,* 1543

1 O— God of— love, O— King of peace, Make
2 Re - mem - ber,— Lord, your— works of old, The
3 Whom— shall we— trust but— you, O Lord? Where

1 wars through-out the world to cease; The wrath of— sin - ful
2 won - ders that our fa - thers told; Re - mem - ber—not— our
3 rest but on your faith - ful word? None ev - er—called—on

1 man— re - strain; Give peace, O God, give peace a - gain!
2 sin's— dark stain; Give peace, O God, give peace a - gain!
3 you— in vain; Give peace, O God, give peace a - gain!

ETERNAL RULER
John W. Chadwick, 1864
522
Higher Key at No. 215
YORKSHIRE (STOCKPORT)
10 10. 10 10. 10 10
John Wainwright, 1750
1 E - ter - nal Rul - er of the cease - less
2 We are of thee, the chil - dren of thy
3 We would be one in ha - tred of all
4 O clothe us with thy heav'n - ly ar - mor,
1 round Of circ - ling plan - ets sing - ing
2 love, The broth - ers of thy well - be -
3 wrong, One in our love of all things
4 Lord, Thy trust - y shield, thy sword of
1 on their way; Guide of the
2 lov - èd Son; De - scend, O
3 sweet and fair, One with the
4 love di - vine; Our in - spi -
1 na - tions from the night pro - found
2 Ho - ly Spir - it, like a dove,
3 joy that breaks out in - to song,
4 ra - tion be thy con - stant word;

SOCIAL RELIGION

1 In - to the glo - ry of the per - fect
2 In - to our hearts, that we may be as
3 One with the grief that trem - bles in - to
4 We ask no vic - to - ries that are not
1 day; Rule in our hearts, that
2 one: As one with thee, to
3 prayer, One in the pow'r that
4 thine: Give or with - hold, let
1 we may ev - er be Guid - ed and
2 whom we ev - er tend; As one with
3 makes thy chil - dren free To fol - low
4 pain or pleas - ure be; E - nough to
1 strength - ened and up - held by thee.
2 him, our Broth - er and our Friend.
3 truth, and thus to fol - low thee.
4 know that we are serv - ing thee.

THE GOD WHO RULES THIS EARTH
Richard G. Jones, b. 1926

523[1]
Higher Key

ARTHUR'S SEAT
66. 66. 88
John Goss, 1874

1 The God who rules this earth Gave life to
2 But sin in - fects us all, Dis - torts the
3 Be - tween the West and East, Yet nei - ther
4 That Man a - lone com - bines All lives with -
1 ev - 'ry race; He chose its day of
2 com - mon good; The u - ni - ver - sal
3 black nor white Be - hold God's Son re -
4 in his own; That Man a - lone en -
1 birth, The col - or of its face;
2 fall Cor - rupts all broth - er - hood;
3 leased, In whom all men u - nite.
4 shrines All flesh, all blood, all bone;
1 So none may claim su - pe - rior grade
2 So ra - cial pride and col - or strife
3 He comes with un - re - strict - ed grace
4 That man ac - cepts all hu - man pain,

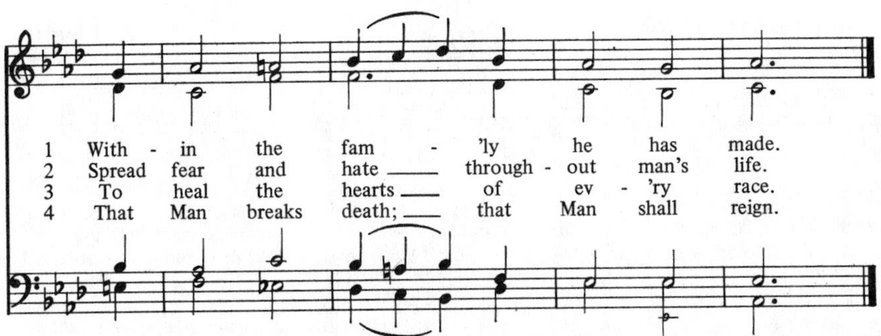
1 With - in the fam - 'ly he has made.
2 Spread fear and hate ___ through - out man's life.
3 To heal the hearts ___ of ev - 'ry race.
4 That Man breaks death; ___ that Man shall reign.

5 To him we bring our praise,
On him all hopes depend;
Sole Master of our days,
In him we see the End;
Man's final Lord, God's perfect Son,
In Jesus Christ are all made one!

523[2]

Lower Key

FATHER, LORD OF ALL CREATION
Stewart Cross, b. 1928
524
SANCTUS
87. 87. D.
John Richards (Isalaw), 1843-1908
1 Fa - ther, Lord of all Cre - a - tion, Ground of Be - ing, Life and Love,
2 Je - sus Christ, the Man for O - thers, We, your peo - ple, make our prayer:
3 Ho - ly Spir - it, rush - ing, burn - ing Wind and flame of Pen - te - cost,
1 Height and depth be - yond des - crip - tion On - ly life in you can prove:
2 Give us grace to love as broth - ers All whose bur - dens we can share.
3 Fire our hearts a - fresh with yearn - ing To re - gain what we have lost.
1 You are mor - tal life's de-pen-dence:Thought,speech,sight are ours by grace;
2 Where your name binds us to - geth - er You, Lord Christ, will sure - ly be;
3 May your love u - nite our ac - tion, Nev - er - more to speak a - lone:
1 Yours is ev - 'ry hour's ex - ist- ence, Sov -'reign Lord of time and space.
2 Where no self - ish - ness can sev - er, There your love may all men see.
3 God, in us a - bol - ish fac - tion, God, through us your love make known.

CHRIST FOR THE WORLD WE SING
Samuel Wolcott, 2 Feb. 1869, alt.

525

Higher Key at No. 411

MOSCOW (ITALIAN HYMN)
664. 6664
Felice De Giardini, 1769, alt.

1 Christ for the world we sing! The world to Christ we bring With lov - ing zeal;
2 Christ for the world we sing! The world to Christ we bring With fer - vent prayer;
3 Christ for the world we sing! The world to Christ we bring With one ac - cord;
4 Christ for the world we sing! The world to Christ we bring With joy - ful song;
1 The poor, and them that mourn, The faint and o - ver - borne, Sin - sick and sor - row - worn, Whom Christ would heal.
2 The way - ward and the lost, By rest - less pas - sions tossed, Re - deemed at count - less cost From dark des - pair.
3 With us the work to share, With us re - proach to dare, With us the cross to bear For Christ, our Lord.
4 The new - born souls, whose days, Re - claimed from er - ror's ways, In - spired with hope and praise, To Christ be - long.

CREATION'S LORD
William DeWitt Hyde, 1903, alt.

526

SEABURY
L. M.
Claude Means, 1941

1 Cre - a - tion's Lord, we give you thanks That this your world is in - com - plete,
2 That you have not yet fin - ished man, That we are in the mak - ing still
3 What though the king - dom long de - lay And still with man - y foes must cope?
4 Since what we choose is what we are And what we love we yet shall be,
1 That bat - tle calls our mar - shaled ranks, That work a - waits our hands and feet,
2 As friends who share the Mak - er's plan, As sons who know the Fa - ther's will.
3 It gives us that for which to pray, A field for toil and faith and hope.
4 The goal may ev - er shine a - far; The will to win it makes us free!

527

Psalm 72
HAIL TO THE LORD'S ANOINTED
James Montgomery, 1821

WOODBIRD
76. 76. D.
Traditional German Melody

1 All hail the Lord's a - noint - ed, Great Da - vid's great - er Son!
2 He shall come down like show - ers Up - on the fruit - ful earth;
3 Kings shall bow down be - fore him, And gold and in - cense bring;
4 He comes with aid so speed - y To those who suf - fer wrong,
1 Hail, in the time ap - point - ed, His reign on earth be - gun!
2 And love, joy, hope, like flow - ers, In his path spring to birth.
3 All na - tions shall a - dore him, His praise all peo - ples sing,
4 To help the poor and need - y, And bid the weak be strong;
1 He comes to break op - pres - sion, To set the cap - tive free,
2 Be - fore him on the moun - tains Shall peace, the her - ald, go;
3 For he shall have do - min - ion O'er riv - er, sea, and shore
4 To give them songs for sigh - ing, Their dark - ness turn to light,
1 To take a - way trans - gres - sion, And rule in eq - ui - ty.
2 And right - eous - ness in foun - tains From hill to val - ley flow.
3 Far as the ea - gle's pin - ion, Or dove's light wing can soar.
4 Whose souls, con - demned and dy - ing, Were pre - cious in his sight.

5 The time of time shall never
His covenant destroy;
His name shall stand forever,
His name of love and joy.

And, over foes victorious,
Upon his throne he'll rest,
From age to age more glorious,
All-blessing and all-blest!

528

Psalm 46
GOD IS OUR REFUGE
Metrical Version Anonymous

EIN' FESTE BURG
87. 87. 66. 66. 7
Martin Luther, 1529

1 God is our ref - uge and_our strength, A help - er ev - er near__ us;
2 God's cit - y is__for ev - er blest With liv - ing wa - ters well - ing;
3 Be - hold what God has done_on earth; His wrath brings des - o - la - tion;
1 We will not fear_tho' earth_ be moved, For God is near to cheer__ us.
2 Since God is there, she stands un - moved 'Mid tu - mults round her swell - ing;
3 His grace, com - mand - ing wars_ to cease, Brings peace to ev - 'ry na - tion.
1 Al - though the moun - tains quake And earth's foun - da - tions shake, Tho' an - gry
2 God speaks and all is peace, From war the na - tions cease; The Lord of
3 Be still, for he is Lord, By all the earth a - dored; The Lord of
1 bil - lows roar And break a - gainst the shore, Our might - y God will hear__ us.
2 hosts is nigh, Our fa - ther's God most high Is our e - ter - nal dwell - ing.
3 hosts is nigh, Our fa - ther's God most high Is our strong hab - i - ta - tion.

LEAD ON, O KING ETERNAL
Ernest Warburton Shurtleff, 1887, alt.
529
Lower Key at No. 280
LANCASHIRE
76. 76. D.
Henry Smart, 1836
1 Lead on, O King e - ter - nal; The day of march has come;
2 Lead on, O King e - ter - nal; Till sin's fierce war shall cease,
3 Lead on, O King e - ter - nal; We fol - low, not in fears;
1 Hence - forth in fields of con - quest Your tents shall be our home:
2 And ho - li - ness shall whis - per The sweet "A - men" of peace;
3 For glad - ness breaks like morn - ing Wher - e'er your face ap - pears;
1 Through days of prep - a - ra - tion Your grace has made us strong,—
2 For, not with swords loud clash - ing, Nor roll of stir - ring drums,—
3 Your cross is lift - ed o'er us; We jour - ney in its light:—
1 And now, O King e - ter - nal, We lift our bat - tle - song.
2 But deeds of love and mer - cy, The heav'n - ly king - dom comes.
3 The crown a - waits the con - quest: Lead on, O God of might!

IGJENNEM NAT OG TRÄNGSEL
Bernhardt Severin Ingemann, 1825
Tr., Sabine Baring-Gould, 1867, alt.
530
Higher Key at No. 471
AUSTRIA (HAYDN)
87. 87. D.
Franz Joseph Haydn, 1797
1 Through the night of doubt and sor - row
2 One the light of God's own pres - ence,
3 One the hymn which lips of thou - sands
4 On - ward, there - fore, pil - grim broth - ers!
1 On - ward goes the pil - grim band,
2 O'er his ran - somed peo - ple shed,
3 Lift as from the heart of one;
4 On - ward with the cross our aid!
1 Sing - ing songs of ex - pec - ta - tion,
2 Chas - ing far the gloom and ter - ror,
3 One the con - flict, one the per - il,
4 Bear its shame and fight its bat - tles
1 March - ing to the Prom - ised Land.
2 Bright - 'ning all the path we tread;
3 One the march in God be - gun;
4 Till we rest be - neath its shade.

1 Clear be - fore us, through the dark - ness,
2 One the ob - ject of our jour - ney,
3 One the glad - ness of re - joic - ing
4 Soon shall come the great a - wak - 'ning,
1 Gleams and burns the guid - ing light,
2 One the faith which nev - er tires,
3 On the far e - ter - nal shore,
4 Soon the break - ing of the tomb;
1 Broth - er clasps the hand of broth - er,
2 One the ear - nest look - ing for - ward,
3 Where the one al - might - y Fa - ther
4 Then the scat - t'ring of all shad - ows,
1 Step - ping, fear - less, through the night.
2 One the hope our God in - spires.
3 Reigns in love for - ev - er - more.
4 And the end of toil and gloom.

LET SAINTS ON EARTH
Charles Wesley, 1759, alt.

531

Higher Key at No. 436

ST. PETER
C. M.
Alexander R. Reinagle, ca. 1836

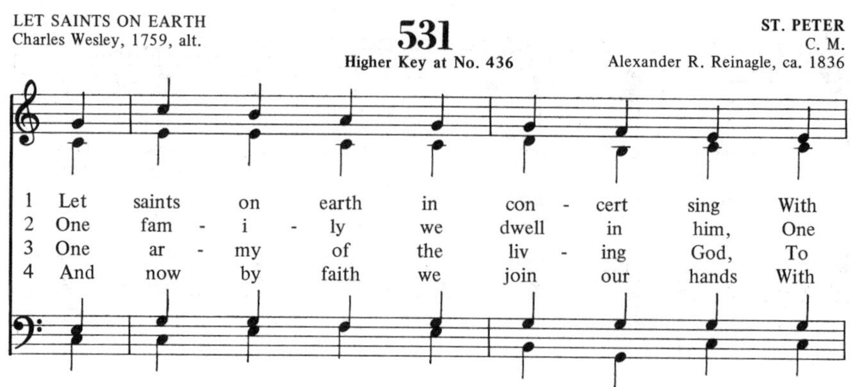
1 Let saints on earth in con - cert sing With
2 One fam - i - ly we dwell in him, One
3 One ar - my of the liv - ing God, To
4 And now by faith we join our hands With

1 those whose work is done; For all the ser - vants
2 Church, a - bove, be - neath, Though now di - vid - ed
3 his com - mand we bow; Part of the host has
4 those that went be - fore, .And greet the ev - er -

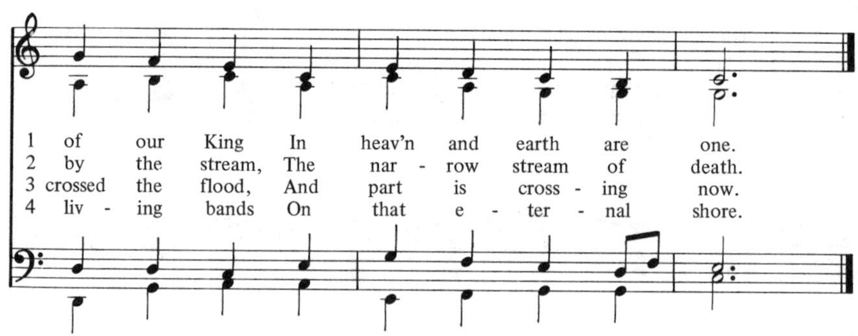
1 of our King In heav'n and earth are one.
2 by the stream, The nar - row stream of death.
3 crossed the flood, And part is cross - ing now.
4 liv - ing bands On that e - ter - nal shore.

5 O Jesus, be our constant Guide;
Then, when the word is giv'n,
Bid Jordan's narrow stream divide,
And bring us safe to heav'n.

YE HOLY ANGELS BRIGHT
Richard Baxter, 1672 *and*
John Hampden Gurney, 1838
532
DARWALL'S 148th
66. 66. 44. 44
John Darwall, 1770, alt., ca. 1778
1 O ho - ly an - gels bright, Who wait at God's right hand,
2 O bless - èd souls at rest, Who ran this earth - ly race
3 O saints, who toil be - low, A - dore your heavn - 'ly King,
4 My soul, O bear your part, Re - joice in God a - bove;
1 Or through the realms of light Fly at your
2 And now, from sin re - leased, Be - hold the
3 And as you on - ward go Some joy - ful
4 And with a well - tuned heart Sing him your
1 Lord's com - mand, As - sist our song, For else the theme
2 Sav - ior's face, God's prais - es sound, As in his sight
3 an - them sing; Take what he gives And praise him still,
4 songs of love! Let all your days Till life shall end,
1 Too high would seem For mor - tal tongue.
2 With sweet de - light You now a - bound.
3 Through good or ill, Who ev - er lives!
4 What - e'er he send, Be filled with praise!

Services for Morning and Evening Prayer

Morning and Evening Prayer

Christ's own earthly life was one of prayer. The gospels constantly portray him as a man of prayer. He habitually prayed early in the morning and late into the night. His ministry was marked by prayer—before the calling of the apostles, in his prayer for his disciples, and for those he healed. His ministry began with forty days of prayer, and closed with the prayer in the garden at Gethsemani and with his prayer on the cross. The gospels describe Jesus as a typical, devout Jew who regularly took part in the services of the synagogue and who described the temple at Jerusalem as a house of prayer. Both the epistle to the Romans and the epistle to the Hebrews describe Christ's risen life as a continuation of his life of prayer—he lives to intercede for us before the Father.

Christ's life of prayer reveals his mission as Son of God. By his prayer he expresses the intimacy and confidence which mark his loving attitude toward the Father. Through our own baptism, we are privileged to share in Christ's life of intimacy and love with the Father. We are baptized to share in Christ's own life as God's sons and daughters. We share in the life of the Spirit of God which enables us to call upon God as a loving Father.

The Church, then, is a community of prayer. It is called to follow Christ in loving union with the Father. When we pray, Christ prays with us and for us. The Holy Spirit makes us one with Christ and leads us to the Father. The prayer of the Church together, clergy and laity, has a special significance. By gathering for common prayer, we acknowledge that we are to be called to be one in the Spirit, one with Christ before the Father. God does not call us to be his children simply as individuals but as one people. Christ promises: "Where two or three are gathered together in my name, there I am in the midst of them" (Mt. 18:20).

The celebration of morning and evening prayer is more than just an ordinary devotional exercise. It is one of the most important ways in which the Church lives its mission to be a community of prayer. The life of every Christian community—diocese, parish, religious community, and other groups—should be marked by the frequent celebration of morning and evening prayer. As far as possible, it should be a real gathering of and for the whole Church. Those who are ordained to ministry in the Church should take their place as leaders of common prayer. The time and place of morning and evening prayer, as well as the manner of celebration, should be such that lay people can take an active part.

Following Jewish prayer patterns, and in imitation of their Lord, the early Christians marked the beginning and the close of day with prayer. Whenever possible, the whole Church, clergy and laity, gathered for morning and evening prayer. For many centuries, the daily round of prayer at morning and evening was characteristic of the public services of the Church.

The General Instruction on the Liturgy of the Hours calls for a renewal of public prayer in the tradition of the Church. This means prayer which is attuned to the scriptures, appropriate to time of day, and accessible to ordinary lay people. It encourages the development of forms of worship in which the whole Church can take part and in which its many ministries can be exercised.

Those familiar with new forms of the breviary will notice some slight departure from typical breviary patterns. This is to be expected, since a breviary is by nature a book for private use, and is not an appropriate or useful instrument for full public worship. It may be useful to note that the General Instruction does not promote the private breviary of the priest as the normative form of the Liturgy of the Hours. Rather, the norm of the Instruction is that of public celebration. According to the Instruction, the primary duty of the priest is not the saying of the breviary, but of gathering and guiding his people in public prayer.

This section of the *The Catholic Liturgy Book* provides a form of morning and evening prayer which can be celebrated by parishes and other groups of ordinary Christians. In accordance with the General Instruction on the Liturgy of the Hours, the special character of morning and evening prayer has been restored.

CHARACTER OF MORNING AND EVENING PRAYER

MORNING PRAYER

Morning prayer is fundamentally a praise to God for a new day, thanking him for it, and offering the day to his care. In the Christian tradition, it takes on a resurrectional note: our own rising to the life of a new day is a recalling of the Lord's resurrection from the dead.

EVENING PRAYER

Evening prayer has a dual character—praise for the gift of the day gone by and penitence for the sins we have committed. It sets the approach of night within the context of Christian hope, and is marked by a strong sense of God's mercy and hope for the coming of Christ who is the light of the world. It is also a special time to pray for the needs of the Church and mankind. Accordingly, provision is made for expanded prayer of intercession.

INTRODUCTION

Each service begins with a call to worship, consisting of three parts: (a) versicles and responses which acknowledge God's presence in our midst; (b) a hymn of praise and thanksgiving; (c) the celebrant's prayer. In the evening, the call to worship takes the form of a thanksgiving for the light of creation and the light of Christ. All stand for this section of the liturgy.

PSALMODY

The psalms are chosen according to their appropriateness for the time of the day. In the evening, Psalm 141 is invariably used to give expression to the penitential side of evening prayer. For Christians, the psalms are prayed in the light of the coming of Christ. Psalmody in morning and evening prayer includes antiphons which highlight the Christian mystery, just as is done with praise of the Trinity at the end of each psalm. So that the psalms can be truly our prayer, there should be a generous pause after each one. The celebrant's prayer (psalm prayer) brings the pause to its conclusion.

PROCLAMATION OF THE WORD

While morning and evening prayer are chiefly prayer services, it is the word of God which informs and shapes true Christian prayer, and the reading is a central part of morning and evening prayer. It may, on ocasion, be followed by a brief homily. The significance of the word is highlighted by the subsequent pause for silence and a canticle. The hearing of the word is prolonged in reflection and prayer.

INTERCESSIONS

Prayer in union with Christ, and with his Spirit, is not complete without prayer for the needs of mankind. It is our special privilege as members of Christ's body to pray with Christ, the high priest who intercedes before the Father. In the morning, the intercessions take the character of prayers commending the day. In the evening, they are more prolonged and detailed. At either time, the pause for free prayer should be used generously. The intercessions are concluded with the Lord's own prayer, the Our Father. On weekdays, the intercessions are said kneeling. On Sunday (including Saturday evening) they are said standing.

BLESSING AND DISMISSAL

Morning and evening prayer conclude with the blessing and dismissal by the one who presides.

MINISTRIES

The format of morning and evening prayer as it is used here encourages a diversity of ministries—one to preside, singers, a reader, and, if desired, a leader of the intercessions. The president says the opening versicle and the prayers which follow the hymns and psalms, invites the congregation to pray the Lord's Prayer, and gives the final blessing and dismissal. After the reading, he (or another person) may deliver a brief homily. In addition to reading, the reader may also lead the intercessions if another person is not available to do so.

The Catholic Church has never restricted presiding over morning and evening prayer to the ordained or to men alone. It may be noted that in Catholic liturgical custom, those who are not ordained do not use the greeting "The Lord be with you" and the formula for blessings is "May the Lord Bless *us*."

THE CELEBRANT

If possible, a bishop, priest, or deacon should preside. The celebrant presides over the celebration as a whole. He invites the people to pray with the opening versicle, says the prayer after the hymn and the psalm prayers, leads the Lord's Prayer, and gives the final blessing. If there is no bishop, priest, or deacon available, any lay person may preside as celebrant.

THE DEACON

A deacon or another assistant minister leads the litanies of intercession, and is the minister of light and incense when these are used.

THE CANTOR

A cantor intones and leads the hymns, psalms, and canticles.

THE READER

A reader is responsible for the reading, and may lead the intercessions as well.

POSTURE

In worship, as indeed in all of life, persons use their bodies to express in a visible, tangible way their inner thoughts, feelings and attitudes. The following postures are suggested:

Stand—for hymns, canticles, and for the Sunday gospel. The celebrant stands to say the psalm prayers.

Sit—for psalms and readings.

Kneel—for the intercessions.

Bow—during the praise to the Trinity (Doxology) at the end of hymns, psalms and canticles, and for the blessing.

LIGHT

From time immemorial, light has been a powerful symbol of divinity. In christian usage, the lighted candle is the principal symbol of the risen Lord. Candles and/or lamps should be lighted during the services, especially on the eves of Sundays and solemnities.

INCENSE

Incense offerings are a normal accompaniment of morning and evening prayer. Its use is a symbol of prayer rising before God and a sign of fragrant cleansing from sin. Incense may be burnt in a fixed container (standing before the altar or in the midst of the congregation) or in a portable thurible. It is especially appropriate on solemnities and Sundays during the singing of the morning and evening canticles (Te Deum and Magnificat). Here, the altar may be incensed first, and then the celebrant and the people.

SILENCE AND SPONTANEITY

Opportunities for silent, personal prayer after the psalms and readings should be scrupulously observed and jealously guarded against erosion. There is also provision for silent reflection and/or spontaneous prayer in the litanies of intercession.

SEASONS

Although it is not possible to make full provision for the four principal seasons of the liturgical year in a book of this sort, a little imagination and some familiarity with morning and evening prayer will enable you to employ seasonal hymns, readings, and prayers from the sacramentary to highlight the emphasis of Advent, Christmas, Lent and Easter for yourselves. Saints are also appropriately commemorated during the litanies of intercession.

SUGGESTIONS

Alternative Readings: Communities which use morning and evening prayer every day may use one of the readings from the Lectionary for Mass from an alternative year—e.g., if Cycle A is being read at Mass, a reading for the day from Cycle B may be used.

Alternative Intercessions: At evening prayer, one of the sample formulas for the general intercessions may be used. Other intercessions may also be composed or taken from other sources.

Psalm Prayers: The celebrant may freely compose alternative psalm prayers.

Song is an integral part of the public celebration of morning and evening prayer, and every effort should be made to avoid the monotony of mere recitation. At the same time, the format of the services used exactly as it is presented here may tax the resources of some parishes, especially at the beginning. It may prove useful to have less musical variation than this format provides. Thus the following suggestions are made:

Hymns for Morning and Evening: The hymns for morning prayer are interchangeable, as are those for evening prayer. It may be desirable to select a single hymn for invariable use at morning or evening. The *Phos Hilaron* is especially appropriate as an evening hymn.

Psalms: It may not be possible to sing both of the psalms at each hour. If this is the case, one of them can be read slowly and meditatively to the congregation by a reader—if possible with music played slowly as a background.

Canticles: In place of the designated canticle, it may be desirable each day to use the Song of Zechariah (Benedictus) for morning prayer and the Song of Mary (Magnificat) for evening prayer.

Other groups may wish more variation than is provided in this format. After each musical selection, alternative suggestions are provided.

SATURDAY EVENING

An old week and old life is past, and a new one waits in vigil.

LIGHT SERVICE

Stand.
As the evening lights are lit, the deacon or celebrant sings:

All
Christ our Light!
Praise to you, Lord Christ!

PHOS HILARON
3rd cent.
Tr., Peter Scagnelli, 1975

JESU DULCIS MEMORIA
L.M.
Plainsong Melody

1. O joyful light, O image blest Of our immortal Father's face! O heaven's glory, Jesus Christ, Eternal, holy, full of grace!
2. At sunset, Lord, we come to pray, As we behold the evening's light: Praise Father, Son and Spirit blest, One holy God of power and might!
3. O Son of God, all creatures sing: How worthy to receive our praise! You give us life and thus the world Gives glory, Lord, through endless days.

SATURDAY EVENING

THANKSGIVING—Apostolic Constitutions, c. 380.

After the evening hymn, the deacon or celebrant stands at the lectern and sings:

All:
Deacon:
The Lord be with you.
And al - so with you.
Let us give thanks to the
All:
Lord our God.
It is right to give him thanks and praise.
Deacon:
All praise and thanks to you, Lord God, holy and e - ter - nal,
Fa - ther all powerful, without beginning and with - out end:
through Christ you created our world and preserve it in be - ing,

SATURDAY EVENING

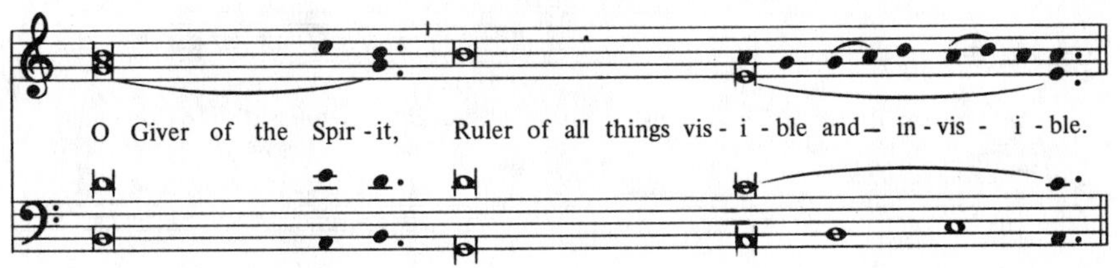
O Giver of the Spir - it, Ruler of all things vis - i - ble and— in - vis - i - ble.

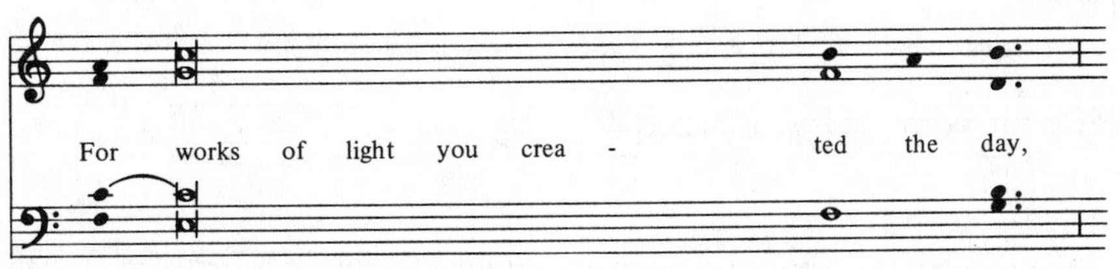
For works of light you crea - ted the day,

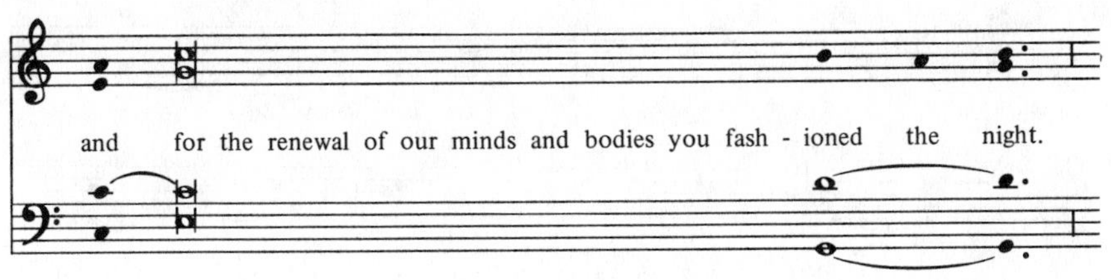
and for the renewal of our minds and bodies you fash - ioned the night.

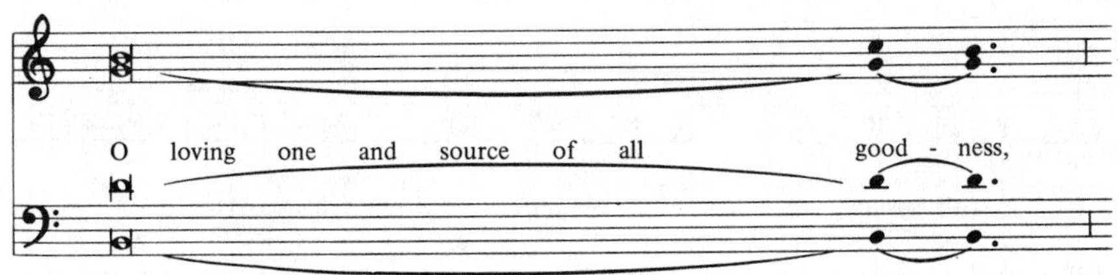
O loving one and source of all good - ness,

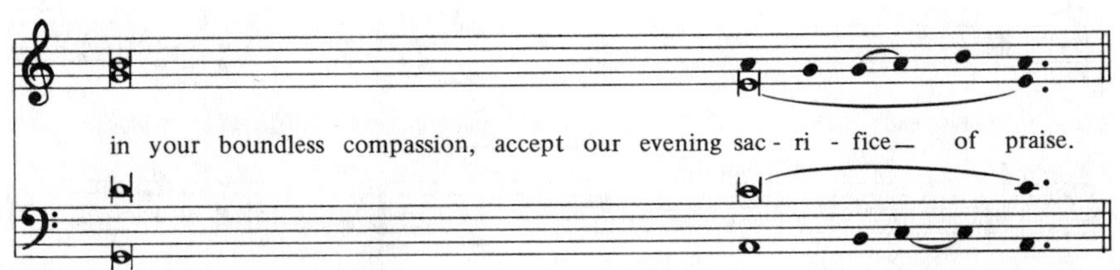
in your boundless compassion, accept our evening sac - ri - fice— of praise.

SATURDAY EVENING

As you have guided us safely through this day and brought us to night's be - gin - ning,
keep us throughout this night in Christ, grant us a peaceful and sin - less rest,
and bring us one day to eternal life in your heav - en - ly king - dom.
We ask this Fa-ther, through your beloved Son, our Lord Je - sus Christ,
to whom with you, and the Ho - ly Spir - it, be all praise, thankgiving and wor-ship:
now and always and for - ev - er and ev - er. A - men.

SATURDAY EVENING

PSALMODY

Sit.
Incense may be burnt in a fixed container or portable censer during the singing of this psalm.

Psalm 141 An evening prayer for repentance.

From the angel's hand the smoke of the incense went up before God with the prayers of his people (Revelation 8:4).

Antiphon
Let my prayer rise before you like in - cense.

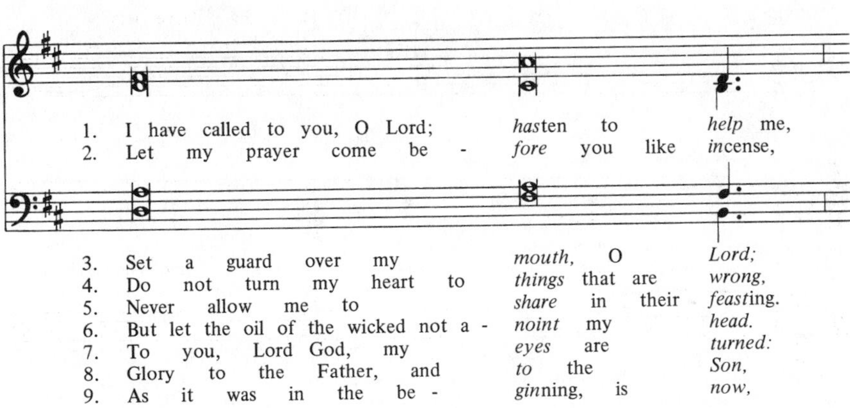
1. I have called to you, O Lord; hasten to help me,
2. Let my prayer come be - fore you like incense,
3. Set a guard over my mouth, O Lord;
4. Do not turn my heart to things that are wrong,
5. Never allow me to share in their feasting.
6. But let the oil of the wicked not a - noint my head.
7. To you, Lord God, my eyes are turned:
8. Glory to the Father, and to the Son,
9. As it was in the be - ginning, is now,

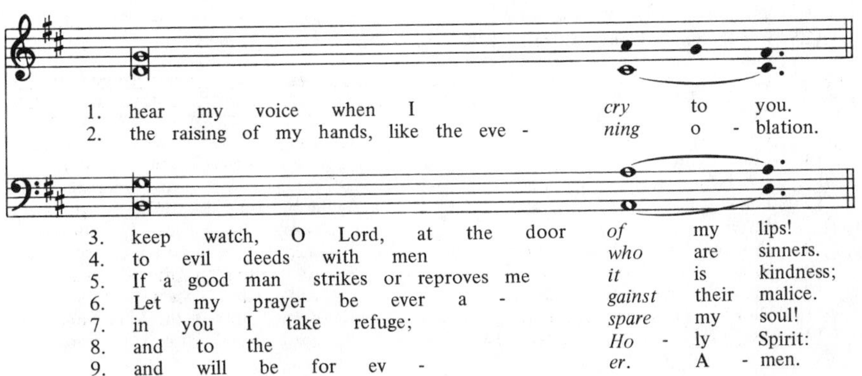
1. hear my voice when I cry to you.
2. the raising of my hands, like the eve - ning o - blation.
3. keep watch, O Lord, at the door of my lips!
4. to evil deeds with men who are sinners.
5. If a good man strikes or reproves me it is kindness;
6. Let my prayer be ever a - gainst their malice.
7. in you I take refuge; spare my soul!
8. and to the Ho - ly Spirit:
9. and will be for ev - er. A - men.

SATURDAY EVENING

PSALM PRAYER

Celebrant: Let us pray.

Pause for silence.

Let the incense of our repentant prayer arise to you, O Lord. As we raise our voices in prayer, teach us to raise our hearts to you in sincere devotion. Through Christ our Lord.

Or,

Heavenly Father, accept the incense of our repentant prayer. Purify us of sin and renew within us your Holy Spirit. In your great mercy, turn our hearts from all that is wrong and preserve us from all harm. Through Christ our Lord.

Or,

Because we turn to you, O Lord, deliver us from all evil and free us from our sins. Let no harm come to those who trust you and find in you a home. Through Christ our Lord.

All: **Amen.**

Psalm 142 Confidence in God.

Everyone deserted me. . . but the Lord stood by me, and strengthened me (2 Timothy 4:16-17).

Antiphon

Lord, you are my ref - uge, all I have left
in the land of the liv - ing.

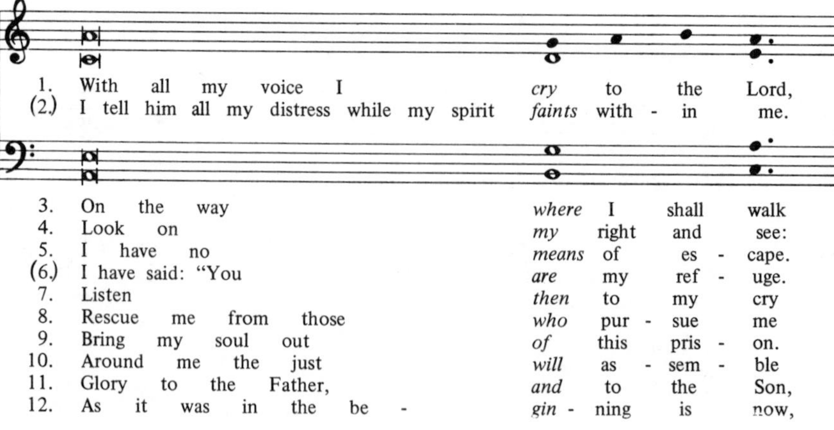
1. With all my voice I *cry* to the Lord,
(2.) I tell him all my distress while my spirit *faints* with - in me.
3. On the way *where* I shall walk
4. Look on *my* right and see:
5. I have no *means* of es - cape.
(6.) I have said: "You *are* my ref - uge.
7. Listen *then* to my cry
8. Rescue me from those *who* pur - sue me
9. Bring my soul out *of* this pris - on.
10. Around me the just *will* as - sem - ble
11. Glory to the Father, *and* to the Son,
12. As it was in the be - *gin* - ning is now,

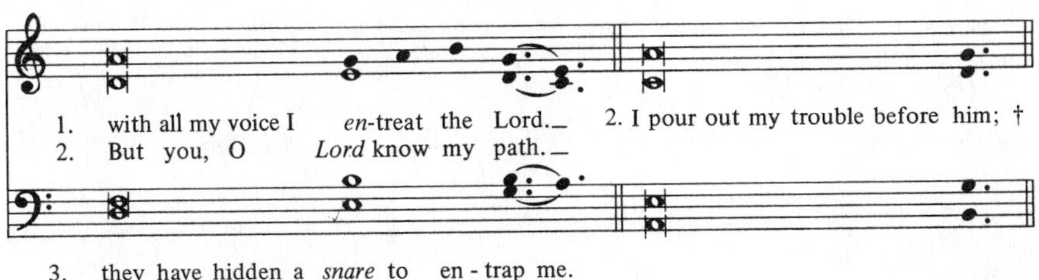
1. with all my voice I en-treat the Lord.— 2. I pour out my trouble before him; †
2. But you, O Lord know my path.—

3. they have hidden a *snare* to en - trap me.
4. there is not one *who* takes my part.—
5. not one who *cares* for my soul.— 6. I cry to you, O Lord. †
6. all that I have left in the *land* of the liv - ing."
7. for I am in the depths *of* my dis- tress.—
8. for they are *strong* - er than I.—
9. and then I *shall* praise your name.—
10. because of your *good* - ness to me.—
11. and to *the* Ho - ly Spir-it:
12. and will be for *ev* - er. A - men.—

Celebrant: Let us pray.

Pause for silence.

Lord, you have been our refuge from one generation to the next. As we ponder the brevity of life, teach us the wisdom of living only for you in your spirit. Through Christ our Lord.

All: **Amen.**

READINGS

Sit.

First Reading *Romans 1:3-6*

This news is about the Son of God who, according to the human nature he took, was a descendant of David: it is about Jesus Christ our Lord who, in the order of the spirit, the spirit of holiness that was in him, was proclaimed Son of God in all his power through his resurrection from the dead. Through him we received grace and our apostolic mission to preach the obedience of faith to all pagan nations in the honor of his name.—This is the Word of the Lord.

All: **Thanks be to God.**

Pause for silent prayer.

Stand.

The Gospel of the Resurrection *Mark 16:1-7*

The proclamation of the gospel of the resurrection according to Mark.
When the sabbath was over, Mary of Magdala, Mary the mother of James, and Salome, brought spices with which to go and anoint him. And very early in the morning on the first day of the week they went to the tomb, just as the sun was rising.

They had been saying to one another, "Who will roll away the stone for us from the entrance to the tomb?" But when they looked they could see that the stone—which was very big—had already been rolled back. On entering the tomb they saw a young man in a white robe seated on the right-hand side, and they were struck with amazement. But he said to them, "There is no need for alarm. You are looking for Jesus of Nazareth, who was crucified: He has risen, he is not here. See, here is the place where they laid him." This is the Gospel of the Lord.

All: **Praise to you, Lord Jesus Christ.**

SATURDAY EVENING

Alternate readings for the Gospel of the Resurrection may be used: Mark 16:9-20; Matthew 28:1-10; Matthew 28:16-20; Luke 24:1-12; Luke 24:13-35; Luke 24:36-45; John 20:1-10; John 20:11-18; John 21:1-14.

After the readings, a period of silence or a homily may follow.

CANTICLE Hymn of Praise (Te Deum)

Stand.

During the Canticle, the altar may be honored with incense.

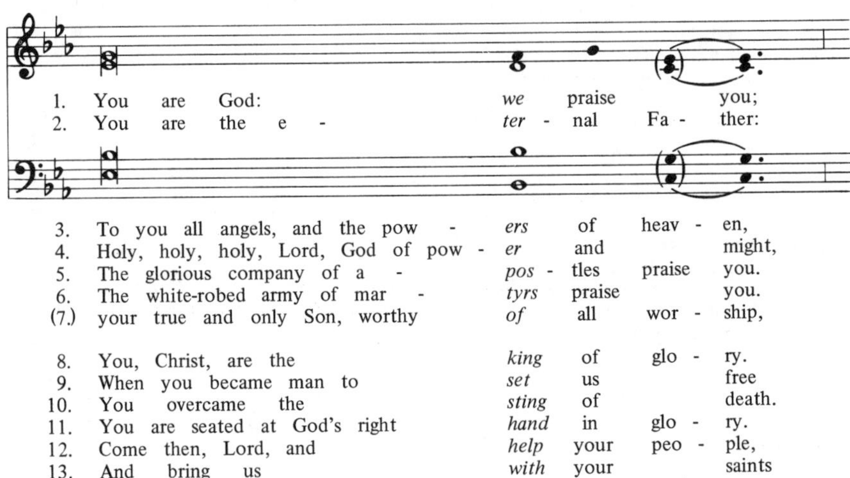
1. You are God: we praise you;
2. You are the e - ter - nal Fa - ther:
3. To you all angels, and the pow - ers of heav - en,
4. Holy, holy, holy, Lord, God of pow - er and might,
5. The glorious company of a - pos - tles praise you.
6. The white-robed army of mar - tyrs praise you.
(7.) your true and only Son, worthy of all wor - ship,
8. You, Christ, are the king of glo - ry.
9. When you became man to set us free
10. You overcame the sting of death.
11. You are seated at God's right hand in glo - ry.
12. Come then, Lord, and help your peo - ple,
13. And bring us with your saints

1. you are the Lord: we ac - claim you;
2. all creation wor - ships you.
3. Cherubim and Seraphim, sing in end - less praise:
4. heaven and earth are full of your glo - ry.
5. The noble fellowship of proph - ets praise you.
6. Throughout the world the holy church ac - claims you: 7. Father, of majesty un-bounded,†
7. and the holy spirit, ad - vo - cate and guide.
8. the eternal Son of the Father.
9. you did not spurn the Vir - gin's womb.
10. and opened the kingdom of heaven to all be - liev - ers.
11. We believe that you will come, and be our judge.
12. bought with the price of your own blood,
13. to glory ev - er last - ing.

INTERCESSIONS

SATURDAY EVENING

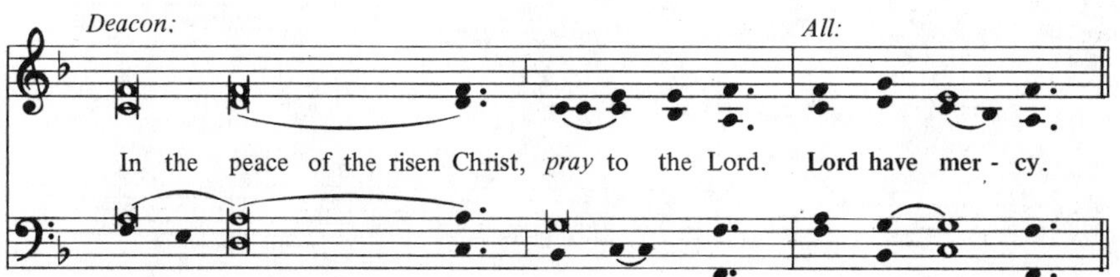
Deacon:
All:
In the peace of the risen Christ, pray to the Lord. Lord have mer - cy.

Deacon: For the holy church of God, throughout the world, for its unity, peace and protection, let us *pray* to the Lord.

All: **Lord, have mercy.**

Deacon: For an outpouring of the Spirit on all bishops and other servants of the Gospel, let us *pray* to the Lord.

All: **Lord, have mercy.**

Deacon: For the leaders of nations and all who serve us in public office, that God may direct their hearts towards justice and peace, let us *pray* to the Lord.

All: **Lord, have mercy.**

Deacon: For all who seek the one true God, let us *pray* to the Lord.

All: **Lord, have mercy.**

Deacon: For the elimination of famine and disease, violence and war, for peace and harmony among all peoples, let us *pray* to the Lord.

All: **Lord, have mercy.**

Deacon: For the proclamation of the gospel, the freeing of captives, and for the consolation of the afflicted, let us *pray* to the Lord.

All: **Lord, have mercy.**

Deacon: For those gone before us in the fellowship of Christian faith, let us *pray* to the Lord.

All: **Lord, have mercy.**

Deacon: Help, save, pity and defend us, O God, by your grace.
Pause for free prayer, silent and spontaneous.
Rejoicing in the fellowship of the Virgin Mary, of Saint N., and of all the saints, let us commend ourselves, one another and our whole life to *Christ* our Lord.

All: **To you, O Lord.**

Celebrant: Let us make our prayer perfect in the prayer of *God's* own Son.

All join in reciting or singing the Lord's Prayer.

SATURDAY EVENING

All:
Our Fa - ther, who art in heav - en, hal - lowed be thy name;
thy king-dom come; thy will be done on earth as it is in heav - en.
Give us this day our dai - ly bread; and for - give us our tres - pass - es
as we for - give those who tres - pass a - gainst us; and lead us
not in - to temp - ta - tion, but de - liv - er us from e - vil.

Lower key at No. 101.

SATURDAY EVENING

All:
Our Fa - ther in heav - en, hal-lowed be your name, your king-dom come,
your will be done, on earth as in — heav - en. Give us to -
day our dai - ly bread. For - give us our sins as we for - give
those who sin — a - gainst — us. Save us from the time of trial,
and de - liv - er us — from e - vil. For the king - dom, the
pow - er and the glo - ry are yours now and for - ev - er.

For additional settings of the Lord's Prayer see No. 100, 101, and 102.

BLESSING AND DISMISSAL

Celebrant: May Christ our Lord, risen form the dead, bless † and keep us, for he is good, and loves mankind.
All: **Amen.**
Celebrant: Let us bless the Lord.
All: **Thanks be to God.**

SUNDAY MORNING

This is the day the Lord has made: let us be glad and rejoice in it!

Stand.
Celebrant: O Lord, open our lips.
All: **And we shall praise your name.**

LUBECK
77. 77
Freylinghausen's
Geistreiches Gesangbuch, 1704

DIE PARENTE TEMPORUM
Le Mans Breviary, 1748
Tr., Henry Williams Baker, 1821-44, alt.

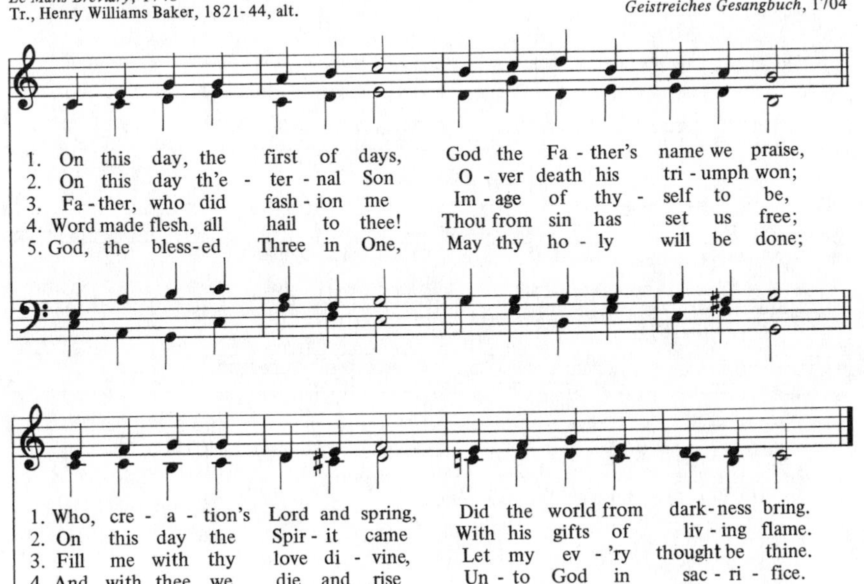
1. On this day, the first of days, God the Fa - ther's name we praise,
2. On this day th'e - ter - nal Son O - ver death his tri - umph won;
3. Fa - ther, who did fash - ion me Im - age of thy - self to be,
4. Word made flesh, all hail to thee! Thou from sin has set us free;
5. God, the bless-ed Three in One, May thy ho - ly will be done;
1. Who, cre - a - tion's Lord and spring, Did the world from dark-ness bring.
2. On this day the Spir - it came With his gifts of liv - ing flame.
3. Fill me with thy love di - vine, Let my ev - 'ry thought be thine.
4. And with thee we die and rise Un - to God in sac - ri - fice.
5. In thy word our souls are free, And we rest this day with thee.

For lower key, see No. 476.

OPENING PRAYER

Celebrant: The Lord be with you.
All: **And also with you.**
Celebrant: Let us pray:
Pause for silent prayer.
Lord, God,
you give us joy every week
in our remembrance of the glorious resurrection
of your Son, Jesus Christ.
Renew us this day through our worship,
that the days to come
may be spent in your service.
We ask this through the Christ our Lord.
All: **Amen.**

The opening prayer of the day from the sacramentary may be used in place of the above.

SUNDAY MORNING

PSALMODY

Sit.

Psalm 63 Longing for God

The water I shall give, will become within him a fountain of water springing up to eternal life (John 4:14).

Antiphon
O God, you are my God, for you I long, to see your strength and your glo - ry.
1. O God, you are my God, for you I long;
2. My bo - dy pines for you
3. For your love is bet - ter than life,
4. So I will bless you all my life,
5. My soul shall be filled as with a ban - quet,
6. On you I muse through the night for you have been my help;
7. My soul clings to you;
8. Glory to the Father, and to the Son,
9. As it was in the be - gin - ning, is now,
1. for you my soul is thirst - ing.
2. like a dry, weary land with - out wa - ter.
3. my lips will speak your praise.
4. in your name I will lift up my hands.
5. my mouth shall praise you with joy.
6. in the shadow of your wings I re - joice.
7. your right hand holds me fast
8. and to the Ho - ly Spir - it:
9. and will be for - ev - er. A - men.
On my bed I remember you. †

Celebrant: Let us pray.
Pause for silent prayer.
Your love is better than life itself, O Lord, and fills our days with joy and hope. As our lips sing your praises, may our lives be spent in your grateful service; Through Jesus Christ our Lord.

All: **Amen.**

Sit.

READING *1 Corinthians 15:3-8*

I taught you what I had been taught myself, namely that Christ died for our sins, in accordance with the Scriptures; that he was buried; and that he was raised to life on the third day, in accordance with the Scriptures; that he appeared first to Cephas and secondly to the Twelve. Next he appeared to more than five hundred of the brothers at the same time, most of whom are still alive, though some have died; then he appeared to James, and then to all the apostles; and last of all he appeared to me too.—This is the Word of the Lord.

All: **Thanks be to God.**

After the reading, a period of silent prayer or a homily may follow.

CANTICLE Song of Zechariah (Benedictus) *Luke 1:68-79*

Stand.

The altar may be honored with incense during the singing of this canticle.

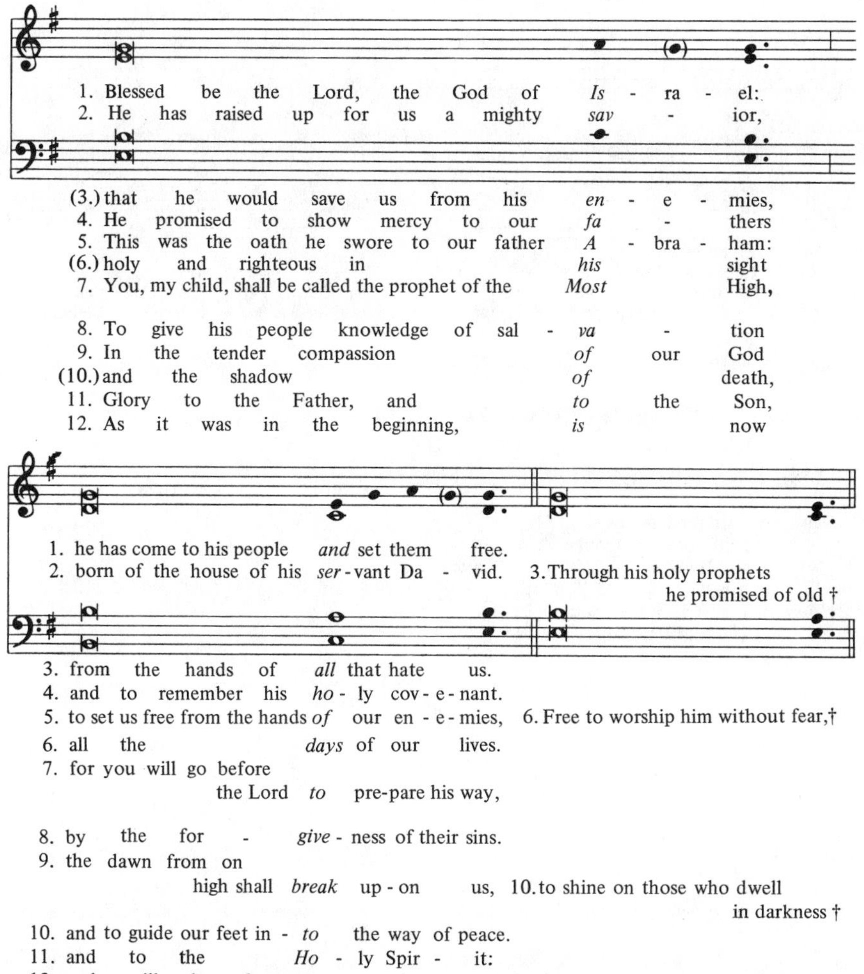
1. Blessed be the Lord, the God of *Is* - ra - el:
2. He has raised up for us a mighty *sav* - ior,
(3.) that he would save us from his *en* - e - mies,
4. He promised to show mercy to our *fa* - thers
5. This was the oath he swore to our father *A* - bra - ham:
(6.) holy and righteous in *his* sight
7. You, my child, shall be called the prophet of the *Most* High,
8. To give his people knowledge of sal - *va* - tion
9. In the tender compassion *of* our God
(10.) and the shadow *of* death,
11. Glory to the Father, and *to* the Son,
12. As it was in the beginning, *is* now
1. he has come to his people *and* set them free.
2. born of the house of his *ser* - vant Da - vid.
3. Through his holy prophets he promised of old †
3. from the hands of *all* that hate us.
4. and to remember his *ho* - ly cov - e - nant.
5. to set us free from the hands *of* our en - e - mies,
6. Free to worship him without fear, †
6. all the *days* of our lives.
7. for you will go before the Lord *to* pre-pare his way,
8. by the for - *give* - ness of their sins.
9. the dawn from on high shall *break* up - on us,
10. to shine on those who dwell in darkness †
10. and to guide our feet in - *to* the way of peace.
11. and to the *Ho* - ly Spir - it:
12. and will be for - *ev* - er. A - men.

INTERCESSIONS

The deacon or reader sings or recites the petition and the people the response after each petition.

Deacon:
1. Creator and Father of us all,
2. Called in Christ and baptized into his death,
3. Send forth the Spirit of your light and truth.
4. Giver of the true bread that has come down from heav - en,
5. Make us faithful witnesses of your Son in all the world,
Celebrant: 6. Let us make our prayer perfect in the prayer of God's own Son.
All:
1. help us live as children fashioned in your im - age.
2. may we live with him in new - ness of life.
3. Confirm his gifts of grace with - in us.
4. nourish us always at your Son's ho - ly ta - ble.
5. to the praise and glory of your ho - ly name.

All join in reciting or singing the Lord's Prayer, p. 468.

BLESSING AND DISMISSAL

Celebrant: May the Lord bless us †
and protect us from evil,
and bring us to a life that will never end.
All: **Amen.**
Celebrant: Let us bless the Lord.
All: **Thanks be to God.**

SUNDAY EVENING

The Lord reigns as messiah and priest in the great eucharistic celebration of his resurrection. Therefore, Christians sing praise in the assembly and rejoice in the covenant which gathers them together as one.

LIGHT SERVICE

Stand.
As the evening lights are lit, the deacon or celebrant sings:

Jesus Christ is the light of the world.
A light no darkness can ex-tin-guish.

EVENING HYMN

The evening hymn is begun immediately.

PHOS HILARON
3rd cent.
Tr., Peter Scagnelli, 1975

JESU DULCIS MEMORIA
L.M.
Plainsong Melody

1. O joy - ful light, O im - age blest Of our im -
2. At sun - set, Lord, we come to pray, As we . be -
3. O Son of God, all crea - tures sing: How wor - thy

1. mor - tal Fa - ther's face! O heav - en's glo - ry, Je - sus
2. hold the eve - ning's light: Praise Fa - ther, Son and Spir - it
3. to re - ceive our praise! You give us life and thus the

1. Christ, ——— E - ter - nal, ho - ly, full of grace!
2. blest, ——— One ho - ly God of power and might!
3. world ——— Gives glo - ry, Lord, through end - less days.

SUNDAY EVENING

THANKSGIVING: Apostolic Tradition, c. 215

Deacon:
All praise and thanks to you, Lord God our Fa - ther, through your be -

lov - ed Son, our Lord Je - sus Christ: Through him you have filled us with light,

by re- veal - ing the light ___ which nev - er fades. Night is fall - ing now,

SUNDAY EVENING

and the hours of day-light draw to a close, and your gift of day's bright-ness is crowned

by your gift of eve-ning lights to guide — us through — this night.

And so we give you all glo-ry, praise, and thanks-giv-ing, O Fa-ther, through Je-sus Christ your

Son, in the Ho-ly Spir-it: one God — now and for-ev - er. A-men. —

SUNDAY EVENING

PSALMODY

***Psalm 141**, An Evening Prayer for Repentance, may be prayed.* *See p. 463.*

Psalm 118

It was for you in the first place that God raised up his servant and sent him to bless you.

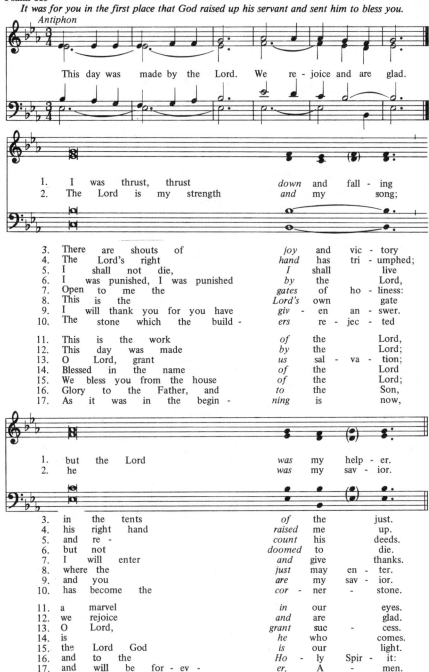

Antiphon

This day was made by the Lord. We re - joice and are glad.

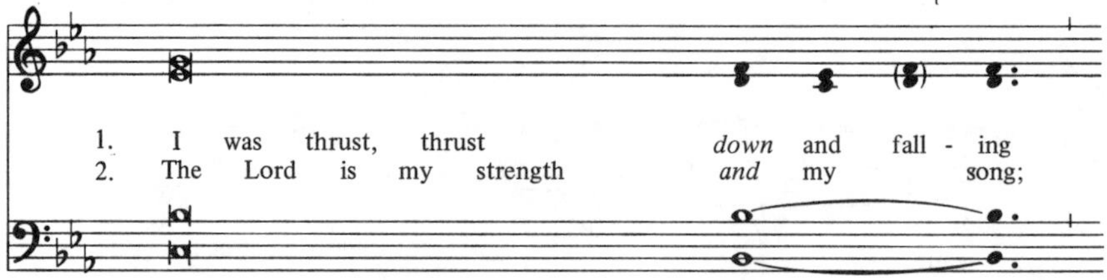

1. I was thrust, thrust *down* and fall - ing
2. The Lord is my strength *and* my song;
3. There are shouts of *joy* and vic - tory
4. The Lord's right *hand* has tri - umphed;
5. I shall not die, *I* shall live
6. I was punished, I was punished *by* the Lord,
7. Open to me the *gates* of ho - liness:
8. This is the *Lord's* own gate
9. I will thank you for you have *giv* - en an - swer.
10. The stone which the build - *ers* re - jec - ted

11. This is the work *of* the Lord,
12. This day was made *by* the Lord;
13. O Lord, grant *us* sal - va - tion;
14. Blessed in the name *of* the Lord
15. We bless you from the house *of* the Lord;
16. Glory to the Father, and *to* the Son,
17. As it was in the begin - *ning* is now,

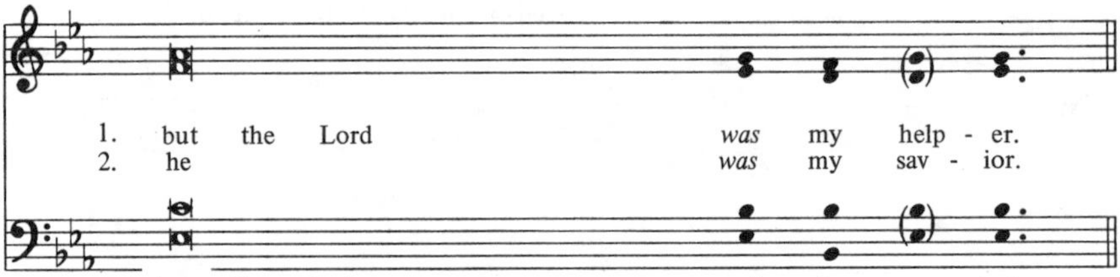

1. but the Lord *was* my help - er.
2. he *was* my sav - ior.
3. in the tents *of* the just.
4. his right hand *raised* me up.
5. and re - *count* his deeds.
6. but not *doomed* to die.
7. I will enter *and* give thanks.
8. where the *just* may en - ter.
9. and you *are* my sav - ior.
10. has become the *cor* - ner - stone.

11. a marvel *in* our eyes.
12. we rejoice *and* are glad.
13. O Lord, *grant* suc - cess.
14. is *he* who comes.
15. the Lord God *is* our light.
16. and to the *Ho* - ly Spir - it:
17. and will be for - ev - *er.* A - men.

SUNDAY EVENING

PSALM PRAYER

Celebrant: Let us pray.
Pause for silent prayer.
Lord Jesus Christ, faithful witness and first-born from the dead, ruler of the kings of the earth, wash away our sins in your blood and make us a line of kings and priests to serve your God and Father; to Him be honor and glory forever and ever.

All: **Amen.**

READING *1 John 4:15-16*

If anyone acknowledges that Jesus is the Son of God, God lives in him, and he is God. We ourselves have known and have put our faith in God's love towards ourselves. God is love and anyone who lives in love lives in God, and God lives in him.—This is the Word of the Lord.

All: **Thanks be to God.**

After the reading, a period of silence or a homily may follow.

CANTICLE Song of Mary (Magnificat) *Luke 1:47-55*

Stand.
The altar may be honored with incense during the singing of this canticle.

Antiphon
My heart sings for joy and o - ver
flows with glad - ness, for the Lord is my Sav -
ior. Al - le - lu - ia.

SUNDAY EVENING

1. My soul proclaims the greatness of the Lord,† my spirit rejoices in *God* my Sa - vior
2. From this day all genera - tions will call me blessed:† the Almighty has *done* great things for me,

3. He has mercy on *those* who fear him
4. He has shown the *strength* of his arm,
5. He has cast down the *might* - y from their thrones,
6. He has filled the *hun* - gry with good things,

7. He has come to the help of his *ser* - vant Is - ra - el
8. The promise he made *to* our Fa - thers,
9. Glory to the Father, *and* to the Son,
10. As it was in the be-*gin* - ning, is now,

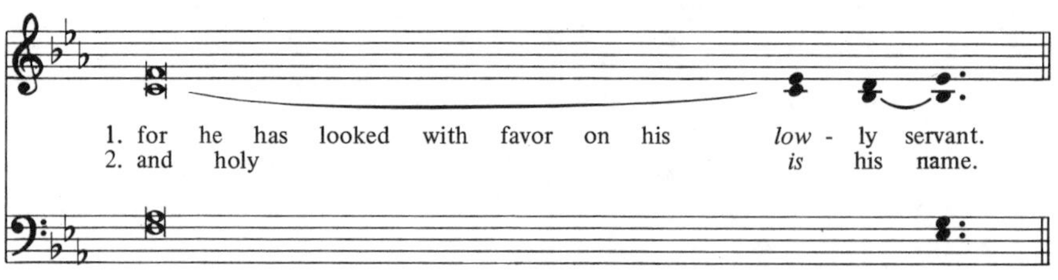
1. for he has looked with favor on his *low* - ly servant.
2. and holy *is* his name.

3. in every *gen* - er - ation.
4. he has scattered the proud in *their* con - ceit.
5. and has lifted *up* the lowly.
6. and the rich he has sent *a* - way empty.

7. for he has remembered his prom - *ise* of mercy,
8. to Abraham and his chil - *dren* for - ever.
9. and to the *Ho* - ly Spirit:
10. and will be for - *ev* - er. Amen.

SUNDAY EVENING

INTERCESSIONS

The deacon or reader sings or recites the petition and the people the response after each petition.

Deacon:
All:
In peace, let us *pray* to the Lord. Lord have mer - cy.

Deacon: For that peace which is from on high and for the salvation of our souls, let us *pray* to the Lord.
All: **Lord, have mercy.**
Deacon: For peace in all the world, the well-being of the holy Churches of God and the unity of all, let us *pray* to the Lord.
All: **Lord, have mercy.**
Deacon: For this holy place (parish family) and for all who come to pray with us in faith, reverence, and fear of God, let us *pray* to the Lord.
All: **Lord, have mercy.**
Deacon: For our holy Father, N., our bishop, N., all bishops, priests, deacons and all God's people, let us *pray* to the Lord.
All: **Lord, have mercy.**
Deacon: For all who serve us in public office, and work for the common good, that they be helped and strengthened in every good deed, let us *pray* to the Lord.
All: **Lord, have mercy.**
Deacon: For pleasant weather, a fruitful harvest, and peaceful times, let us *pray* to the Lord.
All: **Lord, have mercy.**
Deacon: For travelers by sea, air, and land, for the sick, the suffering, the imprisoned, and for their salvation, let us *pray* to the Lord.
All: **Lord, have mercy.**
Deacon: Help, save, pity and defend us, O God by your grace.
Pause for free prayer, silent and spontaneous.
Rejoicing in the fellowship of the Virgin Mary, of Saint N., and of all the saints, let us commend ourselves, one another, and our whole life to *Christ* our Lord.
All: **To you, O Lord.**
Celebrant: Let us make our prayer perfect in the prayer of *God's* own Son.

All join in reciting or singing the Lord's Prayer, p. 468.

BLESSING AND DISMISSAL

Celebrant: May Christ our God, risen from the dead, bless† and keep us, for he is good, and loves mankind.
All: **Amen.**
Cellebrant: Let us bless the Lord.
All: **Thanks be to God.**

MONDAY MORNING

A new week is just beginning, and all men and women are called to share God's creative artistry.

Celebrant: O Lord, open our lips.

All: **And we shall praise your name**

Psalm 95
Tr., James Quinn, S.J., 1969

DARWALL'S 148th
66. 66. 44. 44
John Darwall, 1770, alt., ca. 1778

1. To God with glad - ness sing, Your Rock and Sav - ior bless; With -
2. He cra - dles in his hand The heights and depths of earth; He
3. Your heav'n-ly Fa - ther praise, Ac - claim his on - ly Son, Your

in his tem - ple bring Your songs of thank - ful - ness! O God of
made the sea and land, He brought the world to birth! O God most
voice in hom - age raise To him who makes all one! O Dove of

might, To you we sing, En - throned as King On heav - en's height!
high, We are your sheep; On us you keep Your Shep - herd's eye!
peace, On us de - scend That strife may end And joy in - crease!

Alternate Hymns: no.323 through 326.

OPENING PRAYER

Celebrant: The Lord be with you.
All: **And also with you.**
Celebrant: Let us pray.
Pause for silent prayer.
Lord God, king of heaven and earth, direct and sanctify, guide and govern our minds and bodies, our thoughts, words and deeds throughout this day: that we might live by your spirit and follow your way safe from evil and free from sin. We ask this through Christ our Lord.
All: **Amen.**

The opening prayer of the day from the sacramentary may be used in place of the above.

MONDAY MORNING

PSALMODY

Sit.

Psalm 146 Hymn to the God of help.

Go out quickly into the streets and alleys. . . and bring in the poor and the crippled, the blind and the lame (Luke 14:21).

Antiphon
I will praise the Lord all my days.
1. My soul, give praise to the Lord: † I will praise the Lord all my days,
2. Put no trust in prin - ces,
3. Take their breath, they re - turn to clay
4. He is happy who is helped by Ja - cob's God,
5. Who alone made heaven and earth,
6. It is he who keeps faith for ev - er,
7. It is he who gives bread to the hun - gry,
8. The Lord who gives sight to the blind,
9. The Lord, who pro - tects the stranger
10. It is the Lord who loves the just
11. The Lord will reign for - ev - er,
12. Glory to the Father, and to the Son,
13. As it was in the beginning, is now,
1. make music to my God while I live.
2. in mortal men in whom there is no help.
3. and their plans that day come to no - thing.
4. whose hope is in the Lord his God,
5. the seas and all they con - tain.
6. who is just to those who are op - pressed.
7. the Lord, who sets pris - on - ers free,
8. who raises up those who are bowed down,
9. and upholds the wid - ow and or - phan.
10. but thwarts the path of the wick - ed.
11. Sion's God, from age to age.
12. and to the Ho - ly Spir - it:
13. and will be for - ev - er A - men.

MONDAY MORNING

PSALM PRAYER

Celebrant: Let us pray.
Pause for silent prayer.
Be attentive to our prayers, loving Father. Teach us to share our love and compassion for the poor. May we so live today as to praise you in sincerity and truth. Through Christ our Lord.

All: **Amen.**

READING *Romans 13:11-14*

The time has come: you must wake up now: our salvation is even nearer than it was when we were converted. The night is almost over, it will be daylight soon—let us give up all the things we prefer to do under cover of the dark; let us arm ourselves and appear in the light. Let us live decently as people do in the daytime: no drunken orgies, no promiscuity or licentiousness, and no wrangling or jealousy. Let your armor be the Lord Jesus Christ; forget about satisfying your bodies with all their cravings.—This is the Word of the Lord.

All: **Thanks be to God.**

After the reading, a period of silent prayer or a homily may follow.

The traditional morning canticle, the Song of Zechariah (p.473), or the following canticle may be used.

CANTICLE Second song of Isaiah *Isaiah 55:6-11*

Antiphon
God has blessed us with all spir - it - ual bless-ings in Christ.
1. Seek the Lord while he wills to *be* found;
2. Let the wicked forsake *his* way,
3. And let him turn to the Lord, and he will have com - *pas* - sion,
4. For my thoughts are not *your* thoughts,
(5.) so are my ways higher than *your* ways,
6. For as rain and snow fall from the *heav* - ens,
7. Bringing forth life, and *giv* - ing growth,
8. So is my word that goes forth from *my* mouth:
9. But it will accomplish that which I have *pur* - posed,
10. Glory to the Father, and *to* the Son,
11. As it was in the beginning, *is* now,

MONDAY MORNING

1. call upon him *when* he draws near.
2. and the e - *vil* man his thoughts;

3. and to our God, for he will *rich*-ly par-don.
4. nor your ways my *ways,* says the Lord. 5. For as the heavens are higher than the earth, †
5. and my thoughts high-*er* than your thoughts.
6. and return not again, but *wa* - ter the earth,
7. seed for sowing and *bread* for eat - ing,

8. it will not return *to* me emp - ty;
9. and prosper in that for *which* I sent it.
10. and to the *Ho* - ly Spir - it:
11. and will be for - *ev* - er. A - men.

INTERCESSIONS

The deacon or reader sings or recites the petitions and the people the response after each petition.

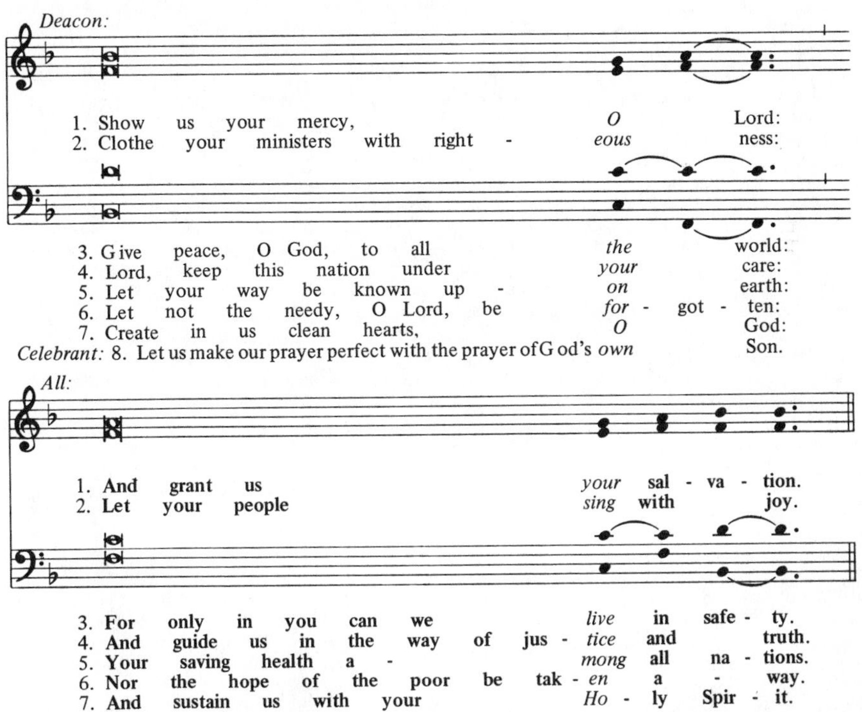
Deacon:
1. Show us your mercy, *O* Lord:
2. Clothe your ministers with right - *eous* ness:
3. Give peace, O God, to all *the* world:
4. Lord, keep this nation under *your* care:
5. Let your way be known up - *on* earth:
6. Let not the needy, O Lord, be *for* - got - ten:
7. Create in us clean hearts, *O* God:
Celebrant: 8. Let us make our prayer perfect with the prayer of God's *own* Son.
All:
1. And grant us *your* sal - va - tion.
2. Let your people *sing* with joy.
3. For only in you can we *live* in safe - ty.
4. And guide us in the way of jus - *tice* and truth.
5. Your saving health a - *mong* all na - tions.
6. Nor the hope of the poor be tak - *en* a - way.
7. And sustain us with your *Ho* - ly Spir - it.

MONDAY MORNING

All join in reciting or singing the Lord's Prayer, p.468.

BLESSING AND DISMISSAL

Celebrant: May the Lord bless us,
protect us from evil,
and bring us to a life that will never end.
All: **Amen.**
Celebrant: Let us bless the Lord.
All: **Thanks be to God.**

MONDAY EVENING

As the day ends, our prayer focuses on God's abiding presence with us.

LIGHT SERVICE

Stand.

As the evening lights are lit, the deacon or celebrant sings:

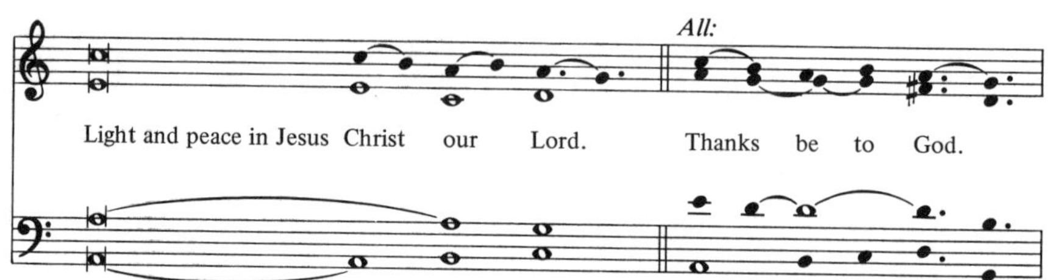

All:
Light and peace in Jesus Christ our Lord.
Thanks be to God.

Te Lucis Ante Terminum
7th cent.
Tr., Peter Scagnelli, 1973

L.M.
Oreste Ravenello

1. Be - fore the end - ing of the day,
2. Let ev - 'ry heart rest free from fear:
3. Let peace - ful rest the strength re - new
4. Al - might - y Fa - ther, hear our cry,

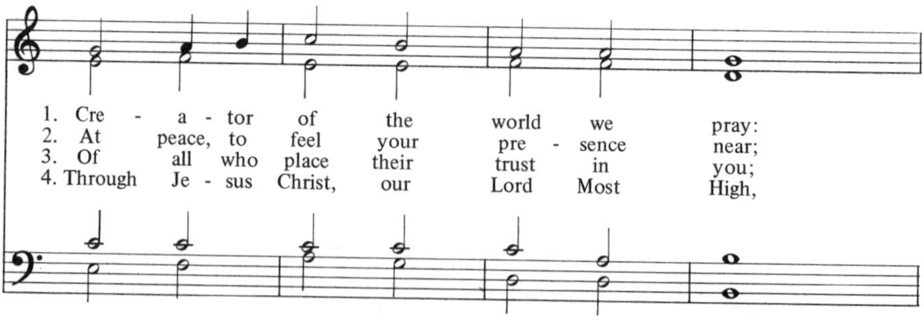

1. Cre - a - tor of the world we pray:
2. At peace, to feel your pre - sence near;
3. Of all who place their trust in you;
4. Through Je - sus Christ, our Lord Most High,

MONDAY EVENING

1. Pro - tect us by your love and might
2. Our souls, through hours ___ veiled in sleep,
3. Let e - vil nev - er have its way:
4. And with the Spir - it, Par - a - clete,
1. And keep us safe through - out the ___ night!
2. In your blest light, their vig - il ___ keep.
3. Pre - serve us for an - oth - er ___ day.
4. Whose reign the end - less a - ges ___ greet. A - men.

THANKSGIVING

After the evening hymn, the deacon or celebrant stands at the lectern and sings or recites (music from page 460 may be used):

Deacon: The Lord be with you.
All: **And also with you.**
Deacon: Let us give thanks to the Lord our God.
All: **It is right to give him thanks and praise.**
Deacon: Blessed are you, Lord God of all creation,
maker of light and darkness,
source and preserver of all that exists.
Remember your Church, O Lord,
keep it safe from evil,
make it perfect in your love,
gather it from the four winds,
into the kingdom of your beloved Son,
for yours is the power and the glory
now and always, and forever and ever.
All: **Amen.**

Or, the following prayer may be used:

Grant, O Lord, that the light of charity which never fails, may shine within us and shed its light on those around us. By its brightness may our world be blessed with the vision of that holy city where dwells the true and never-failing light, Jesus Christ our Lord.

MONDAY EVENING

PSALMODY

Sit.

***Psalm 141,** An Evening Prayer for Repentance, may be prayed.* *See p. 463.*

Psalm 46 Trust in God's Power.

They will call him Immanuel (Matthew 1:23).

Antiphon
The Lord of hosts is with us; the God of Ja - cob is our strong - hold.
1. God is for us a ref - *uge* and strength,
2. So we shall not fear though the *earth* should rock,
3. Even though its waters *rage* and foam,
4. The waters of a river give joy *to* God's city,
5. God is within, it can - *not* be shaken:
6. Nations are in tumult, king - *doms* are shaken:
7. Come, consider the works *of* the Lord
(8.) the bow he breaks, the *spear* he snaps.
9. "Be still and know that *I* am God,
10. Glory to the Father, and *to* the Son,
11. As it was in the begin - *ning,* is now,
1. a helper close at hand, in time *of* dis - tress:
2. though the mountains fall into the depths *of* the sea,

3. even though the mountains be shaken *by* its waves.
4. the holy place where the *Most* High dwells.
5. God will help it at the dawning *of* the day.
6. he lifts his voice, the earth *shrinks* a - way.
7. the redoubtable deeds he has done *on* the earth. 8. He puts end to wars over all the earth: †
8. He burns *shields* with fire.
9. supreme among nations, supreme *on* the earth!"
10. and to the *Ho* - ly Spirit:
11. and will be for - ev - *er.* A - men.

MONDAY EVENING

PSALM PRAYER

Celebrant: Let us pray.
Pause for silent prayer.
Almighty God, you are the Lord of our lives from the rising of the sun even to its setting. Help us to ponder what you have been for us today. Give us a clear vision of your truth, faith in your power, and confident assurance of your love. Through Christ our Lord.

All: **Amen.**

READING *Romans 12:1-2*

Think of God's mercy, my brothers, and worship him, I beg you, in a way that is worthy of thinking beings, by offering your living bodies as a holy sacrifice, truly pleasing to God. Do not model yourselves on the behavior of the world around you, but let your behavior change, modeled by your new mind. This is the only way to discover the will of God and know what is good, what it is that God wants, what is the perfect thing to do.—This is the Word of the Lord.

All: **Thanks be to God.**

After the reading, a period of silent prayer or a homily may follow.

The traditional evening canticle, the Song of Mary (P. 479), or the following canticle may be used.

CANTICLE Song of Simeon (*Nunc Dimittis*) *Luke 2:29-32*

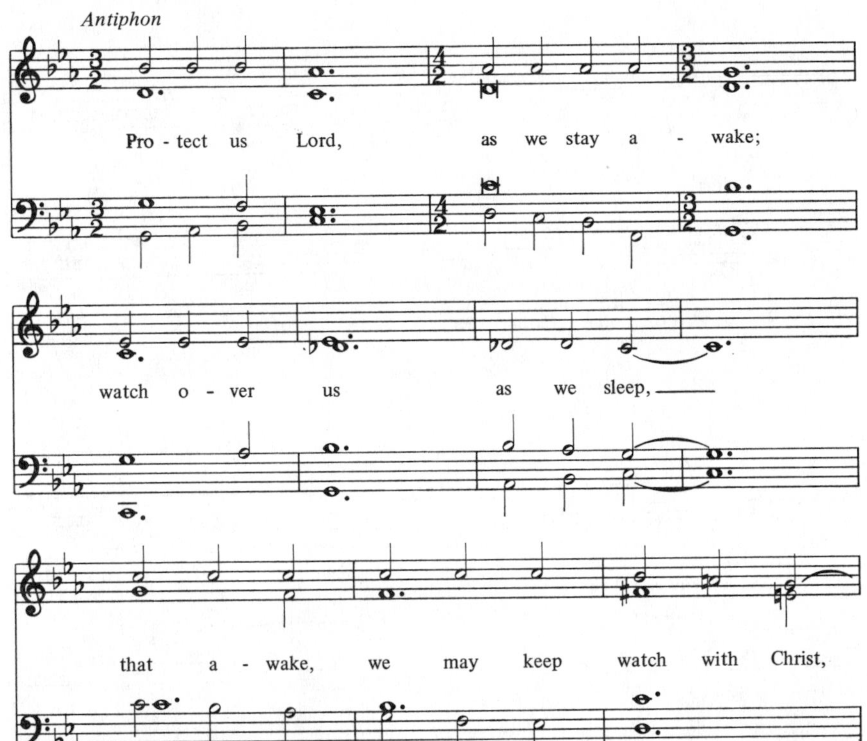
Antiphon
Pro - tect us Lord, as we stay a - wake;
watch o - ver us as we sleep,
that a - wake, we may keep watch with Christ,

MONDAY EVENING

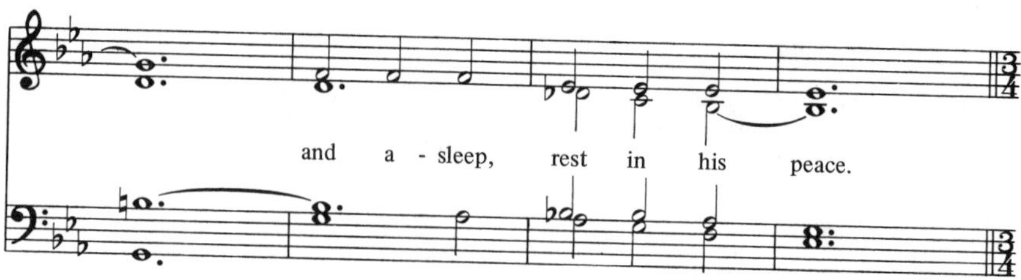

and a - sleep, rest in his peace.

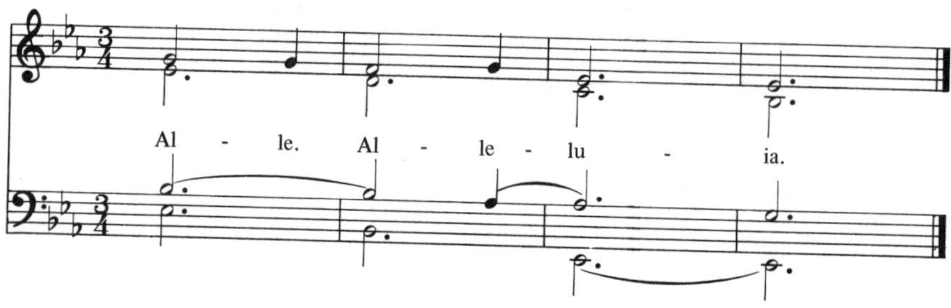

Al - le. Al - le - lu - ia.

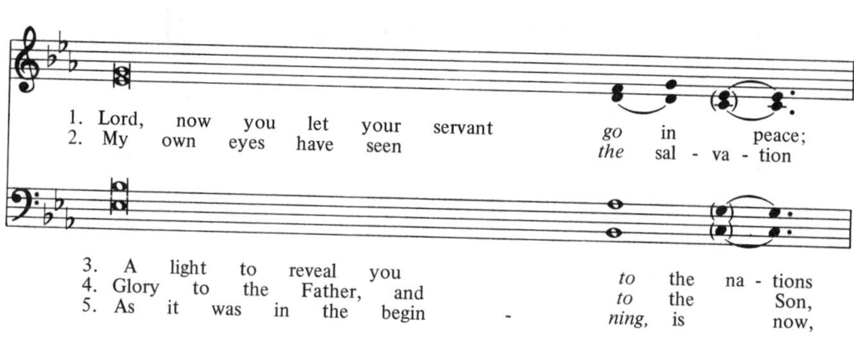

1. Lord, now you let your servant go in peace;
2. My own eyes have seen the sal - va - tion
3. A light to reveal you to the na - tions
4. Glory to the Father, and to the Son,
5. As it was in the begin - ning, is now,

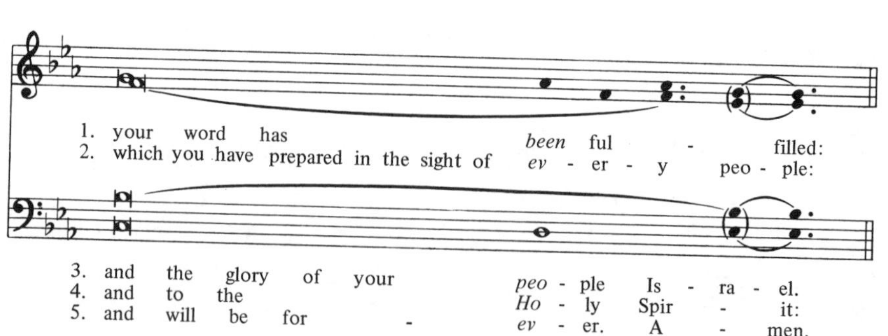

1. your word has been ful - filled:
2. which you have prepared in the sight of ev - er - y peo - ple:
3. and the glory of your peo - ple Is - ra - el.
4. and to the Ho - ly Spir - it:
5. and will be for - ev - er. A - men.

MONDAY EVENING

INTERCESSIONS

Kneel.

The deacon or reader sings or recites the petitions and the people the response after each petition.

Deacon:
All:
In peace, let us *pray* to the Lord. **Lord have mer - cy.**

Deacon: For the one, holy, catholic, and apostolic Church of God, in all its communities throughout the world, let us *pray* to the Lord.
All: **Lord, have mercy.**
Deacon: For ardent preachers of the gospel in this and every land, let us *pray* to the Lord.

All: **Lord, have mercy.**
Deacon: For union of charity, the bond of perfection, and the gift of the spirit, let us *pray* to the Lord.
All: **Lord, have mercy.**
Deacon: For those who serve the needs and defend the rights of the human family, let us *pray* to the Lord.
All: **Lord, have mercy.**
Deacon: For those who love us and for those who hate us, let us *pray* to the Lord.
All: **Lord, have mercy.**
Deacon: Help, save, pity and defend us, O *God,* by your grace.
Pause for free prayer, silent and spontaneous.
Rejoicing in the fellowship of the Blessed Virgin Mary, of Saint N., and of all the saints, let us commend ourselves, one another, and our whole life to Christ our Lord.
All: **To you, O Lord.**
Celebrant: Let us make our prayer perfect in the prayer of *God's* own Son.

All join in reciting or singing the Lord's Prayer, *p. 468.*

BLESSING AND DISMISSAL

Celebrant: May the Lord bless us and keep us.
May the Lord let his face shine upon us and be gracious to us.
May the Lord look upon us kindly and give us peace: in the name of the Father, the Son, † and the Holy Spirit.
All: **Amen.**
Celebrant: Let us bless the Lord.
All: **Thanks be to God.**

TUESDAY MORNING

Early in the week Christians are reminded of their glory and their call to share in all that God does for his world.

Celebrant: O Lord, open our lips.
All: **And we shall praise your name.**

NOCTE SURGENTES
10th cent.
Tr., Percy Dearmer, 1906, alt.

11.11.11.5
F.V. Strahan

1. Fa - ther, we praise you, now that night is o - ver, Ac - tive and watch-ful,
2. Ru - ler of all things, fit us for your ser - vice; Ban - ish our weak-ness,
3. All - ho - ly Fa - ther, Son, and Ho - ly Spir - it, Trin - i - ty bless - ed,
1. stand we all be - fore you; Sing - ing, we of - fer
2. health and whole - ness send - ing; Lead us to heav - en,
3. send us your sal - va - tion; Yours is the glo - ry,
1. pray'r and med - i - ta - tion: Thus we a - dore you.
2. with your saints u - ni - ted, Joy with - out end - ing.
3. gleam - ing and re - sound - ing Through all cre - a - tion.

Alternative hymns: No. 323-326.

OPENING PRAYER

Celebrant: The Lord be with you.
All: **And also with you.**
Celebrant: Let us pray.
Pause for silent prayer.
Lord God, our Father, the wonder of creation and the beauty that surrounds us are yours and your gifts to us. May we begin this new day rejoicing in your love, and spend it by serving you in the needs of others.
We ask this through Christ our Lord.
All: **Amen.**

The opening prayer of the mass of the day from the Sacramentary may be used in place of the above prayer.

TUESDAY MORNING

PSALMODY

Sit.

Psalm 8 The majesty of God and the dignity of man.

He has put all things under Christ's feet and has made him thus exalted head of the Church (Ephesians 1:22).

Antiphon
How great is your name, O Lord — our God, through all — the earth.
1. How great is your name, O *Lord* our God,
2. Your majesty is praised above the *heav* - ens;
3. You have found praise to foil your *en* - e - my,
4. When I see the heavens, the work of *your* hands,
5. What is man that you should keep *him* in mind,
6. Yet you have made him a little less than *a* god;
7. Gave him power over the works of *your* hand,
8. All of them, sheep and *cat* - tle,
9. Birds of the *air,* and fish
10. Glory to the Father, and *to* the Son,
11. As it was in the beginning, *is* now,

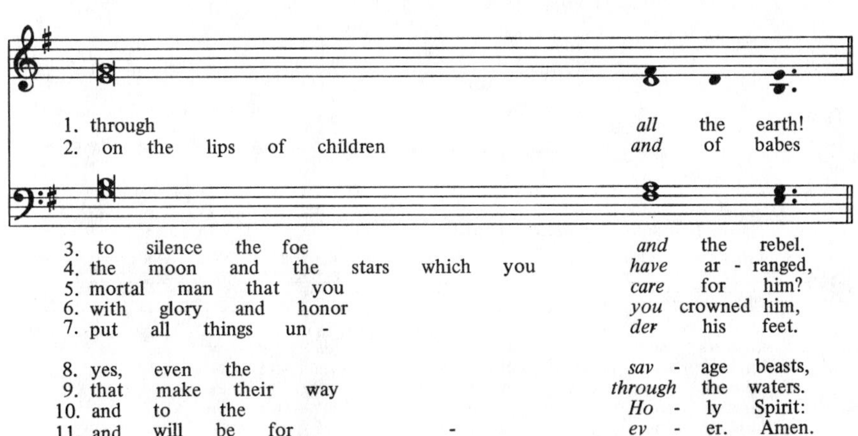

1. through *all* the earth!
2. on the lips of children *and* of babes
3. to silence the foe *and* the rebel.
4. the moon and the stars which you *have* ar - ranged,
5. mortal man that you *care* for him?
6. with glory and honor *you* crowned him,
7. put all things un - *der* his feet.
8. yes, even the *sav* - age beasts,
9. that make their way *through* the waters.
10. and to the *Ho* - ly Spirit:
11. and will be for - *ev* - er. Amen.

TUESDAY MORNING

PSALM PRAYER

Celebrant: Let us pray.
Pause for silent prayer.
Heavenly Father, you fashioned us in your image and called us to the dignity of your sons and daughters. Be with us today as we struggle to reflect your love in our lives. Let our humanity mirror that of the Word made flesh, Jesus Christ your Son our Lord.

All: **Amen.**

READING *Ephesians 6:10-11, 14-17*

Put God's armor on so as to be able to resist the devil's tactics. Stand your ground, with truth buckled around your waist, and integrity for a breast plate, wearing for shoes on your feet the eagerness to spread the gospel of peace and always carrying the shield of faith so that you can use it to put out the burning arrows of the evil one. And then you must accept salvation from God to be your sword.—This is the Word of the Lord.

All: **Thanks be to God.**

After the reading a period of silent prayer or a homily may follow.

The traditional morning canticle, the Song of Zechariah (p. 473), or the following canticle may be used.

CANTICLE Song of the Three Young Men *Daniel 3:29-34*

Cantor

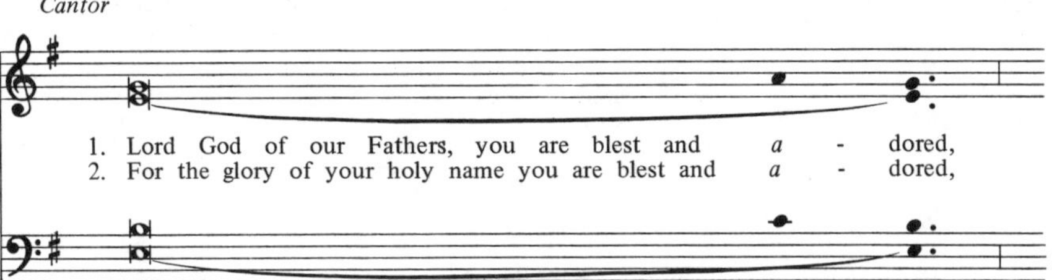
1. Lord God of our Fathers, you are blest and *a* - dored,
2. For the glory of your holy name you are blest and *a* - dored,

3. In the splendor of your Temple you are blest and *a* - dored,
4. On the throne of your majesty you are blest and *a* - dored,
5. Throned above the Cherubim, plumbing the depths, you are blest and *a* - dored,
6. In the high vault of heaven you are blest and *a* - dored,
7. Father, Son, and Holy Spirit, you are blest and *a* - dored,

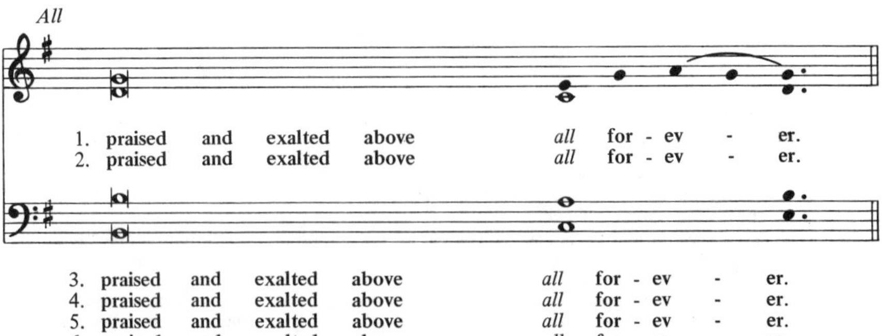
All
1. **praised and exalted above *all* for - ev - er.**
2. **praised and exalted above *all* for - ev - er.**

3. **praised and exalted above *all* for - ev - er.**
4. **praised and exalted above *all* for - ev - er.**
5. **praised and exalted above *all* for - ev - er.**
6. **praised and exalted above *all* for - ev - er.**
7. **praised and exalted above *all* for - ev - er.**

TUESDAY MORNING

INTERCESSIONS

Kneel.

The deacon or reader sings or recites the petitions and the people the response after each petition.

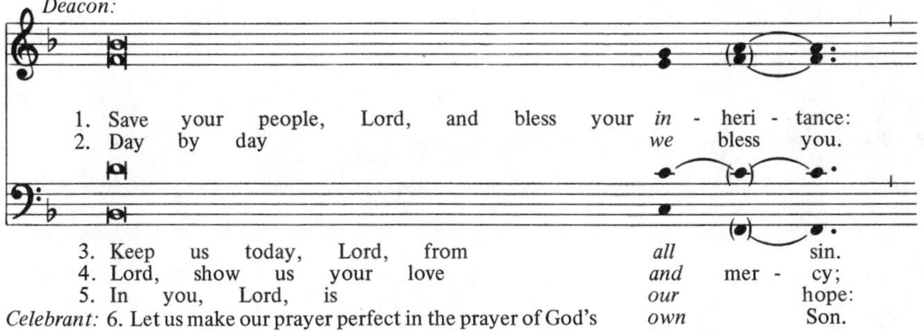

Deacon:
1. Save your people, Lord, and bless your *in* - heri - tance:
2. Day by day *we* bless you.
3. Keep us today, Lord, from *all* sin.
4. Lord, show us your love *and* mer - cy;
5. In you, Lord, is *our* hope:
Celebrant: 6. Let us make our prayer perfect in the prayer of God's *own* Son.

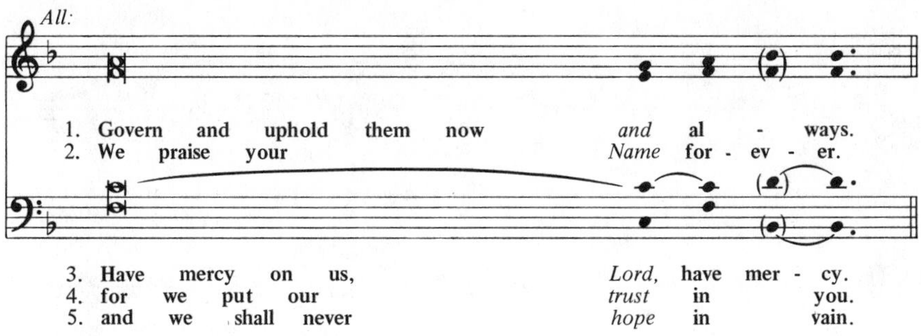

All:
1. Govern and uphold them now *and* al - ways.
2. We praise your *Name* for - ev - er.
3. Have mercy on us, *Lord,* have mer - cy.
4. for we put our *trust* in you.
5. and we shall never *hope* in vain.

All join in reciting or singing the Lord's Prayer, *p.* 468.

BLESSING AND DISMISSAL

Celebrant: May the Lord bless us and keep us.
May the Lord let his face shine upon us and be gracious to us.
May the lord look upon us kindly and give us peace: in the name of the Father, the Son †, and the Holy Spirit.
All: **Amen.**
Celebrant: Let us bless the Lord.
All: **Thanks be to God.**

TUESDAY EVENING

Blest with unique dignity and called to awesome responsibility, the child of God gives thanks and prays for strength.

LIGHT SERVICE

As the evening lights are lit, the deacon or celebrant sings:

All:
Christ our Light!
Praise to you, Lord Christ!

HYMN AT COMPLINE
St. Joseph's Abbey, 1972

Irish Air
L.M.

Em C Am G Am

1. When— ev' - ning comes we turn to you, the— mak - er of— all
2. Give— glo - ry to the Fa - ther who is— source of all— that

G Em C Am G Am

1. things. We— seek that peace and com - fort which your— kind - ness al - ways
2. is. Give— glo - ry to the Son who died that— we might all— be

Em Bm G7 Am Bm

1. brings. Pro - tect us from— all dan - gers now and—
2. His. Give— glo - ry to— the Spir - it Blest whom—

TUESDAY EVENING

G
Am
G
Em
1. all through-out — the night, that — we may rise — once —
2. they to earth — do send. Give — glo - ry to — our —
C
Am
G
Am7
Em
Am
Em
more with Christ, who — is our truth — and light.
Tri - une God, whose — rule will nev - er end. A - men.

THANKSGIVING

After the evening hymn, the deacon or celebrant stands at the lectern and sings or recites (music from p. 460 may be used):

Celebrant: The Lord be with you.
All: **And also with you.**
Celebrant: Let us give thanks to the Lord our God.
All: **It is right to give him thanks and praise.**
Celebrant: Blessed are you, O Lord, the holy God.
You are holy and your name is holy,
and the holy ones praise you every day.
We will sanctify your name in the world
even as they sanctify it in the highest heavens.
Throughout all generations we will declare your greatness
and to all eternity we will proclaim your holiness.
Your praise, our God, will never depart from our mouth,
for you are a great and holy God and king,
and we glorify you, Father, Son and Holy Spirit,
now and forever.
All: **Amen.**

Or the following prayer may be used:

O Lord, God almighty, you created the morning and the evening and called them day. You have taught the sun the hour of its setting. Dispel the darkness of our hearts: that by your brightness we may know you to be the true God and eternal light living for ever and ever.

PSALMODY

Sit.

Psalm 141, *An Evening Prayer for Repentance, may be prayed.* *See p. 463.*

Psalm 139 In praise of God's presence.
Who could ever know the mind of the Lord? Who could ever be his counselor? (Romans 11:34).

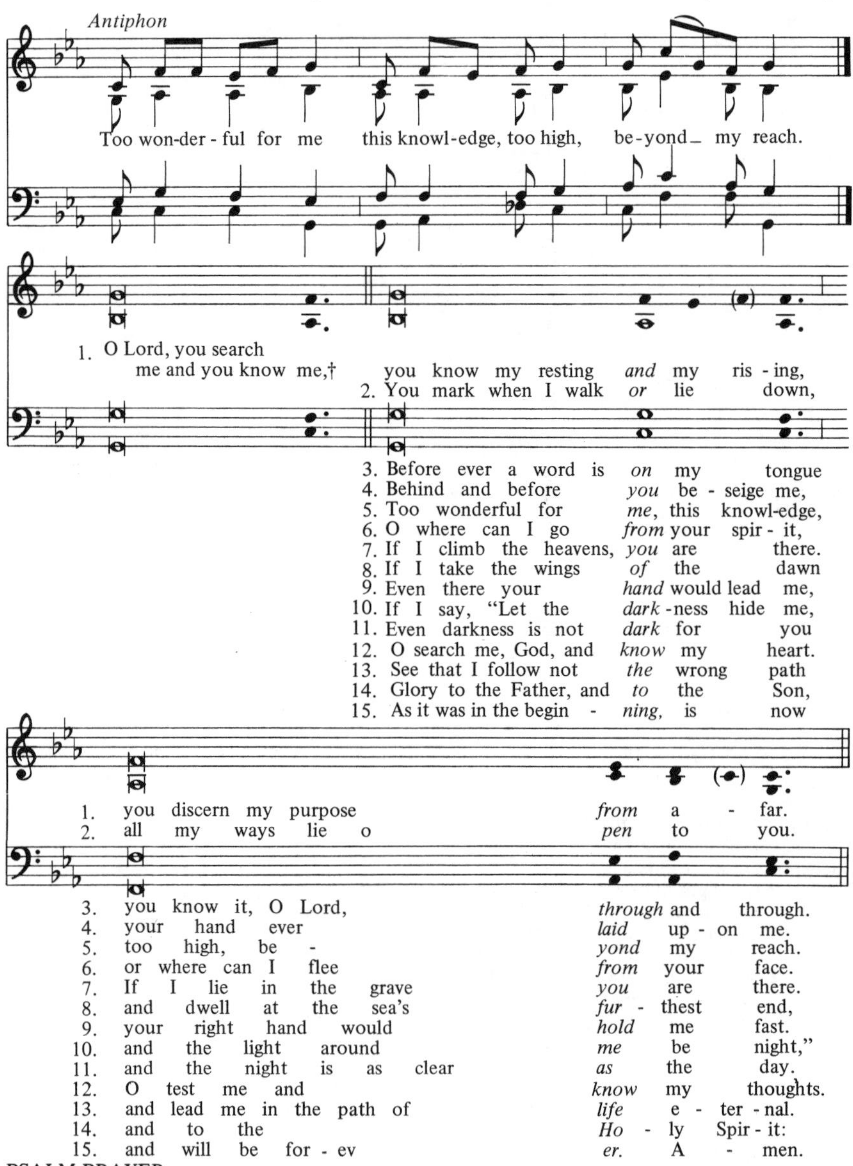
Antiphon
Too won-der - ful for me this knowl-edge, too high, be-yond my reach.
1. O Lord, you search me and you know me,† you know my resting and my ris - ing,
2. You mark when I walk or lie down,
3. Before ever a word is on my tongue
4. Behind and before you be - seige me,
5. Too wonderful for me, this knowl-edge,
6. O where can I go from your spir - it,
7. If I climb the heavens, you are there.
8. If I take the wings of the dawn
9. Even there your hand would lead me,
10. If I say, "Let the dark -ness hide me,
11. Even darkness is not dark for you
12. O search me, God, and know my heart.
13. See that I follow not the wrong path
14. Glory to the Father, and to the Son,
15. As it was in the begin - ning, is now
1. you discern my purpose from a - far.
2. all my ways lie o pen to you.
3. you know it, O Lord, through and through.
4. your hand ever laid up - on me.
5. too high, be - yond my reach.
6. or where can I flee from your face.
7. If I lie in the grave you are there.
8. and dwell at the sea's fur - thest end,
9. your right hand would hold me fast.
10. and the light around me be night,"
11. and the night is as clear as the day.
12. O test me and know my thoughts.
13. and lead me in the path of life e - ter - nal.
14. and to the Ho - ly Spir - it:
15. and will be for - ev er. A - men.

PSALM PRAYER

Celebrant: Let us pray.
Pause for silent prayer.
Lord God, both day and night belong to you. May the light of your presence always shine in our hearts. and may we live in that light forever. Through Christ our Lord.

All: **Amen.**

TUESDAY EVENING

READING *Romans 13:8-10*

Avoid getting into debt, except the debt of mutual love. If you love your fellow men you have carried out your obligations. All the commandments: You shall not commit adultery, you shall not kill, you shall not steal, you shall not covet, and so on, are summed up in this single command: You must love your neighbor as yourself. Love is the one thing that cannot hurt your neighbor; that is why it is the answer to every one of the commandments.—This is the Word of the Lord.

All: **Thanks be to God.**

After the reading, a period of silent prayer or a homily may follow.

The traditional evening canticle, the Song of Mary (p. 479), or the following canticle may be used.

CANTICLE The Song of the Redeemed *Revelation 15:3-4*

Antiphon
Your ways are the ways of right - eous - ness and truth, O, king of the ag - es.
1. O ruler of the universe, Lord God, † 1. great deeds are they that you have done,
2. Your ways are ways of righteous - ness and truth,
3. Who can fail to do you homage, Lord, † and sing the praises of your name?
4. All nations will draw near, and fall down be - fore you,
5. Glory to the Father, and to the Son,
6. As it was in the beginning, is now,
1. surpassing human un - der - stand - ing.
2. O King of all a - ges.
3. for you only are the Ho ly One.
4. Because your just and holy works have been re - vealed.
5. and to the Ho - ly Spir - it:
6. and will be for ev - er. A - men.

INTERCESSIONS

Kneel.
The deacon or reader sings or recites the petition and the people the response after each petition.

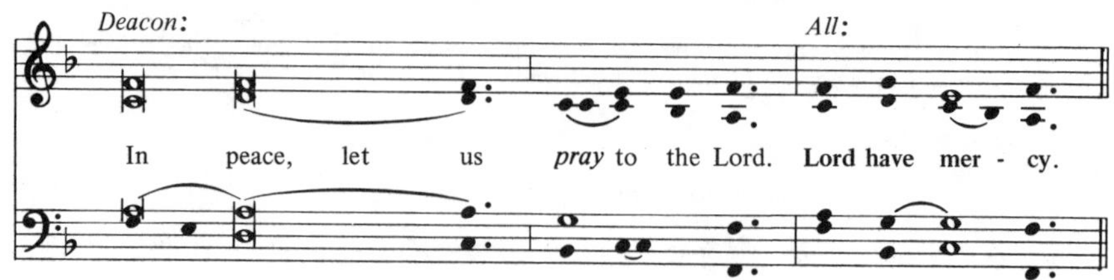
Deacon:
All:
In peace, let us *pray* to the Lord. **Lord have mer - cy.**

Deacon:	That this evening may be restful and peaceful, holy and perfect, free from sin and in Christ, let us *pray* to the Lord.
All:	**Lord, have mercy.**
Deacon:	For an angel of peace, a faithful guardian of our souls and bodies, let us *pray* to the Lord.
All:	**Lord, have mercy.**
Deacon:	For the forgiveness of our sins and the correction of our failings, let us *pray* to the Lord.
All:	**Lord, have mercy.**
Deacon:	For our fidelity in holiness and charity with the Church of God throughout the world, let us *pray* to the Lord.
All:	**Lord, have mercy.**
Deacon:	For whatever is good and helpful for ourselves, for all the human family and the salvation of all, let us *pray* to the Lord.
All:	**Lord, have mercy.**
Deacon:	That the end of our life may be Christian, painless, free from shame and peaceful, and for a good defense before the awesome judgement seat of Christ, let us *pray* to the Lord.
All:	**Lord, have mercy.**
Deacon:	Help, save, pity and defend us, O *God,* by your grace. *Pause for free prayer, silent and spontaneous.* Rejoicing in the fellowship of the Virgin Mary, of Saint N., and of *all* the saints, let us commend ourselves, one another, and our whole life to *Christ* our Lord.
All:	**To you, O Lord.**
Celebrant:	Let us make our prayer perfect in the prayer of *God's* own Son.

All join in reciting or singing the Lord's Prayer, *p. 468*

BLESSING AND DISMISSAL

Celebrant:	May the Lord bless us and keep us. May the Lord let his face shine upon us and be gracious to us. May the Lord look upon us kindly and give us peace: in the name of the Father, and of the Son,† and of the Holy Spirit.
All:	**Amen.**
Celebrant:	Let us bless the Lord.
All:	**Thanks be to God.**

WEDNESDAY MORNING

With the changes and chances of life in view, Christians rejoice in the constancy of God's Love.

Celebrant: O Lord, open our lips.
All: **And we shall praise your name.**

PSALM 100
Tr., James Quinn, S.J. 1969

ROUEN
11 11. 11 5
Rouen Church Melody,
harm. by Healey Willan, 1918

1. Sing, all cre - a - tion, sing to God in glad - ness!
2. Know that our God is Lord of all the a - ges!
3. En - ter his tem - ple, ring - ing out his prais - es!
1. Joy - ous - ly serve him, sing - ing hymns of hom - age!
2. He is our mak - er; we are all his crea - tures,
3. Sing in thanks - giv - ing as you come be - fore him!
1. Chant - ing his prais - es, come be - fore his pres - ence!
2. Peo - ple he fash - ioned, sheep he leads to pas - ture!
3. Bless - ing his boun - ty, glo - ri - fy his great - ness!
1. Praise the Al - might - y!
2. Praise the Al - might - y!
3. Praise the Al - might - y!

Alternate hymns: No. 323-326.

WEDNESDAY MORNING

OPENING PRAYER

Celebrant: The Lord be with you.
All: **And also with you.**
Celebrant: Let us pray.
Pause for silent prayer.
Praise to you, Father, almighty and eternal God, for having brought us through the night into the light of this new day. May we pass this day peacefully and free from sin, that we may give you thanks and praise again when evening comes. We ask this through Christ our Lord.
All: **Amen.**

PSALMODY

Sit.

Psalm 96 The glories of the Lord, king of the universe.

Sing a new song before the throne, in the presence of the Lord (Revelation 14:3).

Antiphon
Give_ the Lord, you fam - 'lies of peo - ple, give_ the Lord glo - ry and pow-er.

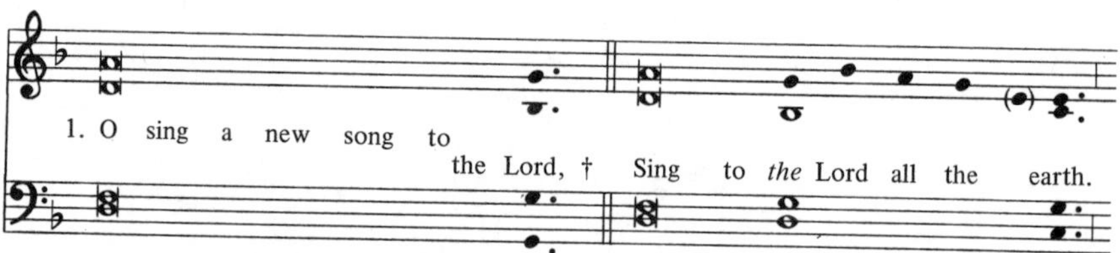

1. O sing a new song to the Lord, † Sing to the Lord all the earth.

2. Proclaim his help day by day, † tell among *the* na - tions his glo - ry
3. The Lord is great and worthy of praise,† to be feared a - bove all gods;
4. It was the Lord who made the heavens, † his are majesty *and* state and pow - er
5. Give the Lord, you families of peoples,† give the Lord *glo* - ry and pow - er,
6. Bring an offering and enter his courts, † worship the *Lord* in his Tem - ple.
7. Proclaim to the nations: "God is king." † The world he *made* firm in its place;
8. Let the heavens rejoice and the earth be glad,† let the sea and all with- *in* it thun-der praise,
9. All the trees of the wood shout for joy † at the presence of *the* Lord for he comes,
10. With justice *he* will rule the world,
11. Glory to the Fa-*ther,* and to the Son,
12. As it was in the *be* - gin - ning, is now,

WEDNESDAY MORNING

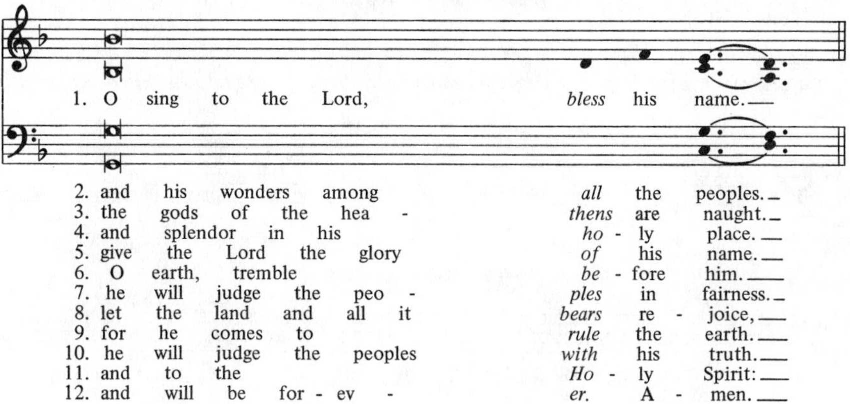
1. O sing to the Lord, bless his name.
2. and his wonders among all the peoples.
3. the gods of the hea - thens are naught.
4. and splendor in his ho - ly place.
5. give the Lord the glory of his name.
6. O earth, tremble be - fore him.
7. he will judge the peo - ples in fairness.
8. let the land and all it bears re - joice,
9. for he comes to rule the earth.
10. he will judge the peoples with his truth.
11. and to the Ho - ly Spirit:
12. and will be for - ev - er. A - men.

PSALM PRAYER

Celebrant: Let us pray.
Pause for silent prayer.
Almighty God, you are the Lord of the universe, the beginning and the end of all that is. Let all creation give praise to you; let all peoples bless your holy name; through Christ our Lord.

All: **Amen.**

READING *Micah 6:8*

What is good has been explained to you, man; this is what Yahweh asks of you: only this, to act justly, to love tenderly and to walk humbly with your God.—This is the Word of the Lord.

All: **Thanks be to God.**

After the reading, a period of silent prayer or a homily may follow.

CANTICLE Song of Zechariah (Benedictus) *Luke 1:68-79*

Stand.

See page 473.

WEDNESDAY MORNING

INTERCESSIONS

Kneel.

The deacon or reader sings or recites the petitions and the people the response after each petition.

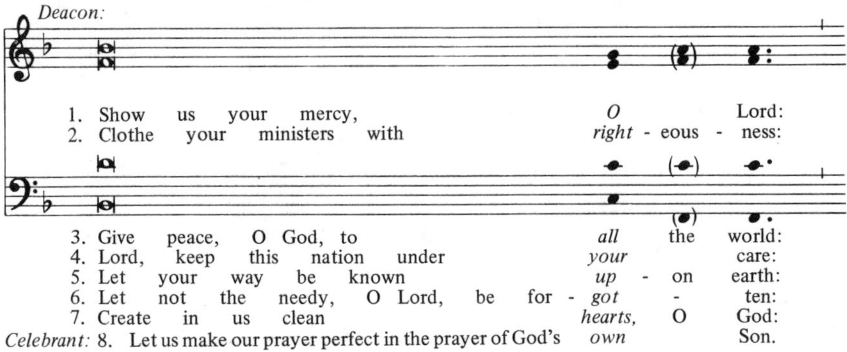
Deacon:
1. Show us your mercy, O Lord:
2. Clothe your ministers with right - eous - ness:
3. Give peace, O God, to all the world:
4. Lord, keep this nation under your care:
5. Let your way be known up - on earth:
6. Let not the needy, O Lord, be for - got - ten:
7. Create in us clean hearts, O God:
Celebrant: 8. Let us make our prayer perfect in the prayer of God's own Son.

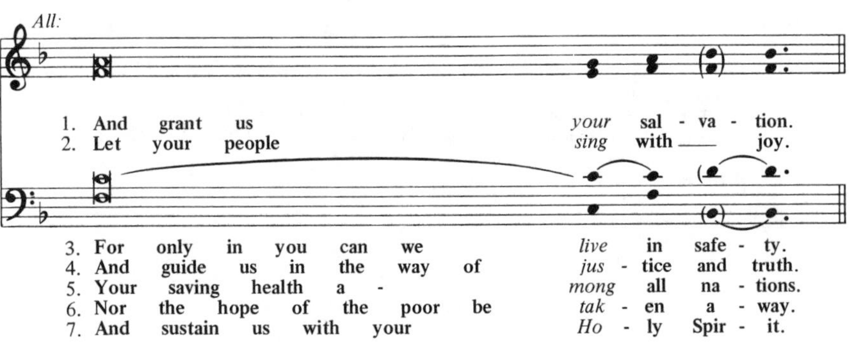
All:
1. And grant us your sal - va - tion.
2. Let your people sing with joy.
3. For only in you can we live in safe - ty.
4. And guide us in the way of jus - tice and truth.
5. Your saving health a - mong all na - tions.
6. Nor the hope of the poor be tak - en a - way.
7. And sustain us with your Ho - ly Spir - it.

All join in reciting or singing the Lord's Prayer, p. 468.

BLESSING AND DISMISSAL

Celebrant: May the Lord bless us, protect us from evil,
and bring us to a life that will never end.
All: **Amen.**
Celebrant: Let us bless the Lord.
All: **Thanks be to God.**

WEDNESDAY EVENING

At mid-week the Church prays that God will continue to bless the work he has begun in us all.

LIGHT SERVICE

Stand.
As the evening lights are lit, the deacon or celebrant sings:

All
Christ our Light!
Praise to you, Lord Christ!
Mane Nobiscum, Domine
Tr., St. Joseph's Abbey, 1967, 1968
L.M.
1. Lord Jesus Christ, abide with us, Now that the sun has run its course; Let hope not be obscured by night, But may faith's darkness be as light.
2. Lord Jesus Christ, grant us your peace, And, when the trials of earth shall cease, Grant us the morning light of grace, The radiant splendor of your face.
3. Immortal, Holy, Three-fold Light, Yours be the kingdom, pow'r and might; All glory be eternally To you, life-giving Trinity! Amen.

WEDNESDAY EVENING

THANKSGIVING

After the evening hymn, the deacon or celebrant stands at the lectern and sings or recites (music from page 460 may be used):

Deacon: The Lord be with you.
All: **And also with you.**
Deacon: Let us give thanks to the Lord, our God.
All: **It is right to give him thanks and praise.**
Deacon: Blessed are you, Lord, God and Father of our Lord Jesus Christ: For in your infinite wisdom you have made us a chosen race, a royal priesthood, a consecrated nation, a people set apart to sing your praise. Strengthen us, O Lord, to live holy and unselfish lives in this world, that we might come to the glory of the world without end, where we shall sing your praise forever.
All: **Amen.**

Or the following may be used:

Lord God, at evening time we offer you our praise. Watch over us always by day and by night; that in the chances and changes of this passing life, we might rest secure in your love. We ask this through Christ our Lord.

PSALMODY

***Psalm 141**, An Evening Prayer for Repentance, may be prayed. See p. 463.*

Psalm 67 Song of Blessing

Take notice that this salvation of God has been sent to the Gentiles; the Gentiles will listen (Acts 28:28).

Antiphon
O God be gra-cious and bless us, and let your light face shed light — up - on — us.

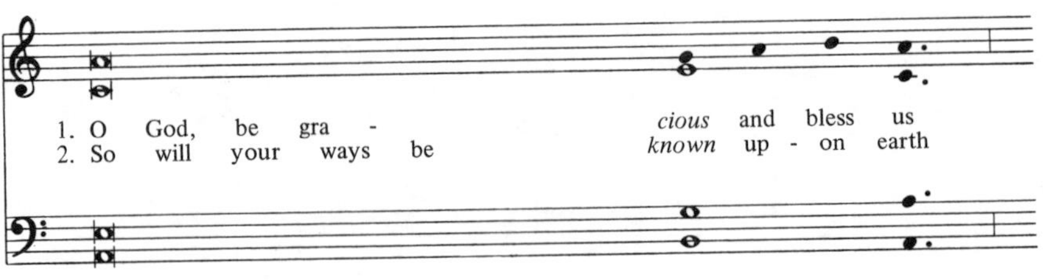
1. O God, be gra - *cious* and bless us
2. So will your ways be *known* up - on earth

3. Let the peoples *praise* you, O God;
4. Let the nations be *glad* and ex - ult
5. With fairness you *rule* the peo - ples,
6. The earth has *yield* - ed its fruit

7. May God still give *us* his bless - ing
8. Let the peoples *praise* you, O God;
9. Glory to the Father, *and* to the Son,
10. As it was in the be - *gin* - ning, is now,

WEDNESDAY EVENING

1. and let your face shed its light up - on us.
2. and all na - tions learn your saving help.
3. let all the peo - ples praise you.
4. for you rule the world with jus - tice.
5. you guide the na - tions on earth.
6. for God, our God, has blessed us.
7. till the ends of the earth re - vere him.
8. let all the peo - ples praise you.
9. and to the Ho - ly Spir - it:
10. and will be forever and ev - er. A - men.

PSALM PRAYER

Celebrant: Let us pray.
Pause for silent prayer.
Loving Father, strengthen our trust in your gracious providence. In your kindness, banish fear from our hearts and surround us with your loving embrace. Through Christ our Lord.

All: **Amen.**

READING *Colossians 3:12, 15-17*

You are God's chosen race, his saints; he loves you, and you should be clothed in sincere compassion, in kindness and humility, gentleness and patience... May the peace of Christ reign in your hearts, because it is for this that you were called together as parts of one body. Always be thankful.

Let the message of Christ, in all its richness, find a home with you. Teach each other, and advise each other, in all wisdom. With gratitude in your hearts sing psalms and hymns and inspired songs to God; and never say or do anything except in the name of the Lord Jesus, giving thanks to God the Father through him.—This is the Word of the Lord.

All: **Thanks be to God.**

After the reading, a period of silent prayer or a homily may follow.

CANTICLE The Song of Mary (Magnificat) *Luke 1:47-55*

Stand.
See p. 479.

INTERCESSIONS

Kneel.
The deacon or reader sings or recites the petition and the people the response after each petition.

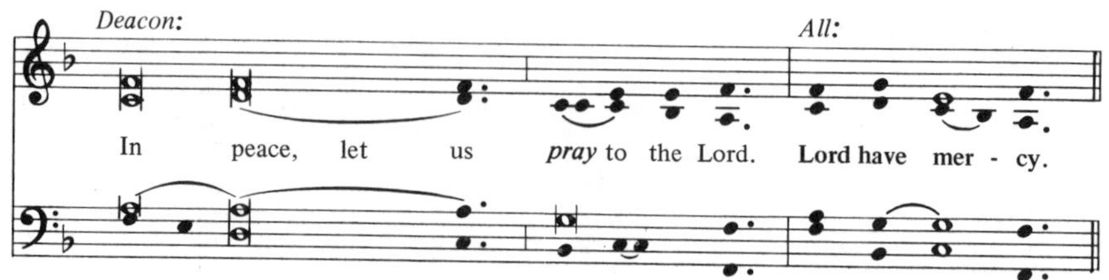
Deacon:
All:
In peace, let us pray to the Lord. Lord have mer - cy.

Deacon: For the royal and priestly people of God throughout the world we *pray* to the Lord.
All: **Lord, have mercy.**
Deacon: For the unity of all Christian believers, and the enlightenment of all unbelievers, we *pray* to the Lord.
All: **Lord, have mercy.**
Deacon: For our persecuted brothers and sisters in the faith, we *pray* to the Lord.
All: **Lord, have mercy.**
Deacon: For peace in our days and for justice among nations, we *pray* to the Lord.
All: **Lord, have mercy.**
Deacon: For light and peace for our beloved dead, we *pray* to the Lord.
All: **Lord, have mercy.**
Deacon: Help, save, pity and defend us, O *God* by your grace.
Pause for free prayer, silent and spontaneous.
Rejoicing in the fellowship of the Blessed Virgin Mary, the Mother of God, of Saint N., and of all the saints, let us commend ourselves, one another, and our whole life to *Christ* our Lord.
All: **To you, O Lord.**
Celebrant: Let us make our prayer perfect in the prayer of *God's* own Son.

All join in reciting or singing the Lord's Prayer, p. 468.

BLESSING AND DISMISSAL

Celebrant: May the Lord bless us and keep us.
May the Lord let his face shine upon us and be gracious to us.
May the Lord look upon us kindly and give us peace: in the name of the Father, and of the Son,† and of the Holy Spirit.
All: **Amen.**
Celebrant: Let us bless the Lord.
All: **Thanks be to God.**

THURSDAY MORNING

On Thursday, all thoughts turn to the Holy Eucharist, the food that sustains Christians during their week of work and prayer.

Celebrant: O Lord, open our lips.
All: **And we shall praise your name.**

MORNING HYMN

DARWALL'S 148th
66. 66. 44. 44
John Darwall, 1770, alt., ca. 1778

Psalm 95
Tr., James Quinn, S.J., 1969

1. To God with glad - ness sing, Your Rock and Sav - ior bless; With - in his tem - ple bring Your songs of thank - ful - ness! O God of might, To you we sing, En - throned as King On heav - en's height!
2. He cra - dles in his hand The heights and depths of earth; He made the sea and land, He brought the world to birth! O God most high, We are your sheep; On us you keep Your Shep - herd's eye!
3. Your heav'n-ly Fa - ther praise, Ac - claim his on - ly Son, Your voice in hom - age raise To him who makes all one! O Dove of peace, On us de - scend That strife may end And joy in - crease!

Alternate Hymns: No. 323 through 326.

OPENING PRAYER

Celebrant: The Lord be with you.
All: **And also with you.**
Celebrant: Let us pray.
Pause for silent prayer.
O Lord, master of our lives, you have brought us in safety and in joy to the dawn of another day. Keep us this day from selfishness and sin. Bless us with humility of heart, with patience and neighborly love: that we may be aware of our failings and not think evil of others. We ask this through Christ our Lord.
All: **Amen.**

THURSDAY MORNING

PSALMODY

Sit.

Psalm 42 Desire for God and his temple.

Let him who is thirsty come forward; let all who desire it accept the gift of the Lord (Revelation 22:17).

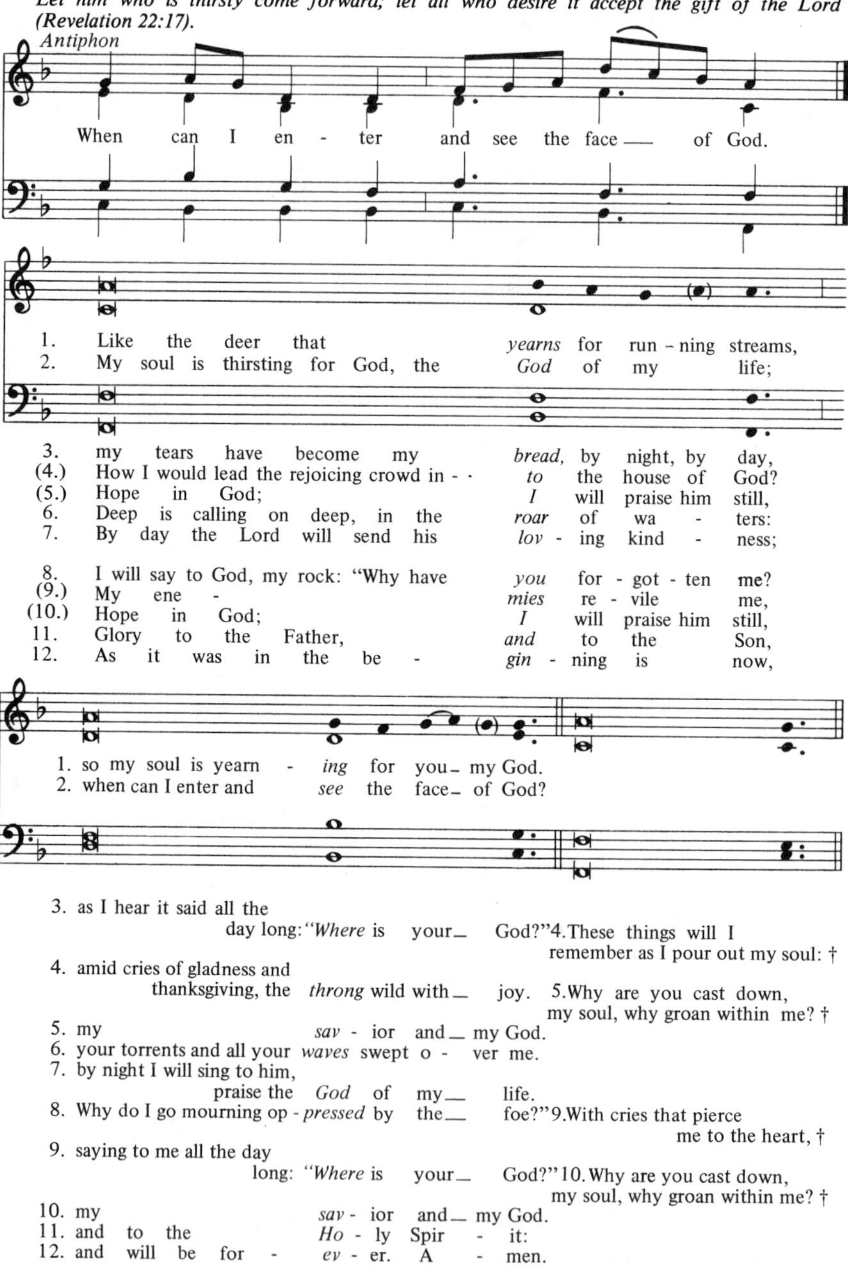

Antiphon
When can I en - ter and see the face — of God.
1. Like the deer that *yearns* for run - ning streams,
2. My soul is thirsting for God, the *God* of my life;
3. my tears have become my *bread,* by night, by day,
(4.) How I would lead the rejoicing crowd in - - *to* the house of God?
(5.) Hope in God; *I* will praise him still,
6. Deep is calling on deep, in the *roar* of wa - ters:
7. By day the Lord will send his *lov* - ing kind - ness;
8. I will say to God, my rock: "Why have *you* for - got - ten me?
(9.) My ene - *mies* re - vile me,
(10.) Hope in God; *I* will praise him still,
11. Glory to the Father, *and* to the Son,
12. As it was in the be - *gin* - ning is now,
1. so my soul is yearn - *ing* for you — my God.
2. when can I enter and *see* the face — of God?
3. as I hear it said all the day long: "*Where* is your — God?" 4. These things will I remember as I pour out my soul: †
4. amid cries of gladness and thanksgiving, the *throng* wild with — joy. 5. Why are you cast down, my soul, why groan within me? †
5. my *sav* - ior and — my God.
6. your torrents and all your *waves* swept o - ver me.
7. by night I will sing to him, praise the *God* of my — life.
8. Why do I go mourning op - *pressed* by the — foe?" 9. With cries that pierce me to the heart, †
9. saying to me all the day long: "*Where* is your — God?" 10. Why are you cast down, my soul, why groan within me? †
10. my *sav* - ior and — my God.
11. and to the *Ho* - ly Spir - it:
12. and will be for - *ev* - er. A - men.

THURSDAY MORNING

PSALM PRAYER

Celebrant: Let us pray.
Pause for silent prayer.
Loving Father, turn our hearts to you and enable us always to see the one thing necessary, to know you and the Lord Jesus whom you sent and who lives and reigns with you forever.
All: **Amen.**

READING *Malachi 1:11*

From the farthest east to the farthest west my name is honored among the nations and everywhere a sacrifice of incense is offered to my name, and a pure offering too, since my name is honored among the nations, says Yahweh Sabbaoth.—This is the Word of God.

All: **Thanks be to God.**

The traditional morning canticle, the Song of Zechariah (p. 473), or the following canticle may be used.

CANTICLE Song of the Lamb *Revelation 4:11, 5:9-10, 13*

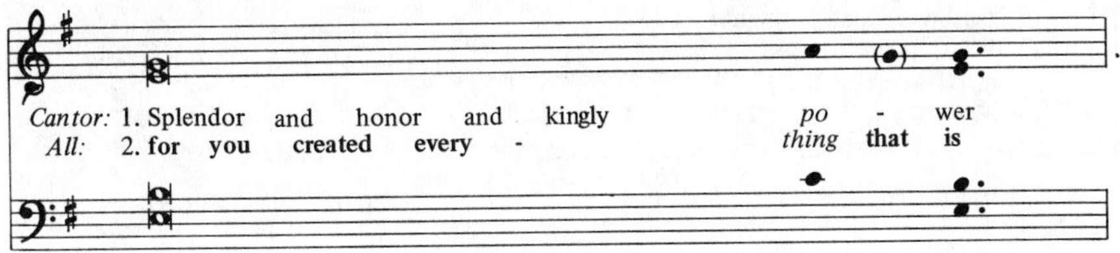
Cantor: 1. Splendor and honor and kingly po - wer
All: 2. for you created every - thing that is

Cantor: 3. And yours by right, O Lamb that *was*— slain,
All: **4. from every family, language, people and** *na* **- tion,**
Cantor: 5. And so, to him who sits up - *on* the throne,
All: **6. be worship and praise, dominion and** *splen* **- dor,**

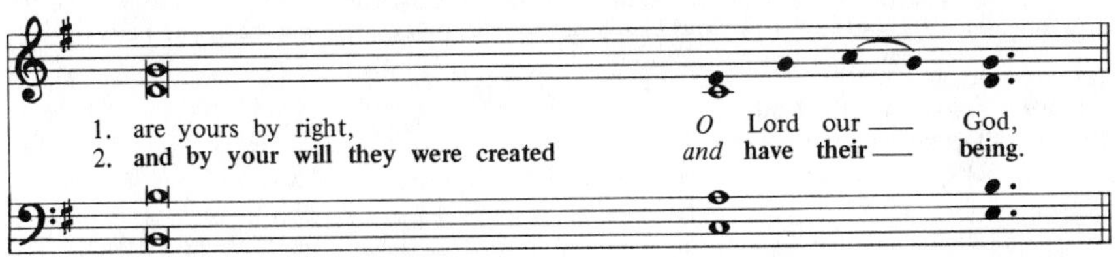
1. are yours by right, O Lord our— God,
2. and by your will they were created and have their— being.

3. for with your blood you have *re* - deemed for— God,
4. a kingdom of priests *to* **serve our— God.**
5. and *to* Christ the— lamb,
6. forever, and *for* **ev - er - more.**

INTERCESSIONS

Kneel.
The deacon or reader sings or recites the petition and the people the response after each petition.

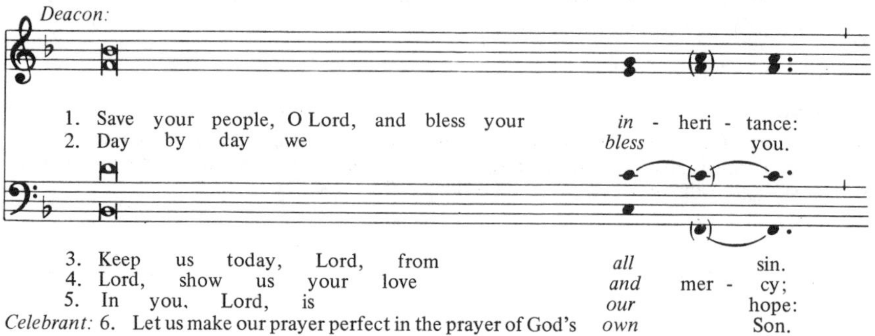
Deacon:
1. Save your people, O Lord, and bless your *in* - heri - tance:
2. Day by day we *bless* you.
3. Keep us today, Lord, from *all* sin.
4. Lord, show us your love *and* mer - cy;
5. In you, Lord, is *our* hope:
Celebrant: 6. Let us make our prayer perfect in the prayer of God's *own* Son.

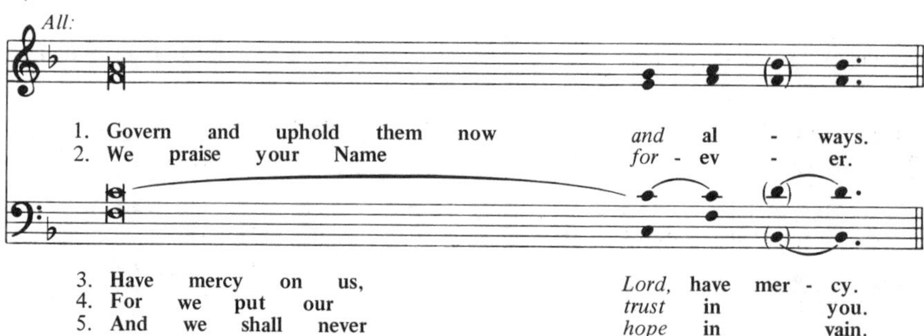
All:
1. Govern and uphold them now *and* al - ways.
2. We praise your Name *for* - ev - er.
3. Have mercy on us, *Lord,* have mer - cy.
4. For we put our *trust* in you.
5. And we shall never *hope* in vain.

All join in reciting or singing the Lord's Prayer, p. 468.

BLESSING AND DISMISSAL

Celebrant: May the Lord bless us and keep us.
May the Lord make his face shine upon us and be gracious to us.
May the Lord look upon us kindly and give us peace: in the name of the Father, Son,† and Holy Spirit.
All: **Amen.**
Celebrant: Let us bless the Lord.
All: **Thanks be to God.**

THURSDAY EVENING

God is our good shepherd and he nourishes us with the food of the eucharist.

LIGHT SERVICE

Stand.
As the evening lights are lit, the deacon or celebrant sings or recites:

All
Christ our Light!
Praise to you, Lord Christ!

EVENING HYMN

The evening hymn is begun immediately.
P. 488, or another appropriate hymn (No. 327-330,) may be sung.

THANKSGIVING

After the evening hymn, the deacon or celebrant stands at the lectern and sings or recites (music from p. 460 may be used):

Deacon: The Lord be with you.
All: **And also with you.**
Deacon: Let us give thanks to the Lord, our God.
All: **It is right to give him thanks and praise.**
Deacon: Blessed are you, O Lord our God,
whose power is without compare,
whose glory is incomprehensible,
whose mercy is beyond all measure,
and whose love for all the human family is beyond words to describe.
From the depths of your compassion, O Master,
look upon your people and upon this holy place:
may we and all those praying for us
obtain the riches of your infinite compassion and loving mercy.
For all honor and glory and worship are your due,
Father, Son and Holy Spirit, one God,
now and always, and forever and ever.
All: **Amen.**

Or, the following prayer may be used:

Father, almighty God, we thank you for bringing us in safety and joy to this evening hour of prayer. May the lifting up of your hands in thanksgiving and praise be a sacrifice acceptable to you. We ask this through Christ our Lord.

THURSDAY EVENING

PSALMODY

Sit.

***Psalm 141,** An Evening prayer for Repentance, may be prayed.* *See page 463.*

Psalm 23 The Good Shepherd

The lamb who is at the throne will be their shepherd and will lead them to springs of living water (Revelation 7:17).

Antiphon
You have pre - pared a ban - quet for me.

1. The Lord *is* my shep - herd; there is nothing *I* shall want.
2. Fresh and green *are* the pas - tures where he gives *me* re - pose.

3. Near restful waters *he* leads me, to revive my *droop*-ing spir - it.
4. He guides me along *the* right path; he is true *to* his name.
5. If I should walk in the *val* - ley of dark-ness no evil *would* I fear.
6. You are there with your crook *and* your staff; with these you *give* me com-fort.
7. You have prepared a *ban*-quet for me in the sight *of* my foes.
8. My head you have a - *noint*-ed with oil; my cup is *ov* - er - flow-ing.
9. Surely goodness and kindness shall *fol* - low me all the days *of* my life.
10. In the Lord's own house *shall* I dwell for - ev - *er* and ev - er.
11. Glory to the Father and *to* the Son, and to the *Ho* - ly Spir - it:
12. As it was in the be - *gin* - ning, is now, and will be for-ev-*er*. A - men.

PSALM PRAYER

Celebrant: Let us pray
Pause for silent prayer.
Heavenly Father, your Son Jesus Christ brings us to life in the waters of baptism, anoints our heads with the oil of gladness and feeds us at his table. Strengthen us as members of his flock. Bring us together in unity and peace. Through Christ our Lord.

All: **Amen.**

READING *1 John 4:7-11*

My dear people, let us love one another since love comes from God and everyone who loves is begotten by God and knows God. Anyone who fails to love can never have known God, because God is love. God's love for us was revealed when God sent into the world his only Son so that we could have life through him; this is the love I mean: not our love for God, but God's love for us when he sent his Son to be the sacrifice that takes our sins away. My dear people, since God has loved us so much, we too should love one another.—This is the Word of the Lord.

All: **Thanks be to God.**

After the reading, a period of silent prayer or a homily may follow.

CANTICLE The Song of Simeon (Nunc Dimittis) *Luke 2:29-32*

The Song of Simeon, p. 491, or the traditional evening canticle, The Song of Mary, p. 479, may be sung or recited.

INTERCESSIONS

Kneel.
The deacon or reader sings or recites the petitions and the people the response after each petition.

Deacon:
All:
In peace, let us *pray* to the Lord.
Lord have mer - cy.

Deacon: For the one, holy, and apostolic Church of God, in all its communities throughout the world, let us *pray* to the Lord.
All: **Lord, have mercy.**
Deacon: For ardent preachers of the gospel in this and every land, let us *pray* to the Lord.
All: **Lord, have mercy.**
Deacon: For the union of charity, the bond of perfection and the gift of the Spirit, let us *pray* to the Lord.
All: **Lord, have mercy.**
Deacon: For those who serve the needs and defend the rights of the human family, let us *pray* to the Lord.
All: **Lord, have mercy.**
Deacon: For those who love us and those who hate us, let us *pray* to the Lord.
All: **Lord, have mercy.**
Deacon: Help, save, pity and defend us, O *God* by your grace.
Pause for free prayer, silent and spontaneous.
Rejoicing in the fellowship of the Blessed Virgin Mary, of Saint N., and of all the saints, let us commend ourselves, one another, and our whole life to *Christ* our Lord.
All: **To you, O Lord.**
Celebrant: Let us make our prayer perfect in the prayer of *God's* own Son.

All join in reciting or singing the Lord's Prayer, p. 468.

BLESSING AND DISMISSAL

Celebrant: May the Lord bless us and keep us.
May the Lord let his face shine upon us and be gracious to us.
May the Lord look upon us kindly and give us peace: in the name of the Father, and of the Son,† and the Holy Spirit.
All: **Amen.**
Celebrant: Let us bless the Lord.
All: **Thanks be to God.**

FRIDAY MORNING

Confronted with sin and the cross, Christians sing in repentance and rejoice in hope.

Celebrant: O Lord, open our lips.
All: **And we shall praise your name.**

MORNING HYMN

NOCTE SURGENTES
10th cent.
Tr., Percy Dearmer, 1906, alt.

11.11.11.5
F.V. Strahan

1. Fa - ther, we praise you, now that night is o - ver, Ac - tive and watch-ful,
2. Ru - ler of all things, fit us for your ser - vice; Ban - ish our weak-ness,
3. All ho - ly Fa - ther, Son, and Ho - ly Spir - it, Trin - i - ty bless - ed,
1. stand we all be - fore you; Sing - ing, we of - fer
2. health and whole-ness send - ing; Lead us to heav - en,
3. send us your sal - va - tion; Yours is the glo - ry,
1. pray'r and med - i - ta - tion: Thus we a - dore you.
2. with your saints u - ni - ted, Joy with - out end - ing.
3. gleam - ing and re - sound - ing Through all cre - a - tion.

Alternative hymns: No. 323-326

OPENING PRAYER

Celebrant: The Lord be with you.
All: **And also with you.**
Celebrant: Let us pray.
Pause for silent prayer.
Lord God almighty, the beginning and the end, the first and the last, dawn of our lives and light of our days: direct our hearts and bodies in the love of your name and the patience of Christ. May we accomplish with joy what you ask us to do and accept with love what you call on us to bear. We ask this through Christ our Lord.
All: **Amen.**

FRIDAY MORNING

PSALMODY

The cantor sings the antiphon and all repeat it initially after him and at the end of each set of verses.

Psalm 51 Prayer of Repentance.

You must be made new in mind and spirit, and put on the new nature of God's creation (Ephesians 4:23-24).

Antiphon
A hum - bled, con - trite heart you will not spurn.

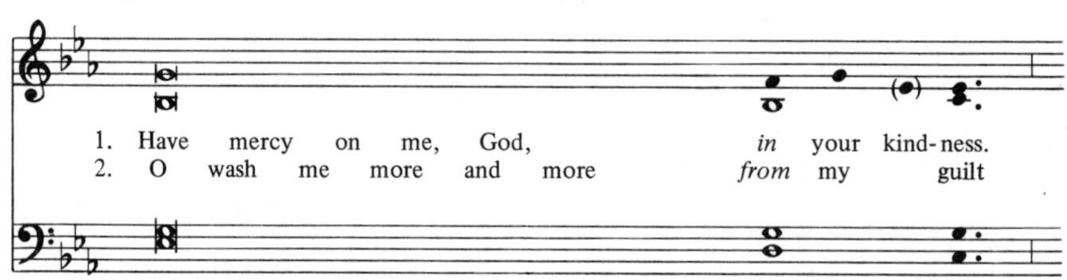
1. Have mercy on me, God, *in* your kind- ness.
2. O wash me more and more *from* my guilt

3.	My offences truly	*I*	know	them;
4.	Against you, you alone,	*have*	I	sin - ned;
5.	That you may be justified when	*you*	give	sen - tence
6.	O see, in guilt	*I*	was	born,
7.	Indeed, you love truth	*in*	the	heart;
8.	O purify me, then I	*shall*	be	clean;
9.	Make me hear rejoicing and	*glad*	-	ness,
10.	From my sins turn a -	*way*	your	face
11.	A pure heart create for	*me,*	O	God,
12.	Do not cast me away	*from*	your	presence,
13.	Give me again the joy	*of*	your	help;
14.	That I may teach transgres -	*sors*	your	ways
15.	O rescue me, God	*my*	help -	er,
16.	O Lord, o -	*pen*	my	lips,
17.	Glory to the Father, and	*to*	the	Son,
18.	As it was in the begin -	*ning,*	is	now

FRIDAY MORNING

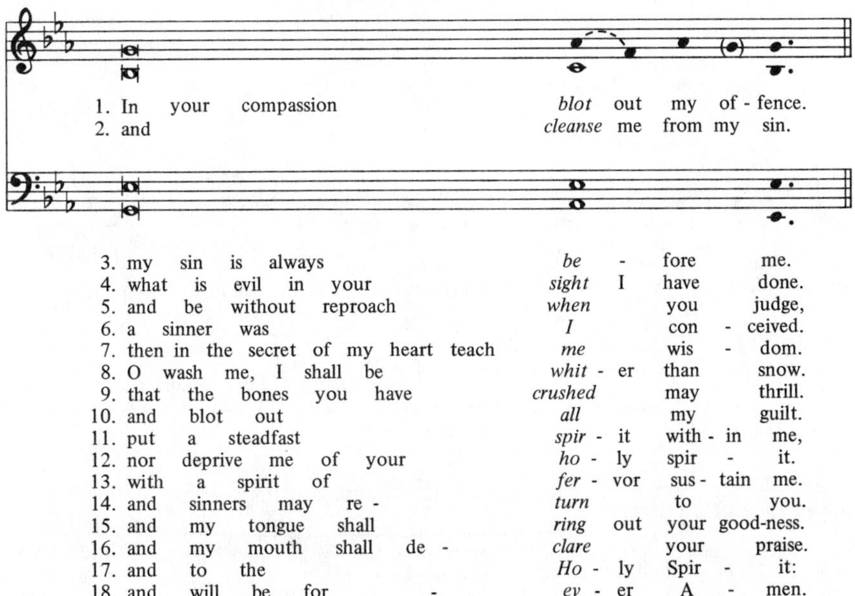
1. In your compassion *blot* out my of - fence.
2. and *cleanse* me from my sin.
3. my sin is always *be* - fore me.
4. what is evil in your *sight* I have done.
5. and be without reproach *when* you judge,
6. a sinner was *I* con - ceived.
7. then in the secret of my heart teach *me* wis - dom.
8. O wash me, I shall be *whit* - er than snow.
9. that the bones you have *crushed* may thrill.
10. and blot out *all* my guilt.
11. put a steadfast *spir* - it with - in me,
12. nor deprive me of your *ho* - ly spir - it.
13. with a spirit of *fer* - vor sus - tain me.
14. and sinners may re - *turn* to you.
15. and my tongue shall *ring* out your good-ness.
16. and my mouth shall de - *clare* your praise.
17. and to the *Ho* - ly Spir - it:
18. and will be for - *ev* - er A - men.

PSALM PRAYER

Celebrant: Let us pray.
Pause for silent prayer.
Almighty and merciful God, you do not desire the death of a sinner, but rather that he turn from his ways and live. In your compassion, forgive our sins, purify our hearts, and recreate your own spirit within us. Through Christ our Lord.

All: **Amen.**

READING *Hebrews 12:1-3*

With so many witnesses in a great cloud on every side of us, we too, then, should throw off everything that hinders us, especially the sin that clings so easily, and keep running steadily in the race we have started. Let us not lose sight of Jesus, who leads us in our faith and brings it to perfection: for the sake of the joy which was still in the future, he endured the cross, disregarding the shamefulness of it, and from now on has taken his place at the right of God's throne. Think of the way he stood such opposition from sinners and then you will not give up for want of courage.—This is the Word of the Lord.

All: **Thanks be to God.**

After the reading, a period of silent prayer or a homily may follow.

FRIDAY MORNING

The traditional morning canticle, the Song of Zechariah (p. 473) or the following canticle may be used.

CANTICLE The First Song of Isaiah *Isaiah 12:2-6*

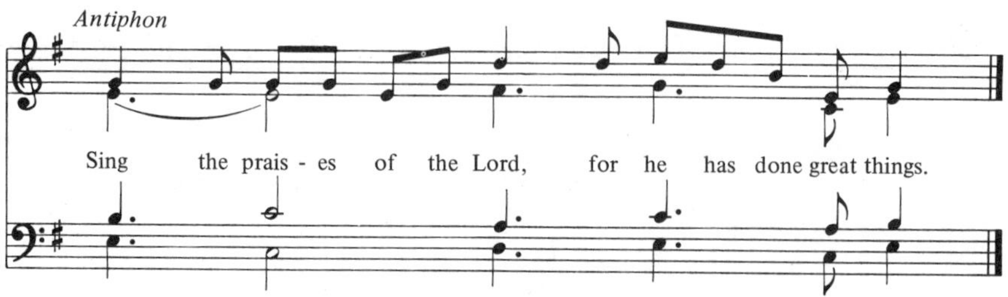

Antiphon
Sing the prais - es of the Lord, for he has done great things.

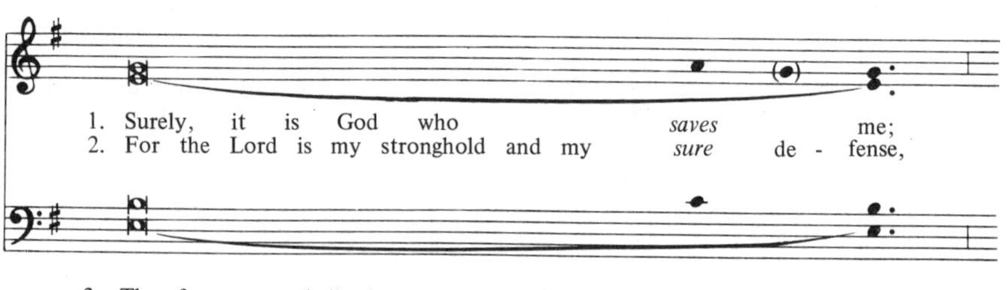

1. Surely, it is God who *saves* me;
2. For the Lord is my stronghold and my *sure* de - fense,

3. Therefore you shall draw water with re - *joic* - ing
4. And on that day *you* will say,
5. Make his deeds known among the *peo* - ples;

(6.) for he has done marve - *lous* things,
(7.) for the great one in the *midst* of you
8. Glory to the Father, and *to* the Son,
9. As in the beginning, *is* now,

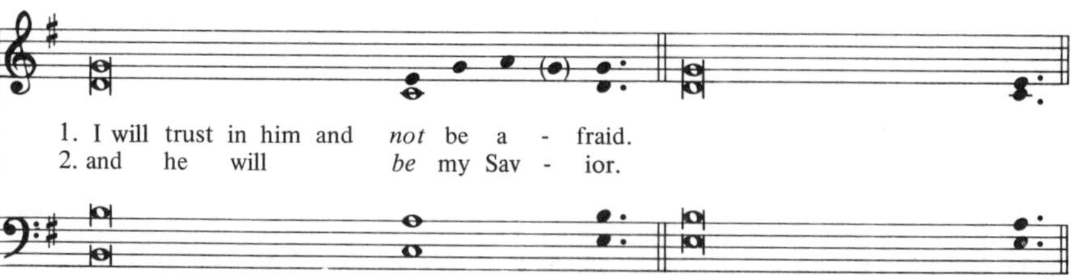

1. I will trust in him and *not* be a - fraid.
2. and he will *be* my Sav - ior.

3. from the springs *of* sal - va - tion.
4. give thanks to the Lord,
and call *up* - on his Name;
5. see that they remember
that his Name *is* ex - al - ted. 6. Sing the praises of the Lord,†

6. and this is known *in* all the world. 7. Cry aloud, ring out your
joy, inhabitants of Zion,†

7. is the Holy *One* of Is - ra - el.
8. and to the *Ho* - ly Spir - it:
9. and will be for - *ev* - er. A - men.

FRIDAY MORNING

INTERCESSIONS

Kneel.

The deacon or reader sings or recites the petitions and the people the response after each petition.

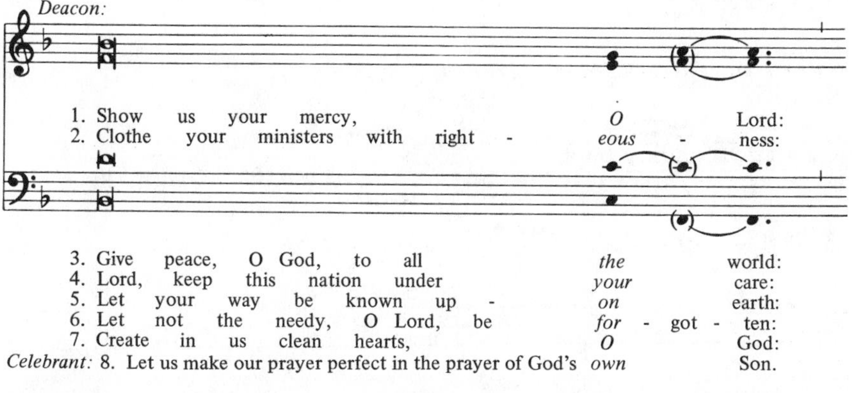

Deacon:
1. Show us your mercy, O Lord:
2. Clothe your ministers with right - eous - ness:

3. Give peace, O God, to all *the* world:
4. Lord, keep this nation under *your* care:
5. Let your way be known up - *on* earth:
6. Let not the needy, O Lord, be *for* - got - ten:
7. Create in us clean hearts, *O* God:

Celebrant: 8. Let us make our prayer perfect in the prayer of God's *own* Son.

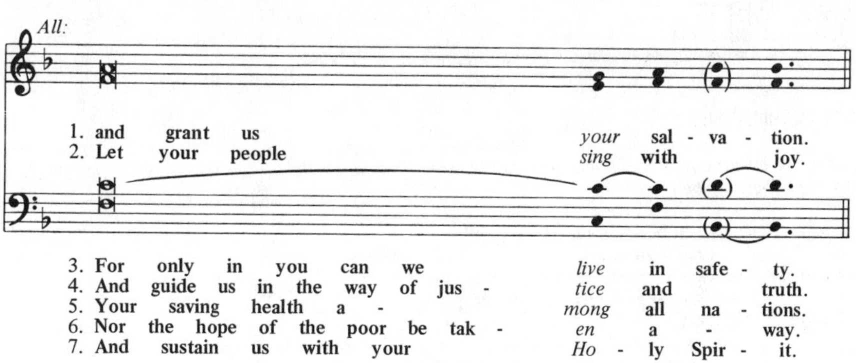

All:
1. and grant us your sal - va - tion.
2. Let your people sing with joy.

3. For only in you can we *live* in safe - ty.
4. And guide us in the way of jus - *tice* and truth.
5. Your saving health a - *mong* all na - tions.
6. Nor the hope of the poor be tak - *en* a - way.
7. And sustain us with your *Ho* - ly Spir - it.

All join in reciting or singing the Lord's Prayer, p. 468.

BLESSING AND DISMISSAL

Celebrant: May the Lord bless us, †
protect us from evil,
and bring us the life that will never end.
All: **Amen.**
Celebrant: Let us bless the Lord.
All: **Thanks be to God.**

FRIDAY EVENING

It is evening on the day of the Lord's passion.

LIGHT SERVICE

Stand.
As the evening lights are lit, the deacon or celebrant sings or recites:

All
Christ our Light!
Praise to you, Lord Christ!

EVENING HYMN

P. 498, or another appropriate hymn may be sung, (No. 327-330.)

THANKSGIVING

After the evening hymn, the deacon or celebrant stands at the lectern and sings or recites (music from p. 460 may be used):

Deacon: The Lord be with you.
All: **And also with you.**
Deacon: Let us give thanks to the Lord our God.
All: **It is right to give him thanks and praise.**
Deacon: Almighty God, Father of all mercies,
we, your unworthy servants, give you humble thanks
for all your goodness and loving kindness to us
and to all your human family.
We bless you for our creation, preservation,
and all the blessings of this life;
but above all for your incomparable love
in the redemption of the world by our Lord Jesus Christ:
for the means of grace, and for the hope of glory.
And, we pray,
give us such an awareness of your mercies,
that with truly thankful hearts
we may make known your praise,
not only with our lips, but in our lives,
by giving up ourselves to your service,
and by walking before you in holiness and righteousness
in all our days; through Jesus Christ, our Lord,
to whom, with you and the Holy Spirit,
be all honor and glory throughout all ages.
All: **Amen.**

Or, the following prayer may be used:

Lord God, by the death of your Son and by his resurrection into glory, you have set us free and given us new life. May we so die each day to sin, that we may live forever in the joy of his resurrection. We ask this in his name, Jesus Christ, our Lord.

FRIDAY EVENING

PSALMODY

Sit.

***Psalm 141,** An Evening Prayer for Repentance, may be prayed.* *See p. 463.*

Psalm 130 Prayer of repentance and trust.

Christ Jesus came into the world to save sinners (1 Timothy 1:15).

Antiphon
With the Lord there is mer - cy and full– ness of re - demp - tion.

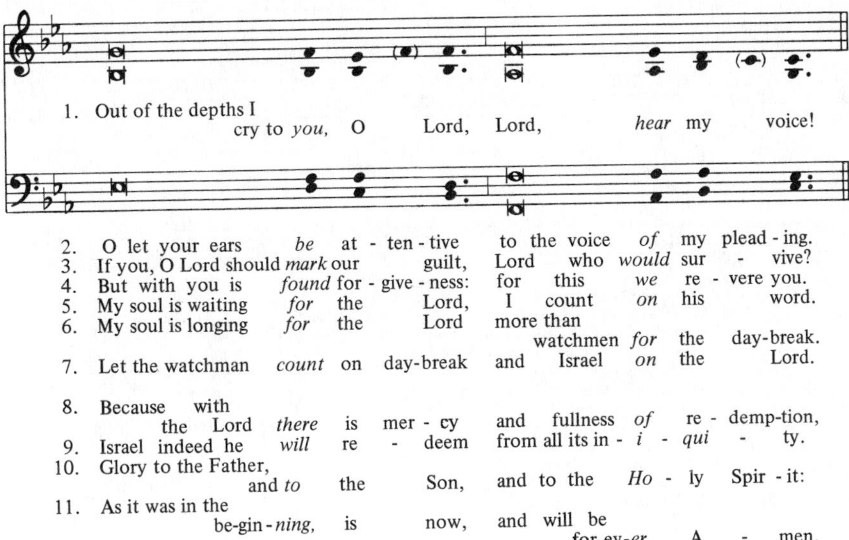
1. Out of the depths I cry to you, O Lord, Lord, hear my voice!
2. O let your ears be at - ten - tive to the voice of my plead - ing.
3. If you, O Lord should mark our guilt, Lord who would sur - vive?
4. But with you is found for - give - ness: for this we re - vere you.
5. My soul is waiting for the Lord, I count on his word.
6. My soul is longing for the Lord more than watchmen for the day-break.
7. Let the watchman count on day-break and Israel on the Lord.
8. Because with the Lord there is mer - cy and fullness of re - demp-tion,
9. Israel indeed he will re - deem from all its in - i - qui - ty.
10. Glory to the Father, and to the Son, and to the Ho - ly Spir - it:
11. As it was in the be-gin-ning, is now, and will be for-ev-er. A - men.

PSALM PRAYER

Celebrant: Let us pray.
Pause for silent prayer.
Lord, our God, you give your word and your light to all who wait in hope. Do not send us away empty, but fill us with the Spirit of your Son, Jesus Christ our Lord.

All: **Amen.**

FRIDAY EVENING

READING

Philippians 2:6-11

His state was divine, yet he did not cling to his equality with God but emptied himself to assume the condition of a slave, and became as men are; he was humbler yet, even to accepting death, death on a cross. But God raised him high and gave the name which is above all other names so that all beings in the heavens, on earth and in the underworld, should bend the knee at the name of Jesus and that every tongue should acclaim Jesus Christ as Lord, to the glory of God the Father.—This is the Word of the Lord.

All: **Thanks be to God.**

After the reading, a period of silent prayer or a homily may follow.

The traditional evening canticle, the Song of Mary (p. 479), or the following canticle may be used.

CANTICLE Christ our Passover

1 Corinthians 5:7-8
Romans 6:9-11

3
3
God has blessed us with all spir - it - ual bless-ings in Christ. —
1. Christ our Passover has been sacri - *ficed* for us;
2. Not with the old *lea* - ven,
3. But with the unleavened bread of sinceri - *ty* and truth.
4. Christ, being raised from the dead, will never *die* a - gain;
5. The death that he died, he died to sin, *once* for all;
6. So also consider yourselves *dead* to sin,
7. Glory to the Father, and *to* the Son,
8. As it was in the beginning, *is* now,
1. therefore let us cele - *brate* the feast,
2. the leaven of *ma* - lice and evil,
3. ——— *Al* - le - lu - ia.
4. death no longer has do - *min* - ion over him.
5. but the life he lives, *he* lives to God.
6. and alive to God in Jesus Christ our Lord. *Al* - le - lu - ia.
7. and to the *Ho* - ly Spir - it:
8. and will be for - *ev* - er. A - men.

FRIDAY EVENING

INTERCESSIONS

Kneel.
The deacon or reader sings or recites the petition and the people the response after each petition.

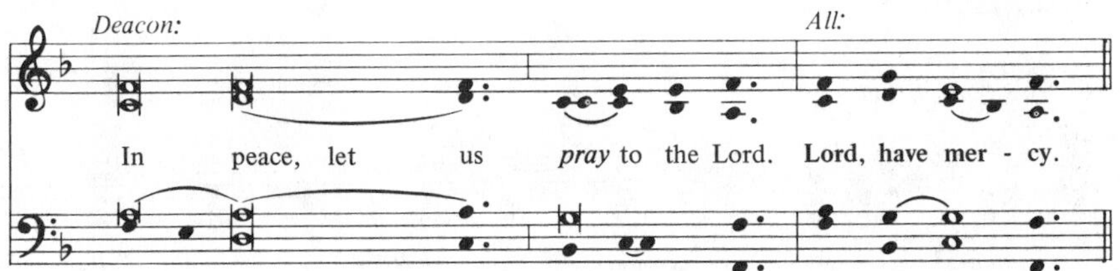

Deacon:
All:
In peace, let us *pray* to the Lord. **Lord, have mer - cy.**

Deacon: That this evening may be restful and peaceful, holy and perfect, free from sin and in Christ, let us *pray* to the Lord.
All: **Lord, have mercy.**
Deacon: For an angel of peace, a faithful guardian of our souls and bodies,
let us *pray* to the Lord.
All: **Lord, have mercy.**
Deacon: For the forgiveness of sins and the correction of our failings, let us *pray* to the Lord.
All: **Lord, have mercy.**
Deacon: For our fidelity in holiness and charity with the Church of God throughout the world, let us *pray* to the Lord.
All: **Lord, have mercy.**
Deacon: For whatever is good and helpful for ourselves, for all the human family and the salvation of all, let us *pray* to the Lord.
All: **Lord, have mercy.**
Deacon: That the end of our life may be Christian, painless, free from shame and peaceful, and for a good defense before the awesome judgement seat of Christ,
let us *pray* to the Lord.
All: **Lord, have mercy.**
Deacon: Help, save, pity and defend us, O God, by your grace.
Pause for free prayer, silent and spontaneous.
Rejoicing in the fellowship of the Blessed Virgin Mary, of Saint N., and of all the saints, let us commend ourselves, one another, and our whole life
to *Christ* our Lord.
All: **To you, O Lord.**
Celebrant: Let us make our prayer perfect in the prayer of *God's* own son.

All join in reciting or singing the Lord's Prayer, p. 468.

BLESSING AND DISMISSAL

Celebrant: May the Lord bless us and keep us.
May the Lord let his face shine upon us and be gracious to us.
May the Lord look upon us kindly and give us peace: in the name of the Father, and of the Son, † and of the Holy Spirit.
All: **Amen.**
Celebrant: Let us bless the Lord.
All: **Thanks be to God.**

SATURDAY MORNING

Christians rejoice with all God's creation for his loving and faithful care.

Celebrant: O Lord, open our lips.
All: **And we shall praise your name.**

MORNING HYMN

ROUEN
11 11. 11 5
Rouen Church Melody,
harm. by Healey Willan, 1918

PSALM 100
Tr., James Quinn, S.J. 1969

1. Sing, all cre - a - tion, sing to God in glad - ness!
2. Know that our God is Lord of all the a - ges!
3. En - ter his tem - ple, ring - ing out his prais - es!
1. Joy - ous - ly serve him, sing - ing hymns of hom - age!
2. He is our mak - er; we are all his crea — tures,
3. Sing in thanks - giv - ing as you come be - fore — him!
1. Chant - ing his prais - es, come be - fore his pres - ence!
2. Peo - ple he fash - ioned, sheep he leads to pas - ture!
3. Bless - ing his boun - ty, glo - ri - fy his great — ness!
1. Praise the Al - might - y!
2. Praise the Al - might - y!
3. Praise the Al - might - y!

Alternate hymns: No. 323-326.

SATURDAY MORNING

OPENING PRAYER

Celebrant: The Lord be with you.
All: **And also with you.**
Celebrant: Let us pray.
Pause for silent prayer.
Free us, Lord God, from the dark night of death and let the light of Christ's resurrection dawn within our hearts: That we might come with joy to the radiance of life everlasting. We ask this through Christ our Lord.
All: **Amen.**

The Opening Prayer of the Mass of the day from the Sacramentary may be used in place of the above.

PSALMODY

Sit.

Psalm 150 A Chorus of Praise to God

To God be all glory in the Church and in Christ Jesus forever and ever (Ephesians 3:21).

Antiphon
Let ev - ry - thing that lives and breathes give praise — to the Lord.
1. Praise God in his ho - ly place, praise him in his might - y heav - ens.
2. Praise him for his pow - er - ful deeds, praise his sur - pass - ing great - ness.
3. O praise him with sound of trumpet, praise him with lute and harp.
4. Praise him with tim-brel and dance, praise him with strings and pipes.
5. Let everything that lives and breathes give praise to the Lord.
6. Glory to the Father, and to the Son, and to the Ho - ly Spir - it:
7. As it was in the begin-ning, is now, and will be for - ev - er. A - men.

PSALM PRAYER

Celebrant: Let us pray.
Pause for silent prayer.
Almighty and ever living God, you are worthy indeed of our praise. Accept our heartfelt worship in union with the praise of all creation; through Christ our Lord.
All: **Amen.**

SATURDAY MORNING

READING *Deuteronomy 6:4-8*

Listen, Israel: Yahweh is our God, Yahweh alone. You shall love Yahweh your God with all your heart, with all your soul, with all your strength. Let these words, I urge on you today, be written in your heart. You shall repeat them to your children and say them over to them whether at rest in your house or walking abroad, at your lying down or at your rising.—This is the Word of the Lord.

All: **Thanks be to God.**

After the reading, a period of silent prayer or a homily may follow.

The traditional morning canticle, the Song of Zechariah (p. 473), or the following canticle may be used.

CANTICLE A Song of Creation *Daniel 3:57-87*

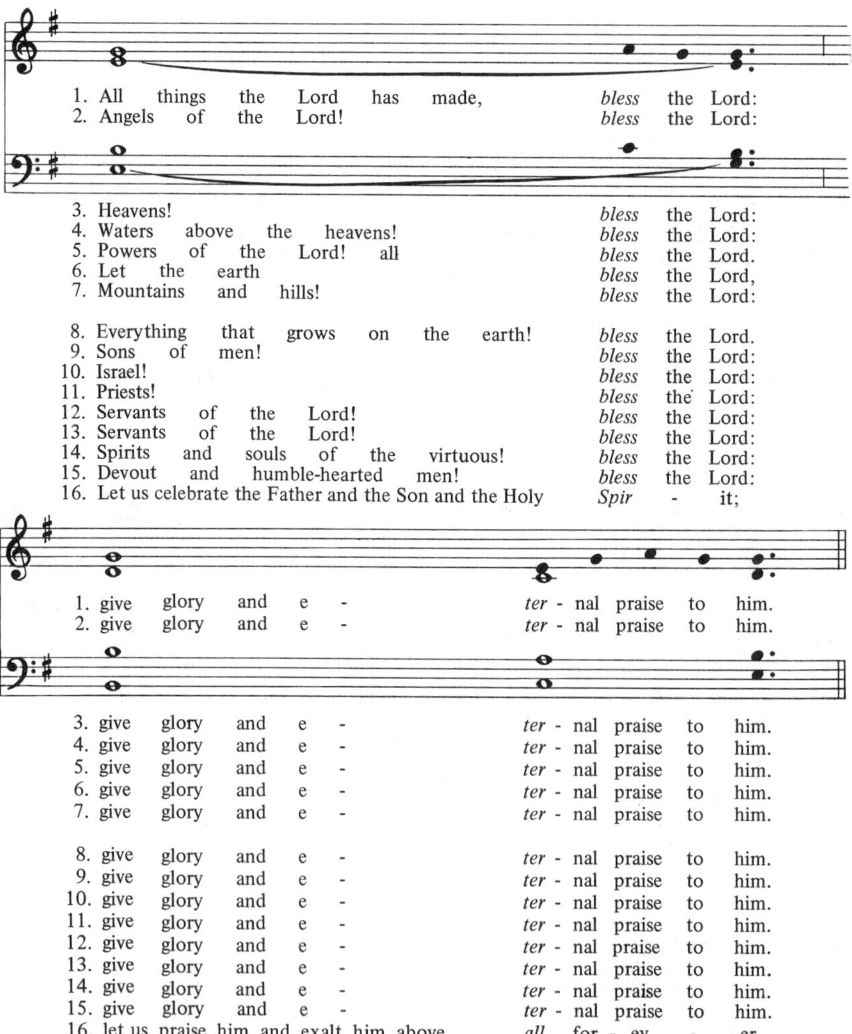
1. All things the Lord has made, bless the Lord:
2. Angels of the Lord! bless the Lord:
3. Heavens! bless the Lord:
4. Waters above the heavens! bless the Lord:
5. Powers of the Lord! all bless the Lord.
6. Let the earth bless the Lord,
7. Mountains and hills! bless the Lord:
8. Everything that grows on the earth! bless the Lord.
9. Sons of men! bless the Lord:
10. Israel! bless the Lord:
11. Priests! bless the Lord:
12. Servants of the Lord! bless the Lord:
13. Servants of the Lord! bless the Lord:
14. Spirits and souls of the virtuous! bless the Lord:
15. Devout and humble-hearted men! bless the Lord:
16. Let us celebrate the Father and the Son and the Holy Spir - it;
1. give glory and e - ter - nal praise to him.
2. give glory and e - ter - nal praise to him.
3. give glory and e - ter - nal praise to him.
4. give glory and e - ter - nal praise to him.
5. give glory and e - ter - nal praise to him.
6. give glory and e - ter - nal praise to him.
7. give glory and e - ter - nal praise to him.
8. give glory and e - ter - nal praise to him.
9. give glory and e - ter - nal praise to him.
10. give glory and e - ter - nal praise to him.
11. give glory and e - ter - nal praise to him.
12. give glory and e - ter - nal praise to him.
13. give glory and e - ter - nal praise to him.
14. give glory and e - ter - nal praise to him.
15. give glory and e - ter - nal praise to him.
16. let us praise him and exalt him above all for - ev - er.

INTERCESSIONS

Kneel.
The deacon or reader sings or recites the petition and the people the response after each petition.

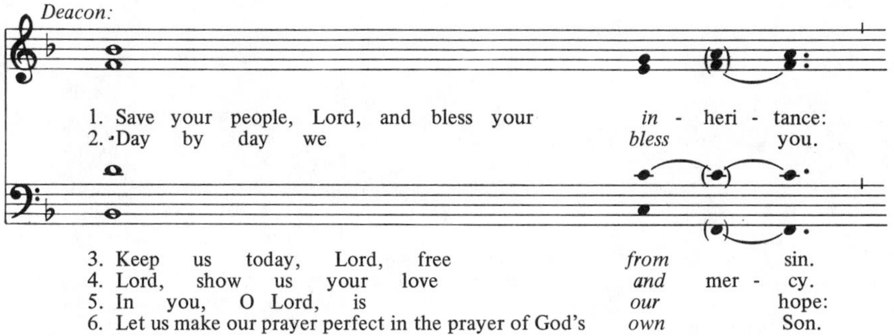
Deacon:
1. Save your people, Lord, and bless your *in* - heri - tance:
2. Day by day we *bless* you.
3. Keep us today, Lord, free *from* sin.
4. Lord, show us your love *and* mer - cy.
5. In you, O Lord, is *our* hope:
6. Let us make our prayer perfect in the prayer of God's *own* Son.

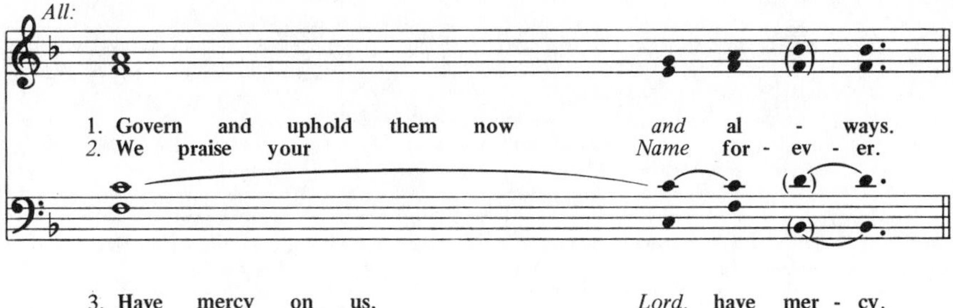
All:
1. **Govern and uphold them now** *and* **al - ways.**
2. **We praise your** *Name* **for - ev - er.**
3. **Have mercy on us,** *Lord,* **have mer - cy.**
4. **For we put our** *trust* **in you.**
5. **And we shall never** *hope* **in vain.**

All join in reciting or singing the Lord's Prayer, P. 468.

BLESSING AND DISMISSAL

Celebrant: May the Lord bless us, † protect us from evil,
and bring us the life that will never end.
All: **Amen.**
Celebrant: Let us bless the Lord.
All: **Thanks be to God.**

Appendix

Appendix

Chants and acclamations for Ash Wednesday, Holy Week, and music for Funeral Mass. Page numbers refer to the Congregation Edition.

ASH WEDNESDAY
Page 117:
Peter Scagnelli, 1975
Harm., J.S.
Be mer - ci - ful, O Lord, for we have sinned.
PALM SUNDAY
Page 129:
R.F. Twynham, 1965
Ho - san - na to the Son of Da - vid!
Bles - sed is he who comes in the name of the Lord. O
King of Is - ra - el: Ho - san - na in_ the_ high - est.

Page 130:

R.F. Twynham, 1965

The children of the Hebrews, bearing olive branches, went to meet the Lord crying aloud and saying, Hosanna in the highest.

HOLY THURSDAY

Page 135:

Roger Nachtwey, 1975
Harm., J.S.

Lord Je - sus Christ, hear us and an - swer our prayer.

Page 140:

R.F. Twynham, 1965

"A new com-mand-ment I give you, that you love one a-
no-ther as I have loved you," says the Lord, says the Lord.

Page 140-141:

Plainsong Melody

Refrain:

Where true char - i - ty and love_ dwell,_ sure - ly God is there.

Verse 1:

The love of Christ_ has_ gath-ered us_ to - geth - er in - to one.

Let us re - joice and be glad in him. Let us fear and love the
Repeat Refrain.
liv - ing God, and love each oth - er from the depths of our hearts.
Verse 2
There - fore when we are to - geth - er, let us take heed not to
be di - vi - ded in mind. Let there be an end to bit - ter - ness and quar -
Repeat Refrain
rels, an end to strife, and in our midst be Christ our God.

Verse 3
And, in com - pa - ny with the bles - sed, may we see your face in glo -
ry, Christ our God, pure and un - bound-ed joy for - ev - er and ev - er.
Fine

GOOD FRIDAY
Page 148:

Harm., J.S.

Priest:
This is the wood of the cross, on which
hung the Sav - ior of the world.
All:
Come, let us wor - ship.

Page 149:
Harm., J.S.
My peo - ple what have I done to you? How have
I of - fend - ed you? An - swer me!
Page 149:
Harm., J.S.
Ho - ly is God! Ho - ly and strong!
Ho - ly im - mor - tal One, have mer - cy on us.
THE EASTER VIGIL
Page 154:
Peter Scagnelli, 1975
Harm., J.S.
Lord, send out your Spir - it, and re - new the face of the earth.

Page 154:

Peter Scagnelli, 1975
Harm., J.S.

The earth is full of the good-ness of God.

Page 155:

Peter Scagnelli, 1975
Harm., J.S.

Keep me safe, O God; you are my hope.

Page 155:

Peter Scagnelli, 1975
Harm., J.S.

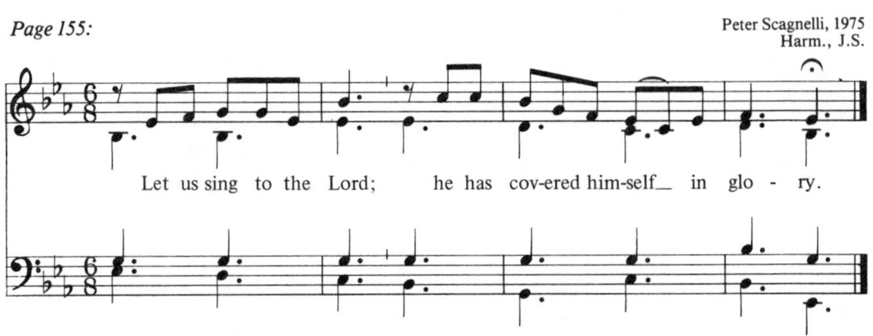
Let us sing to the Lord; he has cov-ered him-self in glo - ry.

Page 155:

Roger Nachtwey, 1975
Harm., J.S.

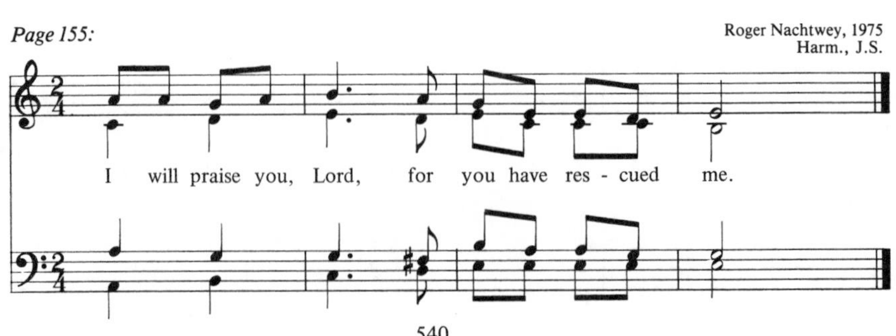
I will praise you, Lord, for you have res - cued me.

Page 156:

Peter Scagnelli, 1975
Harm., J.S.

You will draw wa - ter joy - ful - ly from the springs of sal - va - tion.

Page 156:

Roger Nachtwey, 1975
Harm., J.S.

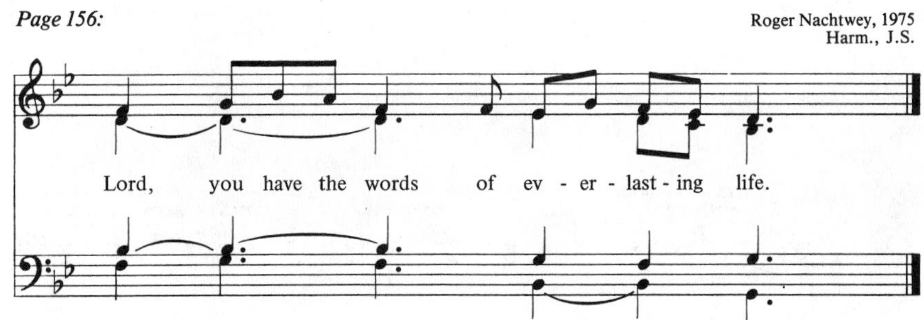
Lord, you have the words of ev - er - last - ing life.

Page 156:

Peter Scagnelli, 1975
Harm., J.S.

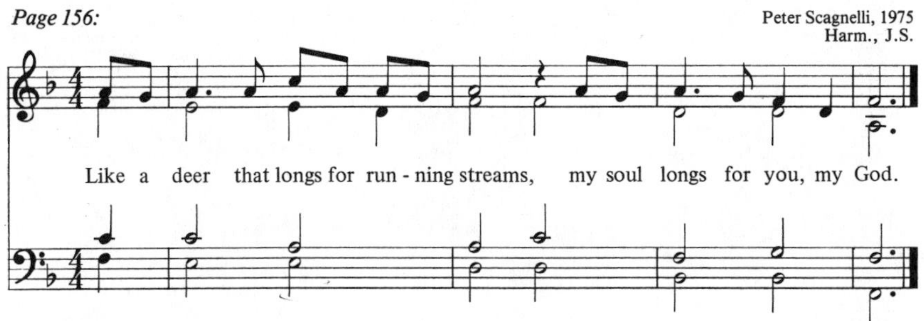
Like a deer that longs for run - ning streams, my soul longs for you, my God.

Page 156:

Peter Scagnelli, 1975
Harm., J.S.

Cre - ate a clean heart in me, O God.

Page 157:

Plainsong

Al - le - lu - ia, al - le - lu - ia, ___ al - le - lu - ia.

Page 157

Plainsong

Al - le - lu - ia. ___

Page 158:

Harm., J.S.

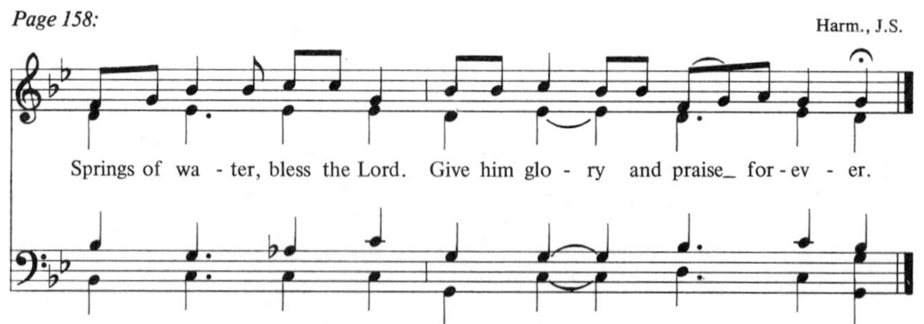
Springs of wa - ter, bless the Lord. Give him glo - ry and praise_ for - ev - er.

THE FUNERAL MASS

Page 677:

Based on "In Paradisum"
MAY FLIGHTS OF ANGELS
James Quinn, 1969

UNDE ET MEMORES
10 10. 10 10. 10 10
William H. Monk, 1875, alt.

May flights of an - gels lead you on your way To par - a - dise and
heav'n's e - ter - nal day. May mar - tyrs greet you af - ter death's dark night,
And bid you en - ter in - to Zi - on's light. May choirs of an - gels
sing you to your rest With once poor Laz - 'rus, now for - ev - er blest.

Lower Key at No. 333

Indices

Index of Authors, Composers and Sources

Metrical Index of Hymns

Index of Hymn Tunes

Topical Index of Hymns

THANKSGIVING

TRINITY SUNDAY

First Line Index of Hymns